INTRODUCTION TO THE FOUNDATIONS OF MATHEMATICS

INTRODUCTION TO

The Foundations of Mathematics

RAYMOND L. WILDER
RESEARCH PROFESSOR OF MATHEMATICS
UNIVERSITY OF MICHIGAN

JOHN WILEY & SONS, INC., NEW YORK
CHAPMAN & HALL, LIMITED, LONDON

SECOND PRINTING, JULY, 1956

Library of Congress Catalog Card Number: 52–10923

Printed in the United States of America

Preface

This book grew out of a course in Foundations of Mathematics which I have given at the University of Michigan for over twenty years. The reason for instituting the course was simply the conviction that it was not good to have teachers, actuaries, statisticians, and others who had specialized in undergraduate mathematics, and who were to base their life's work on mathematics, leave the university without some knowledge of modern mathematics and its foundations. The training of these people consisted chiefly of "classical" mathematics and its applications—that part of mathematics which is based on pre-twentieth-century and, in large part, on pre-Cantorian ideas and methods.

It seemed, too, that a course in Foundations at about the senior level might serve to unify and extend the material covered in the traditional mathematics curriculum. The "compartmentalization" of the preparatory school—arithmetic, algebra, and geometry—is usually continued in college with a further dose of algebra, followed by courses in analytic geometry and calculus in which a little unification of preceding subjects takes place, but no time is spent on the *nature* of the material or its foundation.

Also, the growing realization that mathematical logic is a new and legitimate part of mathematics made it seem advisable to institute a course which would make manifest the importance of studies in the Foundations, and the reasons for inquiring into the nature of mathematics by either the tools of logic or other methods.

To my first class in the course I owe much for inspiration and encouragement. It consisted, with one or two exceptions, of approximately thirty actuarial students, most of them first-year graduate students. Their response was surprising; for I was aware of the antagonism of many professional mathematicians to any inquiry into the nature of mathematics, especially if it leads to any questioning of the validity of time-honored principles and methods (the analogue in mathematics, perhaps, of the historical lag in the cultivation of those sciences that study man's own behavior).

v

Perhaps their reaction was due to the change, possibly refreshing to them, from the type of teaching which treats mathematics as a "discipline," dogmatic in character. Whatever the reason, the course seemed to "take" with them and left no question about the desirability of repeating the experiment. (Even today I occasionally meet members of that original class, many of them now insurance company executives, and find them still able to recall topics that were discussed.)

In a few years the course ceased to be an experiment and became as well established as any other course in the curriculum. This development was aided, no doubt, by the realization that the course was also fulfilling other purposes. For those students who were going on to the doctorate in mathematics, it did spadework in the ideas and methods that were going to form the principal tools in their graduate courses and research. And for mature students in other fields, such as philosophy and the social sciences, it provided an insight into basic mathematical concepts without the necessity of first wading through the traditional courses in algebra, geometry, calculus, etc.

In the belief that such a course ought, perhaps, to be offered in most universities and colleges that train mathematicians either for teaching or for any of the professional fields, I decided to incorporate the material covered in a book which would serve as a basis for such a course. Unfortunately, a book in my own special field of research took precedence and delayed my starting on the present work for at least ten years. Moreover, it seemed desirable to include in the book material that it was not possible to crowd into a one-semester course, and which has usually been suggested for collateral reading; especially material that is in languages other than English. For it continues to be true that the students in American universities are generally not prepared to read in French and German; and most of the older and basic work in Foundations was originally published in German. The material in Chapter X (Intuitionism), for instance, has heretofore been available almost entirely only in German.

In a general way, the idea of the book is similiar to that which motivated J. W. Young's *Fundamental Concepts of Algebra and Geometry*, first published in 1911. In 1932 I discussed with Professor Young the desirability of a book such as this one; he agreed thoroughly that it was desirable to write it, if only to have available a book on fundamental concepts that would take into account the great strides that have been made in Foundations since the publication of his book.

As already indicated, I have given the material in the form of a course of one semester, with a calculus prerequisite. The students who have taken the course have, however, been at all levels, from undergraduate juniors to students already writing doctoral dissertations. Ideally, the course should be given at senior level or first-year graduate level. And, I have found, it is not necessary to insist on the calculus prerequisite for mature students in other fields, such as philosophy. (One of the most enthusiastic students in my experience was a medical student who was taking the course as a "cultural" subject.) No *mathematics* student, however, should take the course without having had calculus, and for the average student it is better that he have taken courses such as advanced calculus and projective geometry in order to develop the maturity requisite for abstract thinking.

Whether I have succeeded in getting down on paper a reasonable facsimile of what I have done in class only the reception of this book can tell. No false modesty prevents me from admitting the success of the course itself, as numerous past students will testify. But the enthusiasm and inspiration which come from facing a group of interested students are hard to duplicate in the seclusion of one's study, and it is difficult to recapture the many spontaneous ideas and illustrations that have revealed themselves in the classroom from time to time over the years. No doubt, now that the book is written, I shall occasionally recall some of them and regret that they are doomed to oblivion.

I have made it a general rule, incidentally, not to reveal to students my own opinion regarding a controversial point, despite frequent requests to do so. It has always seemed better to present, as emphatically as possible from the point of view of their proponents, such topics as are controversial; and frequently, in order to aggravate class discussion, it has been my custom to oppose the point of view of a student while secretly agreeing with him. There is nothing new about such methods of instruction, of course, and I bring them up here largely to afford occasion to remark that I am including my own opinions regarding the nature of mathematics in the material of Chapter XII. In the earlier chapters I have tried to follow my usual rule of acting as advocate for the view presented; and, in thus breaking my rule, I do so not only with a view to getting in my own "innings," but also to furnish additional fuel for the stirring up of controversy which, it seems to me, is the most effective stimulant to original and creative thinking. And if, after reading this book, the student is not aroused to the extent of "thinking about" mathematics, I shall have failed in one of my chief purposes in writing it.

For rapidity and exactness of reference, the decimal system of numbering sections has been employed. Cross references to items in the text are made by citing chapter and section; thus "IV 2.4" refers to

Chapter IV, Section 2.4. However, for reference to a section in the chapter under consideration, only the section number is used; thus "1.2" refers to Section 1.2 of the chapter in which the citation occurs.

The Bibliography is divided into two parts, the first listing books and longer memoirs, the second listing papers and shorter articles. References to the Bibliography are enclosed in brackets, those involving capital letters such as [B], [Ha], [H$_1$] referring to the first part of the Bibliography, and those involving single lower-case letters such as [a], [b] referring to the second part. Page or chapter numbers will frequently be included; thus "Hilbert [H$_3$; 6]" will be found under Hilbert's name in the first part of the Bibliography, item [H$_3$] (the reference, then, is to page 6 of Hilbert's *Foundations of Geometry*). Always, "f" indicates "footnote," and "ff" indicates "and the following page or pages."

To those colleagues and students who have given me encouragement and stimulation, I wish to express sincere thanks. I am especially grateful to Professors E. T. Bell, Leon Henkin, Paul Henle, and Leo Zippin, and to Dr. C. V. Newsom for suggestions and criticisms; but the errors and shortcomings to be found herein are not their fault and are present only in spite of their wise counsel.

For aid in a material way, thanks are due to the Office of Naval Research, under whose Contract N9onr-89300 the first draft of this work was written, as well as to the California Institute of Technology, which generously afforded an office and library facilities during the academic year 1949–1950 for my writing and research.

R. L. WILDER

Ann Arbor, Michigan
September, 1952

Suggestions for Use as a Textbook

The plan of presentation is based on the idea that an appreciation of the need for a study of the Foundations of Mathematics can come only through a prior acquaintance with Fundamental Concepts of Mathematics. It is the nature of these concepts and the contradictions to which their unrestricted use may lead that make one realize the necessity for going deeper into their background—Foundations.

Accordingly the book is divided into two parts: Part I, Fundamental Concepts and Methods of Mathematics, and Part II, Development of Various Viewpoints on Foundations. In Part I are presented those topics which are indispensable for work in modern mathematics. Here the student will become aware of the conventional character of much that he has heretofore taken for granted, as well as of the true intrinsic nature of such concepts as the infinite, the real number continuum, arithmetic, and geometry which he has continually encountered in his elementary and intermediate mathematics courses. When this material has been digested, the student's curiosity about the actual nature of the Foundations has usually been aroused, and he is ready for Part II.

By judicious selection of material, a satisfactory one-semester course can be based on the book. This has been my custom; for instance, such proofs as those of the equivalence of Choice Axiom, Comparability, and Well-ordering in Chapter V can be omitted, and some discussion of the principles involved, the reasons why the equivalence may induce some to reject the Choice Axiom, etc., can be substituted therefor. As a matter of fact, much of the material on the infinite in Chapters IV and V can be summarized with details omitted; and a like comment holds regarding Chapter VII.

However, it is probably best to leave the choice to the judgment of the individual instructor. One may wish to place the main emphasis on Foundations proper, spending most of the time on Part II; the bibliographical references should enable the instructor to supplement the material given, if he so desires. Another may wish to give a course emphasizing Fundamental Concepts, in which case Part I may be used exclusively, or may be supplemented by some discussion of the material in Part II without going into much detail, however.

If the book is used for a two-semester course, probably all details can be covered, although one can introduce variation, if desired, by substituting or augmenting here and there from the Bibliography. Problems are provided for the better understanding of the concepts discussed in Part I; these may be used for class discussion, or as a basis for written work.

Contents

P A R T I

Fundamental Concepts
and
Methods of Mathematics

I

The Axiomatic Method

Since the axiomatic method as it is now understood and practiced by mathematicians is the result of a long evolution in human thought, we shall precede our discussion of it by a brief description of some older uses of the term *axiom*. The modern usage of the term represents a high degree of maturity, and a better understanding of it may be achieved by some acquaintance with the course of its evolution.

1 Evolution of the method

If the reader has at hand a copy of an elementary plane geometry, of a type frequently used in high schools, he may find two groupings of fundamental assumptions, one entitled "Axioms," the other entitled "Postulates." The intent of this grouping may be explained by such accompanying remarks as: *"An axiom is a self-evident truth." "A postulate is a geometrical fact* so simple and obvious that its validity may be assumed." The "axioms" themselves may contain such statements as: "The whole is greater than any of its parts." "The whole is the sum of its parts." "Things equal to the same thing are equal to one another." "Equals added to equals yield equals." It will be noted that such geometric terms as "point" or "line" do not occur in these statements; in some sense the axioms are intended to transcend geometry—to be "universal truths." In contrast, the "postulates" probably contain such statements as: "Through two distinct points one and only one straight line can be drawn." "A line can be extended indefinitely." "If L is a line and P is a point not on L, then through P there can be drawn one and only one line parallel to L." (Some so-called "definitions" of terms usually precede these statements.)

This grouping into "axioms" and "postulates" has its roots in antiquity. Thus we find in Aristotle (384–321 B.C.) the following viewpoint: †

"Every demonstrative science must start from indemonstrable principles; otherwise, the steps of demonstration would be endless. Of these indemonstrable principles some are (a) common to all sciences, others are (b) particular, or peculiar to the particular science; (a) the common principles are the *axioms*, most commonly illustrated by the axiom that, if equals be subtracted from equals, the remainders are equal. In (b) we have first the *genus* or subject-matter, the *existence* of which must be assumed."

1.1   In Euclid's *Elements* (written about 300 B.C.), the two groups occur, respectively labeled "Common notions" and "Postulates." From these and a collection of definitions, Euclid deduced 465 propositions in a logical chain. Although the actual background for Euclid's work is not clear, apparently he did not originate this method of deducing logically from certain unproved propositions, given at the start, all the remaining propositions. As we have just noted, Aristotle, and probably other scholars of the period, had a well-conceived notion of the nature of a demonstrative science; and the logical deduction of mathematical propositions was common in Plato's Academy and perhaps among the Pythagoreans. Nevertheless, the influence of Euclid's work has been tremendous; probably no other document has had a greater influence on scientific thought. For example, modern high school geometries are usually modeled after Euclid's famous work (in England, Euclid is still used as a textbook), thus explaining the still common grouping into "axioms" and "postulates." Also the use in non-mathematical writings of such phrases as "It is axiomatic that . . . ," and "It is a fundamental postulate of . . . ," in the sense of something being "universal" or beyond opposition, is explained by this traditional use of the terms in mathematics.

The method featured in Euclid's work was employed by Archimedes (287–212 B.C.) in his two books which provided a foundation for the science of theoretical mechanics; in Book I of this treatise Archimedes proved 15 propositions from 7 postulates. Newton's famous *Principia*, first published in 1686, is organized as a deductive system in which the well-known laws of motion appear as unproved propositions, or postulates, given at the start. The treatment of analytic mechanics published by Lagrange in 1788 has been consid-

---

† As summarized by T. L. Heath [Hea; I, 119]; quoted by permission of Cambridge University Press. The reader is referred to this book for citations from Aristotle, Proclus, et al.

ered a masterpiece of logical perfection, moving from explicitly stated primary propositions to the other propositions of the system.

1.2   There exists a large literature devoted to the discussion of the *nature* of axioms and postulates and their philosophical background. Most of this is influenced by the fact that only within comparatively recent years have axioms and postulates been very generally employed in parts of mathematics other than geometry. Even though the method popularized by Euclid is acknowledged now as a fundamental part of the scientific method in every realm of human endeavor, our modern understanding of axioms and postulates, as well as our comprehension of deductive methods in general, has resulted to a great extent from studies in the field of geometry. And, since geometry was conceived to be an attempt to describe the actual physical space in which we live, there arose a conviction that axioms and postulates possessed a character of *logical necessity*. For example, Euclid's fifth postulate (the "parallel postulate") was "Let the following be postulated that, if a straight line falling on two straight lines make the interior angles on the same side less than two right angles, the two straight lines, if produced indefinitely, meet on that side on which are the angles less than the two right angles." † Proclus (A.D. 410–485) described vividly in his writings the controversy that was taking place in connection with this postulate even in his time; in fact, he argued in favor of the elimination "from our body of doctrine this merely plausible and un-reasoned statement." † With the renewal of interest in Greek learning during the Renaissance, controversy in regard to the fifth postulate was renewed. Attempts were made to prove the "parallel postulate," often from logical—non-geometrical—principles alone. Surely if a statement is a "logical necessity" the assumption of its invalidity should lead to contradiction—such was the motivation of much of the work on the postulates of geometry. With the invention of non-euclidean geometries the futility of such attempts became clear.

1.3   The development of the non-euclidean geometries was evidence of a growing recognition of the independent nature of the fifth postulate; that is, this postulate cannot be demonstrated as a logical conse-quence of the other axioms and postulates in the euclidean system. By a suitable replacement of the fifth postulate, one may obtain the alternative and logically consistent geometry of Bolyai, Lobachevski, and Gauss in which the fifth postulate of Euclid fails to hold. In it

† Quoted from T. L. Heath [Hea; I, 154-155, 203], by permission of Cambridge University Press.

appears, for example, the proposition that the sum of the interior angles of a triangle is less than two right angles. Riemann in 1854 developed another non-euclidean geometry, likewise composed of a non-contradictory collection of propositions, in which all lines are of finite length and the sum of the interior angles of a triangle is greater than two right angles.

The invention of the non-euclidean geometries was only part of the rapidly moving developments of the nineteenth century that were to lead to the acceptance of formal geometries apart from those that might be regarded as constituting definitive sciences of space or extension. Grassmann's *Ausdehnungslehre*, published in 1844 and a critical landmark during this era of changing ideas, was described by its author in these terms: "My *Ausdehnungslehre* is the abstract foundation for the doctrine of space, i.e., it is free from all spatial intuition, and is a purely mathematical discipline whose application to space yields the science of space. This latter science, since it refers to something given in nature (i.e., space), is no branch of mathematics, but is an application of mathematics to nature." † In explanation of Grassmann's concept of a formal science, Nagel [a; 169] writes: "Formal sciences are characterized by the fact that their sole principles of procedure are the rules of logic as well as by the further fact that their theorems are not 'about' some phase of the existing world but are 'about' whatever is *postulated* by thought." †

1.4 The idea expressed by Grassmann is essentially the one held at the present time; that is, a mathematical system called "geometry" is not necessarily a description of actual space. One must distinguish, of course, between the origin of a theory and the form to which it evolves. Geometry, like arithmetic, originated in things "practical," but to assert that any particular type of geometry is a description of physical space is to make a *physical* assertion, not a mathematical statement. In short, the modern viewpoint is that one must distinguish between mathematics and *applications* of mathematics.

A natural consequence of this change in viewpoint on the significance of a mathematical system was a re-examination of the nature of the basic, unproved propositions. It became clear, for instance, that the euclidean "common notion" that "the whole is greater than the part" has no more of an absolute character than the "parallel postulate" but is contingent upon the meaning of "greater than"; in fact, the proposition may even fail to hold, as in the theory of the in-

---

† As quoted by E. Nagel [a; 172, 169]; used here by permission of E. Nagel and *Osiris*.

finite (cf. Chapter IV). Although there was much discussion as to whether the parallel postulate should be listed as a "postulate" or as a "common notion" (axiom), it was finally realized that neither had any more universality than the other and the distinction might as well be deleted.† Accordingly we find in the classical work of Hilbert on the foundations of geometry,‡ published in 1899, that only one name, "axioms," is applied to the fundamental statements or assumptions, and that certain basic terms such as "point" and "line" are left completely undefined. To be sure, Hilbert made a grouping of his axioms—into five groups—but this pertained only to the technical character of the statements, and not to their relative status of "trueness" or "commonness."

1.5 Although this work of Hilbert has come to be regarded by many as the first to display the axiomatic method in its modern form, it should be recognized that similar ideas were appearing in works of his contemporaries.

In 1882 appeared the first edition of *Vorlesungen über Neuere Geometrie* by M. Pasch [Pa]. Pasch based his treatment of geometry on a small number of so-called "nuclear" concepts and propositions, which are introduced respectively without definition and without demonstration, but which he believes have a common basis of acceptance and understanding in man's experience. After the basic system of propositions (axioms) has been introduced, the logical deduction of the remaining propositions of the system would probably be regarded as quite "rigorous" by modern mathematical scholars. Pasch's ideas in this regard were described by him as follows: §

"Indeed, if geometry is to be deductive, the deduction must everywhere be independent of the *meaning* of geometrical concepts, just as it must be independent of the diagrams; only the *relations* specified in the propositions and definitions employed may legitimately be taken into account. During the deduction it is useful and legitimate, but in *no* way necessary, to think of the meanings of the terms; in fact, if it is necessary to do so, the inadequacy of the proof is made manifest. If, however, a theorem is rigorously derived from a set of propositions—the *basic* set—the deduction has a value which goes beyond

† For an excellent non-technical description of this "revolution" in thought, see E. T. Bell [B₂; XIV].

‡ Hilbert [H₁, H₃]; the work [H₃] is in English, but the seventh edition [H₂], published in 1930, incorporates some of the improvements found by various colleagues of Hilbert in the interval between the first and seventh editions.

§ [Pa; 98–99.] The translation given here is from Nagel [a; 197], with slight change of wording; used here by permission of E. Nagel and *Osiris*.

its original purpose. For if, on replacing the geometric terms in the basic set of propositions by certain other terms, true propositions are obtained, then corresponding replacements may be made in the theorem; in this way one obtains a new theorem as a consequence of the altered basic propositions without having to repeat the proof."

It is probable that the organization and the logical perfection of the work of Pasch were influential in the thinking of Peano. However, of the work of this imaginative Italian, Nagel (loc. cit.) writes: "No phase of Pasch's empiricism is reflected in Peano's version, and pure geometry in his hands became a calculus operating upon variables formally stipulated to be related to one another in certain ways." † Peano's *Principii di Geometria* [P₁], published in 1889, treated the geometric elements as mere "things," and was a demonstration of the idea, which Peano emphasized, that a relatively small number of *undefined* terms can be used in defining all the other terms that occur in geometry; he insisted that there should be as few undefined terms (mere "symbols") as possible. Peano's work employed the language of mathematical logic, of which he was one of the originators, and was based essentially upon an undefined entity called a "point" and an undefined relation of "betweenness." (The concept of betweenness was fundamental in several of the well-conceived organizations of geometry that were constructed during the latter part of the nineteenth century; it was employed by both Pasch and Hilbert.) In later work on the foundations of geometry, published in 1894, Peano [a] discussed *independence* of axioms.

1.6   Such studies as those of Pasch, Peano, Hilbert, and Pieri in euclidean geometry provided a tremendous impetus for investigations of possible formal organizations of the subject matter of this old discipline; these considerations, in turn, provided new understanding of mathematical systems in general and were partly responsible for the remarkable mathematical advances of the twentieth century. Among the other important modern organizations of euclidean geometry may be mentioned the following: Pieri, a member of Peano's school in Italy, published, in the same year (1899) in which Hilbert's book appeared, a treatment of the subject in which he based his development upon an aggregate of "points" and an undefined concept of "motion." ‡ In 1904, Veblen [a] accomplished an organization of euclidean geometry in which the notion of betweenness, as used by Peano and Hilbert, was replaced by an order relation. As a result of suggestions

† From Nagel [a; 199]; quoted by permission of E. Nagel and *Osiris.*
‡ For a discussion of Pieri's system see Young [Y; Lecture XV].

made by R. L. Moore, a revision of Veblen's system appeared in 1911.†
(A rather interesting combination of the axiomatic systems of Hilbert
and Veblen was employed by Robinson [Ro] in a recent treatment of
euclidean geometry.)

It is noteworthy that these early studies in the field of geometry
were revealing the great generality that was inherent in formal mathematical systems. Mathematics was evolving in a direction that was
to compel the development of a method which could *encompass in a
single framework* of undefined terms and basic statements concepts like
group and *abstract space* that were appearing in seemingly unrelated
branches of mathematics. As will be pointed out below, the economy
of effort so achieved is one of the characteristic features of modern
mathematics.

2   Description of the method; the undefined terms and axioms

As commonly used in mathematics today, the axiomatic method
consists in setting forth certain basic statements about the concept
(such as the geometry of the plane) to be studied, using certain undefined technical terms as well as the terms of classical logic. Usually
no description of the meanings of the logical terms is given, and no
rules are stated about their use or the methods allowable for proving
theorems; perhaps these omissions form a weakness of the method.‡§
The basic statements are called *axioms* (or, synonymously, *postulates*). It is assumed that in proving theorems from the axioms the
rules of classical logic regarding contradictions and "excluded middle"
(II 2.1) may be employed; hence the "reductio ad absurdum" type of
proof is in common use. The statements of both the axioms and the
theorems proved from them are said to be *implied by* or *deduced from*
the axioms. An example might be instructive:

2.1   Let us consider again the subject of plane geometry. It will
be unnecessary to recall many details. We may perhaps assume,

---

† See J. W. A. Young [Yo; 3–51].

‡ In modern textbooks of geometry for elementary school use there are of course
directions to the student as to how to go about proving theorems; but such books
do not generally, on the other hand (and for obvious reasons), set forth the subject
in rigorous axiomatic form. See, however, Birkhoff and Beatley [B-B], who attempt
to instill in the minds of high school students the spirit of the modern axiomatic
method.

§ We are not here describing the method as used in modern mathematical logic
or the formalistic treatises of Hilbert and his followers, where the rules for operations
with the basic symbols and formulas are (of necessity) set forth in the language of
ordinary discourse. See Chapters IX and XI.

however, that the reader recalls from his high school course that *points* and *straight lines*, and such notions as that of *parallel* lines, were fundamental. Now, if we were going to set forth an axiomatic system for plane geometry in rigorous modern form, we would first of all select certain basic terms that we would leave undefined; perhaps "point" and "line" would be included here (the adjective "straight" can be omitted, since the *undefined* character of the term "line" enables us to choose to *mean* "straight line" in our thinking as well as in the later selection of statements for the axioms). Next we would scan the propositions of geometry and try to select certain basic ones with an eye to both their simplicity and their adequacy for proving the ones not selected; these we would call our *primary propositions* or *axioms*, to be left unproved in our system.

2.2   To be more explicit, let us proceed as though we were actually carrying out the above procedure; although we do not intend to give a complete system of axioms (cf. II 4), a miniature sample of what the axioms and *secondary propositions* or *theorems* might be like, together with sample proofs of the latter, follows:

Undefined terms: Point; line.
Axiom 1.   Every line is a collection of points.
Axiom 2.   There exist at least two points.
Axiom 3.   If p and q are points, then there exists one and only one line containing p and q.
Axiom 4.   If L is a line, then there exists a point not on L.
Axiom 5.   If L is a line, and p is a point not on L, then there exists one and only one line containing p that is parallel to L.

These axioms would not by any means suffice as a basis for proof of all the theorems of plane geometry, but they will be sufficient to prove a certain number of the theorems found in any organization of plane geometry. Their selection is motivated as follows: In the first place, the undefined terms "point" and "line" are to play a role like that of the variables in algebra. Thus, in the expression

$$x^2 - y^2 = (x - y)(x + y)$$

the x and y are undefined, in the sense that they may represent any individual numbers in a certain domain of numbers (as for instance the domain of ordinary integers). In the present instance, "point" may be any individual in a domain sufficiently delimited as to satisfy the statements set forth in the axioms. On the other hand, "line," as indicated in Axiom 1, has a range of values (= meanings) limited to certain collections of the individuals that are selected as "points." Thus Axiom 1 is designed to set up a *relationship* between the undefined entities *point* and *line*. It is *not* a *definition* of line, since (if the study is carried through) there will be other collections of points (circles, angles, etc.) that are not lines. Furthermore, it enables us, as we shall see presently, to define certain terms needed in the statements of the later axioms. Axiom 2 is the first step toward introducing lines into our geometry, and this is actually accomplished by adding Axiom 3. Before the latter can have meaning, however, we need the following formal definition:

2.3   Definition. If a point p is an element of the collection of points which constitutes a line L (cf. Axiom 1), then we say, variously, that L *contains* p, p is *on* L, or L is a line containing p.

Having stated Axioms 2 and 3, we would have that there exists a line in our geometry, but in order to have *plane* geometry and not merely a *line* or "one-dimensional" geometry we would have to say something to insure that not all points lie on a single line; Axiom 4 is designed to accomplish this. We would now imagine, intuitively (since we have a line L, a point p not on that line, and also a line through p and each point q of L), that we have practically a plane; however, so far as euclidean geometry is concerned, we have not provided, in Axioms 1–4, for the *parallel* to L through p until we have stated Axiom 5. And of course Axiom 5 is not significant until we have the definition:

2.4   Definition. Two lines L_1 and L_2 are called *parallel* if there is no point which is on both L_1 and L_2. (We may also call L_1 "parallel to" L_2, or conversely.)

2.5   Let us denote the above set of five axioms, together with the undefined terms point, line, by Γ and call it the *axiom system* Γ.

(We shall also frequently use the term "axiom system" in a broader sense to include the theorems, etc., implied by the axioms.)

For future purposes we note two aspects of Γ, but we shall not go into these fully at this point: (1) In addition to the *geometrical* ("technical") undefined terms *point, line*, we have used *logical* ("universal") undefined terms such as *collection, there exist, one, every*, and *not*. (2) That Γ is far from being a set of axioms adequate for plane geometry may be shown as follows: Since *point* and *line* are left undefined, we are at liberty to consider possible meanings for them, subject of course to the restriction that we take into account the statements made in the axioms. If we have been educated in the American or English school systems, our reactions to these terms will no doubt immediately be specialized, our geometric experience in the schools having the upper hand in our response. But let us imagine that the terms are entirely unfamiliar, although the logical terms used in the axioms are not unfamiliar, so that we may consider other possible meanings for point and line. Unquestionably this will involve considerable experimentation before suitable meanings are found. For example, we might first try letting "point" mean book and "line" mean library; we know from the statement in Axiom 1 that a line is a collection of points, and libraries form one of the most familiar collections in our daily experience. We can imagine that we live in a city, C, which has two distinct libraries, and that by library we mean either one of the libraries of C, and by book any one of the books in these two libraries. Axiom 2 becomes a valid statement: "There exist at least two books." However, Axiom 3 fails, since, if p and q designate books in different libraries, then there is no library that contains p and q. However, before trying other meanings for point and line, we notice that Axioms 4 and 5 are valid, becoming, respectively, "If L is a library, then there exists a book not on (i.e., in) L," and "If L is a library and p a book not on (i.e., in) L, then there exists one and only one library containing p that is parallel to (has no books in common with) L." †

Now, impressed by our failure to satisfy Axiom 3 on our first attempt at meanings for "point" and "line," we may, with an eye on Axiom 3, try to imagine a community, which we denote by Z, of people in which everyone belongs to some club, but in such a manner that, if p and q are two persons in Z, then there is one and only one club of which p and q are both members. In other words, we may try letting "point" mean a *person in Z* and "line" mean a *club in Z*, and imagine that the club situation in Z is such that the statement just made is valid, so that Axiom 3 is satisfied. We would then have no difficulty in seeing that Axioms 1, 2, and 4 are satisfied: "A club in Z is a collection of people in Z"; "There exist at least two people in Z"; etc. However, Axiom 5 becomes (with suitable change of wording to suit the new meanings): "If L is a club in Z, and p is a person in Z not in the club L, then there exists one and only one club in Z of which p is a member and which has no members in common with L." This is a statement which apparently makes a rather strong convention regarding the club situation in Z, and which may conceivably fail to apply; in any case, the stipulation that only one club have a given

† In parentheses we have placed the terms commonly employed in connection with libraries and books that are indicated by our definition of "on" and "parallel."

pair of persons as members can hardly be expected to suffice for Axiom 5! To clinch the matter suppose that Z is a "ghost" community, there being only three persons, whom we shall designate by a, b and c respectively, living in Z; and that as a result of certain circumstances each pair ab, bc, and ac shares a secret from the third member of the community, so that we may consider this bond between each two as forming them into a club ("secret society") excluding the third member. Now, with the meaning of point and line as before, we see that Axioms 1–4 hold but Axiom 5 does not hold.

Before rejecting the latter attempt as impossible, however, let us imagine that Z has *four* citizens: a, b, c, and d. And suppose that *each pair* of these people forms a club excluding the other two members of the community; that is, there are six clubs consisting of ab, ac, ad, bc, bd, and cd. Now *all* the axioms of Γ are satisfied with the meanings *person in* Z for "point" and *club in* Z for "line"! And we may then notice that we could arrive at a similar example by taking *any* collection Z of *four* things a, b, c, and d, and, by letting "point" mean a member or *element* of the collection Z, and "line" mean any pair of elements of Z, satisfy the statements embodied in the axioms of Γ.

2.6   Although we may experience no particular thrill at this discovery—may, rather, begin to feel that it is a rather trivial game we are playing in toying with possible meanings for the system Γ—we might conceivably be beguiled into seeking an answer to questions such as: How many "points" must a collection have in order to serve as the basis for an example satisfying the statements in Γ? For a given collection at hand, how many "points" must a "line" have in order to satisfy Γ? (For example, a "line" above could not have consisted of *three* persons in Z in the case where Z has exactly four citizens.) Furthermore, if we have already a general knowledge of, or experience with, plane geometry, the above example shows us that Γ is far from being a sufficient basis for euclidean geometry; certainly an adequate set of axioms for plane geometry would exclude the possibility of the geometry permitting a set of only *four* points satisfying all the axioms.

Before proceeding any further with this general discussion, however, let us notice how theorems would be proved from such a system as Γ.

3   Description of the method; the proving of theorems

Having set down a system, such as Γ for instance, we then proceed to see what statements are *implied*, or can be *proved* or *deduced from* the system. Contrary to the manner in which we proceeded in high school, when we brought in all kinds of propositions and assumptions not included in the fundamental terms and axioms (such as "breadth"; "a line has no breadth"), and even drew diagrams and pictures embodying properties that we promptly accepted as part of our equipment,† we take care to use only points and lines, and those relations and properties of points and lines that are given in the axioms. (Of course, after we have proved a statement, we may use it in later proofs instead of going back to the axioms and proving it all over again.) There is no objection to drawing diagrams, provided they are used only to aid in the reasoning process and do not trick us into making assumptions not implied by the axioms; indeed, the professional mathematician uses them constantly. The reader might recall here the quotation from Pasch in 1.5 above.

3.1   Consider the following formal theorem and proof:

Theorem 1.   *Every point is on at least two distinct lines.*
Proof.   Let p denote any point. Since by Axiom 2 there exist at least two points, there must exist a point q distinct from p. And by Axiom 3 there exists a line L containing p and q. Furthermore, by Axiom 4 there exists a point r not on L, and (again by Axiom 3) a line K containing p and r.

Now by Axiom 1 every line is a collection of points. Hence, for two lines to be distinct (i.e., different), the two collections which constitute them must be different; or, what amounts to the same thing, one of them must contain a point that is not on the other. The lines L and K are distinct, then, because K contains the point r which is not on L. As p is on both L and K, the theorem is proved.

3.2   Now it will be noticed that we have used Axioms 1–4 in the proof, but not Axiom 5. We could, then, go back to the example of the community Z, let "point" mean *person in Z* and "line" mean *pair of persons in Z*, rephrase Axioms 1–4 in these terms, and carry through the proof of Theorem 1 in these terms. That is, Theorem 1 is a "true" statement about any example, such as Z, which satisfies the statements embodied in Axioms 1–4 of Γ. In proving Theorem 1, then, *we have in one step proved many different statements about many different examples,* namely the statements corresponding to Theorem 1 as they appear in the different examples that satisfy Axioms 1–4 of Γ. This aspect of the "economy" achieved in using the axiomatic method

† A classical example may be found in the well-known "proof" that all triangles are isosceles, which is based on a diagram that deceives the eye by placing a certain point *within* an angle instead of outside, where rigorous reasoning about the situation would place it. This may be found in J. W. Young [Y; 143–145].

will be, further dwelt upon later (II 4.12). If, because of some diagram or other aid to thought, we had used some property of point or line not stated in Axioms 1–4, we could not expect to make the above assertions, and the "economy" cited would be lost!

Note, too, that Theorem 1 will remain valid in any axiom system (such as Γ) that *contains* the undefined terms point and line as well as Axioms 1–4. In particular, it is valid for euclidean plane geometry, which is only one of the possible geometries embodying these four axioms, and which, as we stated before, would require many more axioms than those stated above.

3.3   Now consider the following statement, which we call a *corollary* of Theorem 1: †

Corollary.   *Every line contains at least one point.*

3.4   Before considering a proof (see 3.5), we hasten to meet an objection which the "uninitiated" might make at this point; to wit, since Axiom 1 explicitly states that a line is a collection of points, *of course* every line contains at least one point, so why should this be repeated as a corollary of Theorem 1? This is not a trivial matter, and it leads directly to a question which causes considerable concern in modern mathematics, namely, what is meant by *collection?* We said above that "collection" is an undefined logical term, and as such we took it for granted that its use is universally understood and employed, just as the word "the" is universally understood and used by anyone familiar with the English language. But now we find ourselves almost immediately in need of explaining the use of the term in the above corollary (see also II 7f).

However, there is nothing so very astonishing about this if we reflect that, whenever we try to make very precise a term in ordinary use, it is usually necessary to adopt certain conventions. For example, such terms as *vegetable, fruit, animal* are commonly "understood" and used by anyone who habitually uses the English language, but, when we come to apply them to certain special objects, it is frequently necessary to agree on some convention; as, for example, that a certain type of living substance shall be called "animal" rather than "fish" (e.g., *whale*). So, for instance, we may want to make the con-

† We assume the reader recalls that this indicates that the statement so designated follows almost directly from Theorem 1. We could avoid the use of the term entirely, of course, by calling the statement "Theorem 2," but then probably the reader familiar with ordinary geometry or axiomatic procedure in general would inquire *why* wasn't the term "corollary" used!

vention that, if person A wishes to talk about "the collection of all coins in B's pockets," he may do so even though person B is literally penniless! In other words, no matter whether there actually are coins in B's pockets or not, the collection of all such coins is to be regarded as an existing entity; we call the collection *empty* if B has no coins. (In case B is penniless, we may also talk about "the coin in B's pocket," but in this case there is no existing entity to which the phrase refers.) And this is the convention that is generally agreed on throughout mathematics and logic, namely, that a collection may "exist," as in the case of the collection of all coins in B's pockets, even though it is empty.

When we come to mention an *algebra* of sets, we shall see another reason for the convention regarding empty collections, analogous to the reason for the introduction of a number *zero* in arithmetic (cf. III 3.4).

3.5   Proof of corollary to Theorem 1.   There exists a point p by Axiom 2, and by Theorem 1 there exist two distinct lines L_1 and L_2 containing p.

Now, if there exists a line L that contains no points, then both L_1 and L_2 are parallel to L (by definition). As this would stand in contradiction to Axiom 5, it follows that there cannot exist such a line L.

3.6   A statement "stronger" than the above corollary is embodied in the next theorem:

Theorem 2.   *Every line contains at least two points.*

Proof.   Let L be any line. By the above corollary, L contains a point p. To show p not the only point on L, we shall use a "proof by contradiction." Suppose p is the only point that L contains. By Theorem 1 there is another line L_1 containing p. Now L_1 must contain at least one other point, q; for otherwise L and L_1 would each contain only p, hence be the same collection of points and ergo the same line (Axiom 1). By Axiom 4 there is a point x which is not on L_1, and by Axiom 5 there is a line L_2 containing x and parallel to L_1. But both L and L_1 are lines containing p and parallel to L_2, in violation of Axiom 5. We must conclude, then, that the supposition that p is the only point on L cannot hold and hence that L contains at least two points.

Now, since by Theorem 2 every line contains at least two points, and since by Axiom 3 two given points can lie simultaneously on only one line, we can state:

Corollary (to Theorem 2). *Every line is completely determined by any two of its points that are distinct.*

3.7   Theorem 3. *There exist at least four distinct points.*

Proof. By Axiom 2 there exist at least two distinct points p and q. By Axiom 3 there exists a line L containing p and q, and by Axiom 4 there exists a point x not on L. By Axiom 5 there exists a line L_1 containing x and parallel to L, and by Theorem 2 L_1 contains at least two distinct points (cf. Definition 2.4).

3.8   Theorem 4. *There exist at least six distinct lines.*

Before proving Theorem 4, we perhaps need to make sure that the meaning of another one of our "common" terms is agreed upon, namely the word "distinct." As we are using the term, two collections are distinct if they are not the *same*. Thus, the lines L and L_1 which figure in the proof of Theorem 2 are distinct, although under the supposition made there L_1 *contains* L, for they are not the *same* line (L_1 contains q and L does not).

Proof of Theorem 4. We proceed, as in the proof of Theorem 3, to obtain the line L containing the points p and q, and the line L_1 parallel to L containing two distinct points (Theorem 2) x and y. By Axiom 3 there exist lines K and K_1 determined respectively by the pairs (p, x), (q, y). Now the point q is not on K, else by Axiom 3 K and L would be the same line (which is impossible since x is not on L). Also, y is not on K, else K and L_1 would be the same line. Similarly, p is not on K_1 and x is not on K_1. Now there also exist lines M and M_1 determined respectively by the pairs (p, y), (q, x); and we can show that q is not on M, x is not on M, p is not on M_1, and y is not on M_1. It follows that no two of the lines L, L_1, K, K_1, M, M_1 are the same.

4 Comment on the above theorems and proofs

If the reader has followed the proofs given above, he has probably resorted to the use of figures by this time! This would be quite natural, since in high school geometry he used figures; and they help to keep the various symbols (L, p, q, $\cdots$) and their significance in mind. However, as we stated above, no special meanings have been assigned to "point" and "line," and consequently the above proofs should, and do, hold just as well if the reader uses coins for "points" and pairs of coins for "lines." As a matter of fact, if *any* collection of four objects is employed, "point" meaning any object of the collection and "line" any pair of the objects, then the reader may follow the above proofs with these meanings in mind.

Of course, the theorems we have stated in the preceding sections are not by any means all the theorems that we might state. For example, we can show that any collection of objects satisfying the axioms of the system Γ must, if not infinite as in ordinary geometry, satisfy certain conditions regarding the number of points (there cannot be just 5 points in the collection, for instance), and that there must be a relation between the number of lines and the number of points in the collection. (See Problems 3–5 at the end of the chapter.) In fact, we can continue the above study to a surprising extent; we could hardly expect to reach a point where we could confidently assert that no more theorems could be proved. It is not our intention to extend the number of theorems, however, since we believe that we have already obtained enough theorems and proofs to serve as specimens for our later purposes. (See Problem 6 at the end of the chapter.)

4.1   As a useful terminology in what follows, let us agree that, when we use the term "statement" in connection with an axiom system Σ, we shall mean a sentence phrased, or phrasable, in the undefined terms and universal terms of Σ; such a statement may be called a Σ-*statement*. Thus the axioms of Γ are Γ-statements (Axiom 5 contains the word "parallel," but this is "phrasable" in the undefined terms and universal terms), as are also the theorems.

4.2   In conformance with the conventions made in Section 2, we shall say that an axiom system Σ *implies* a statement S if S follows by logical argument, such as used above, from Σ. In particular, each axiom is itself implied, trivially. We shall also say S is *logically deducible* from Σ if Σ implies S.

4.3   In the course of our work above we had to pause in two instances to explain the conventions we were making in regard to the use of two words commonly used in ordinary discourse, namely "collection" and "distinct." These words were left undefined, to be sure, in the sense that they are supposedly universally understood nontechnical terms; but, as we discovered, not so "universal" but that it was felt advisable to give some conventions we were making in regard to their use here! On the other hand, the words "point" and "line" we left strictly undefined, saying that any meaning whatsoever could be assigned to them as long as these meanings were consistent with the statements embodied in the axioms. We saw that the "collection = library," "point = book" meanings were not permissible, but that, if C is any collection of four objects, then "point = object of C," "line = pair of objects of C" are permissible meanings. The terms "point," "line," "parallel," etc., we may call *technical* terms of the system, the terms "point" and "line" being the *undefined technical terms*. The terms "collection," "distinct" might be called *universal terms* or *logical terms* (cf. 2.5).

Other examples of universal terms in Γ are "exist" (in Axiom 2), "one" (Axiom 3), "two" (Theorem 1), "four" (Theorem 3), "six" (Theorem 4), "and" (Axiom 3), "or" (Definition 1), "not" (Axiom 4), and "every" (Theorem 1). However, if we were setting up an axiom system for the elementary arithmetic of integers ($1 + 2 = 3$, $2 \times 2 = 4$, etc.), we might use a term like "one" as an undefined technical term. Thus the same term may have different roles in different axiom systems! The sense in which the numbers "one," "two," etc., are used above—that is, in the universal sense—will be discussed in greater detail later (IV 4). As the term "exist" is used above, it is chiefly *permissive* so far as proofs are concerned, and *stipulative* for examples; thus in the proof of Theorem 3 we were permitted to introduce the line L_1 by virtue of Axiom 5, and the example of the "ghost community" containing only three persons (2.5) failed because it could not meet the stipulation concerning the existence of a certain line parallel to another line which is made in Axiom 5. It will be necessary, as we shall see, to distinguish between this type of "existence" and what is generally called "mathematical existence." The terms "and," "or," and "not," as logical terms, will be discussed further later. We also wish to remark about the use of the word "element" in connection with the term "collection" in Definition 1; more will be said about this in the sequel.

5   Source of the axioms

But enough for the moment regarding the *language* used in the axioms. Let us consider more fully the *source of the statements* embodied in the axioms. We chose axioms for *geometry* in our example Γ since we felt that we could assume the reader had studied some elementary geometry in high school. That is, we were careful to pick a subject already familiar! The undefined technical terms "point" and "line" already have a meaning of some sort for us. And, as we shall see, this is the usual way in which axioms are obtained; *they are statements about some concept with which we already have some familiarity*. Thus, if we are already familiar with arithmetic, we might begin to set down axioms for arithmetic. Of course the method is not restricted to mathematics. If we are familiar with some field such as physics, philosophy, chemistry, zoology, economics, for instance, we might choose to set down some axioms for it, or a portion of it, and see what theorems we might logically deduce from them.† We may say, then, that an *axiom*, as used in the modern way, is *a statement which seems to hold for an underlying concept*, an *axiom system* being *a collection of such statements about the concept*.

Thus, in practice, the concept comes first, the axioms later. Theoretically this is not necessary, of course. Thus, we may say "Let us take as undefined terms *aba* and *daba*, and set down some axioms in these and universal logical terms." With no concept in mind, it is difficult to think of anything to say! That is, unless we first *give some meanings* to "aba" and "daba"—that is, introduce some *concept* to talk about—it is difficult to find anything to say at all. And, if we finally do make some statements without first fitting a suitable concept to "aba" and "daba," we shall, very likely, make statements that contradict one another! As we shall see below, the underlying concept is not only a source of the axioms, but it also guides us to *consistency* (about which we shall speak directly).

Thus, we select the concept; then we select the terms that are to be left undefined and the statements that are to form our axioms; and finally we prove theorems as we did above. This is a simplification of the process, to be sure, but in a general way it describes the method. It is to be noted how the procedure, as so formulated, differs from the classical use of the method. In the classical use the axioms were regarded as absolute truths—absolutely true statements about material space—and as having a certain character of necessity. To have stated the parallel axiom, Axiom 5 above, was to have stated something "obviously true," something one took for granted if one had thought about the character of the space in which he lived. It would have been inconceivable before the nineteenth century to state an axiom such as "If L is a line and p a point not on L, then there exist at least two distinct lines containing p and parallel to L." To have in mathematics, simultaneously, two axiom systems Γ_1 and Γ_2 with axioms in Γ_1 denying axioms in Γ_2, as is the case in mathematics today with the euclidean and non-euclidean geometries, would also have been inconceivable! But, if we take the point of view that an axiom is only a statement about some concept,‡ so that axioms con-

---

† As an example in genetics and embryology, see J. H. Woodger [Wo].

‡ It is only in this sense—that an axiom is a statement *true* of some concept—that the word "true" can be used of an axiom.

tradicting one another in different systems only express basic differences in the concepts from which they were derived, we see that no fundamental difficulty exists. What is important is that axioms in the *same* system should not contradict one another. This brings us to the point where we should discuss consistency and other characteristics of an axiom system.

5.1   Remark

The derivation of an axiom system for non-euclidean geometry from axioms for euclidean geometry, using the device of replacing the parallel axiom by one of its denials, is an example of another manner in which new axiom systems may be obtained. In general, we may select a given axiom system and change one or more of the axioms therein in suitable manner to derive a new axiom system. See II 6.1.

SUGGESTED READING

Bell [B₁; 20–46]   Pasch and Dehn [P-D; 185–271]
Hilbert [H₃]   Poincaré [Po; 55–91]
Kerschner and Wilcox [K-W; II, VI]   Richardson [R; II]
Nagel [a]   Veblen [a]
Newsom [Ne]   Veblen and Young [V-Y; 2–7]
Northrop [N; 221–230]   Young [Y; I–IV]

PROBLEMS

1. Obtain other meanings for "point" and "line" which make the axioms of Γ true statements. Also find a collection of *nine* objects (instead of four, as obtained in Section 2.5) "satisfying" these axioms.

2. Do the lines M and M_1, defined in the proof of Theorem 4 in Section 3.8, necessarily have a point in common?

In Problems 3–6, it may be assumed that the number of points is finite. This is, however, an unnecessary assumption in 3 and 4, if familiarity with the notion of cardinal number is assumed (see Chapter IV).

3. Prove as a theorem of the axiom system Γ: The number of points on a line is constant; that is, any two lines have the same number of points.

4. Prove as a theorem of the axiom system Γ: The number of lines containing a given point is constant.

5. If m is the number of lines containing a given point, and r is the number of points on a line (constant according to problem 3), then prove as a theorem of Γ that $m = r + 1$.

6. State and prove other new theorems for the axiom system Γ̇. (For instance, consider how many points there are on all lines, in terms of the number r above.)

7. Make up a simple axiom system of your own and prove a few theorems. (For example, "bee" and "hive" might be used as undefined terms.)

8. As an experiment, try constructing a system of axioms with undefined terms "aba" and "daba" with no meanings in mind for these terms. To what mental devices do you find yourself resorting?

9. In Veblen [a] it is stated: "A definition is an agreement to substitute a single term or symbol for more complex terms or symbols." Discuss. Compare the introductory remarks of Chapter III.

10. In what respect do "definitions" such as those given in Sections 4.1 and 4.2 differ from Definitions 2.3 and 2.4?

11. Would we necessarily become involved in contradictions in an axiom system if, in formulating an axiom as a statement which "seems to hold" for some concept, the statement is actually a false statement about the concept?

12. Why is not the corollary to Theorem 2 a direct consequence of Axiom 3 of the system Γ?

II

Analysis of
the Axiomatic Method

When the undefined terms and the primary propositions or axioms have tentatively been selected, how can it be ascertained that the resulting axiom system is suited to the purposes for which it was set up? If, for example, it was set up to serve as a base on which to prove all theorems of euclidean plane geometry, then we should like some method whereby we can show that it suffices to do so. On the contrary, we may wish an axiom system to serve as an introduction to several different kinds of geometry, sufficing to prove the theorems common to them all, and no more. Another question that might arise would concern the so-called "independence" of the axioms; are any of the axioms provable from the others, and, if so, should we not delete them from the system, relegating them to the body of theorems to be proved later?

Experience has shown, however, that a much more fundamental and critical question is, does the system imply any contradictory theorems? If it does, clearly something is wrong, and it is useless to inquire into other questions until this defect has been eliminated. We shall therefore consider this question first.

1 Consistency of an axiom system

From a logical point of view we can make the following definition:

1.1 Definition. An axiom system Σ is called *consistent* if contradictory statements are not implied by Σ.

Now this definition gives rise to certain questions and criticisms. In the first place, given an axiom system Σ, *how are we going to tell whether it is consistent or not?* Conceivably we might prove two theorems from Σ which contradict one another, and hence conclude that Σ is *not* consistent.

For example, if we added to the system Γ of Chapter I the new axiom, "There exist at most three points," it would become apparent, as soon as Theorem 3 of Γ was proved (cf. I 3.7), that the new system of axioms is not consistent.

But, supposing that this does not happen, are we going to conclude that Σ is consistent? How can we tell that, if we continued stating and proving theorems, we might not ultimately arrive at contradictory statements and hence *inconsistency!* We remarked above (I 4) about the system Γ that we could hardly expect to reach a point where we could say with confidence that no more theorems could be stated. And, unless we could have all possible theorems in front of our eyes, capable of being scanned for contradictions, how could we assert that the system is consistent? We are immediately faced with the problem: Is there any *procedure for proving a system of axioms consistent?* And, if so, on what basis does the proof rest, since the proof cannot be conducted *within* the system as in the case of the theorems of the system!

Another difficulty would arise from the fact that it might be very hard to recognize that a contradiction is implied, when such is the case. There are examples in mathematical literature of cases where considerable material was published concerning systems which later were found to be inconsistent! Until someone suspected the inconsistency and set out to prove it, or (as in some cases) stumbled upon it by chance, the systems seemed quite valid and worth while. It can also happen, for example, that the theorems become so numerous and complicated that we fail to detect a pair of contradictory ones. For example, although two theorems might really be of the form "S" and "not S" respectively, because of the manner in which they are stated it might escape our attention that they contradict one another. In short, the usefulness of the above definition is limited by our ability to recognize a contradiction even when it is staring us in the face, so to speak.

The former objection, that hinging upon the probable impossibility of setting down all theorems implied by the system, is the more serious from the point of view of the working mathematician. And as a consequence the mathematician usually resorts to the procedure described below:

Let us make the definition:

1.2   Definition. If Σ is an axiom system, then an *interpretation* of Σ is the assignment of meanings to the undefined technical terms of Σ in such a way that the axioms become true statements for all values of the variables (such as p and q of Axiom 3, I 2.2, for instance).

This definition requires some explanation. First, as an example we can cite the system Γ above and the meanings "point" = any one of a collection of four coins and "line" = any pair of coins in this collection. The axioms now become statements about the collection of coins and are easily seen to be true thereof. Hence this assignment of meanings is an interpretation of Γ. As the axioms stand, with "point" and "line" having no assigned meanings, they cannot be called either true or not true. (Similarly, we cannot speak of the expression "$x^2 - y^2 = (x - y)(x + y)$" as being either true or false until *meanings*, such as "x and y are integers," are assigned.) But, with the meanings assigned above, they are true statements about a "meaningful" concept. As a rule, we shall use the word "model" to denote the *result* of the assignment of meanings to the undefined terms. Thus the collection of four coins, considered a collection of points and lines according to the meanings assigned above, is a model of Γ. Generally, if an interpretation I is made of an axiom system, we shall denote the model resulting from I by $\mathfrak{M}(I)$.

For some models of an axiom system Σ, certain axioms of Σ may be *vacuously satisfied*. That is, axioms of the form "If . . . , then . . . ," such as Axiom 3 of Γ, which we might call "conditional axioms," may be true as interpreted only because the conditional "If . . ." part is not fulfilled by the model.

Suppose, for example, we delete Axioms 2 and 4 from Γ and denote the resulting system by Γ'. Then a collection of coins containing just one coin is a model for Γ', if we interpret "point" to mean coin and "line" to mean a collection containing just one coin. For in this model the "If . . ." parts of Axioms 3 and 5 are not fulfilled. (Note that, for Axiom 3 to be false of a model $\mathfrak{M}$, there must be *two* points p and q in $\mathfrak{M}$ such that either no line of $\mathfrak{M}$ contains p and q or more than one line of $\mathfrak{M}$ contains p and q.)

This may be better illustrated, perhaps, by the following digression: Suppose boy A tells girl B, "If it happens that the sun shines Sunday, then I will take you boating." And let us suppose that on Sunday it rains all day, the sun not once peeping out between the clouds. Then, no matter whether A takes B boating or not, it cannot asserted that he made her a false promise. For his promise to have been false, (1) the sun must have shone Sunday and (2) A must not have taken B boating. And, in general, for a statement of the form "If . . . , then . . ." to be false, the "If . . ." condition must be fulfilled and the "then . . ." not be fulfilled.

Now we did not have in mind a collection of four coins when we set down the axioms of Γ. We were thinking of something entirely different, namely euclidean geometry as we knew it in high school. "Point" had for us then an entirely different meaning—something "without length, breadth, or thickness"; and "line" meant a "straight" line that had "length, but no breadth or thickness." Do not these meanings also yield a model of Γ—what we might perhaps call an "ideal" model? We may admit that this is so, and, as we shall see later, we resort frequently in mathematics to such ideal models— always, of course, when it happens that every collection of objects serving as a model must of necessity be infinite in number. (Such is the case, for instance, when we have enough axioms in a geometry to insure an infinite number of lines.) We return to this discussion later (see 2.3); at present, let us go on to the so-called "working definition" of consistency:

1.3   Definition.   An axiom system Σ is *satisfiable* if there exists an interpretation of Σ.

Now what is the relation between the two definitions 1.1 and 1.3? What we actually want of any axiom system is that it be consistent in the sense of 1.1. But we saw that 1.1 was not a practicable definition except in cases where contradictory statements are actually found to be implied by the system and inconsistency is thus recognized. Where a system is consistent, we are usually unable to tell the fact from 1.1. But, as in the case of the four-coin interpretation of Γ above, we have a very simple test showing "satisfiability" in the sense of 1.3. Does this imply consistency in the sense of 1.1? The mathematician and the logician take the point of view that it does, and, in order to explain why, we have to go into the domain of logic for a few moments.

2   The proof of consistency of an axiom system

2.1   The Law of Contradiction and the Law of the Excluded Middle

First let us recall two basic "laws" of classical (i.e., Aristotelian) logic, namely the Law of Contradiction and the Law of the Excluded Middle; the latter is also called the Law of the Excluded Third ("tertium non datur"). These are frequently, and loosely, described as follows: If S is any statement, then the Law of Contradiction states that S and a contradiction (i.e., any denial) of S cannot both hold. And the Law of the Excluded Middle states that either S holds or a denial of S holds. For example, let S be the statement "Today is

Tuesday." The Law of Contradiction certainly holds here, for today cannot be *both* Tuesday and Wednesday, for example. And the Law of the Excluded Middle states that either today is Tuesday or it is not Tuesday.

But "things are not so simple as they seem" here. Unless one limits himself to a specified point on the earth (or parallel of longitude), it *can* be both Tuesday and Wednesday at the same time! And, without including in S such a geographical provision, the statement "Either today is Tuesday or it is not Tuesday" can hardly be accepted. As a matter of fact, whenever such statements are made there usually exists a tacit understanding between speaker and listener that their locale at the time is the place being referred to.

Or consider the statement "The king of the United States wears bow ties." Does the Law of the Excluded Middle hold here? Or let S be the statement "All triangles are green."

The upshot of this is merely that, although these "laws" are called "universally valid," some sort of qualifications have to be made with regard to their applicability in order for them to have validity. In so far as axiomatic systems are concerned, the problem is not so great, since we can restrict our use of the term "statement" to the convention already made in section I 4.1 ("Σ-statement"). And this will be our understanding from now on. Further qualifications regarding the applicability of these logical "laws" will be noted in the discussion of completeness below.

2.2   As soon as an interpretation of a system Σ is made, the statements of the system become statements about the resulting model. Let us assume the following, which may be considered *basic principles of applied logic!*

2.2.1   All statements implied by an axiom system Σ hold true for all models of Σ;

2.2.2   The Law of Contradiction holds for all statements about a model of an axiom system Σ, provided they are Σ-statements whose technical terms have the meanings given in the interpretation. We can make this clearer and more precise by introducing the notion of an I-Σ-statement:

2.2.3   If Σ is an axiom system and I denotes an interpretation of Σ, then the result of assigning to the technical terms in a Σ-statement their meanings in I will be called an I-Σ-statement.

Then 2.2.1 and 2.2.2 become respectively:

2.2.1   Every I-Σ-statement, such that the corresponding Σ-statement is implied by Σ, holds true for $\mathfrak{M}(I)$ (cf. 1.2);

2.2.2   Contradictory I-Σ-statements cannot both hold true of $\mathfrak{M}(I)$.

Under the assumption that 2.2.1 and 2.2.2 hold, satisfiability implies consistency. For, if an axiom system Σ implies two contradictory Σ-statements, then by 2.2.1 these statements as I-Σ-statements hold true for the model $\mathfrak{M}(I)$; but the latter is impossible by 2.2.2. Hence we must conclude that, if 2.2.1 and 2.2.2 are valid, then the existence of an interpretation for an axiom system Σ guarantees the consistency of Σ in the sense of 1.1. And this is the basis for the "working definition" 1.3. For example, the existence of the "four-coin interpretation" of the system Γ above guarantees the consistency of Γ if we grant 2.2.1 and 2.2.2.

The reader will have noticed that we have not proved that consistency in the sense of 1.1 implies satisfiability. To go into this question would be impractical, since it would necessitate going into detail concerning formal logical systems (cf. Chapter XI) and is too complicated to describe here.

2.3   In Section 1 we used the term "ideal" model, by way of contrast to such models as that of the four coins for Γ; the latter might be termed a "concrete" model. It was pointed out that, whenever an axiom system Σ requires an infinite collection in each of its models, then of necessity the models are "ideal."

This raises not only the question as to how reliable are "ideal" models, but also the question as to what constitutes an *allowable* model. What we should like, of course, is a criterion which would allow only models that satisfy assumptions 2.2.1, 2.2.2, and especially the latter. If there is any danger that an ideal model may require such a degree of abstraction that it harbors contradictions in violation of 2.2.2, then clearly the use of models is no general guarantee of consistency in spite of what we have said above.

Further light can be shed on this matter by a consideration of well-known examples. It is not an uncommon practice, for instance, to obtain a model of an axiom system Σ in another branch of mathematics —even in a branch of mathematics that is, in its turn, based on an axiom system Σ'! How valid are such models? Do they necessarily satisfy 2.2.2? For example, to establish the consistency of a non-euclidean geometry we give a model of it in euclidean geometry! (See Richardson [R; 418–419] for instance.) But suppose that the euclidean geometry harbors contradictions; what then? Evidently all we can conclude here is that, *if* euclidean geometry is consistent, then so is the non-euclidean geometry whose model we have set up in the euclidean framework.

We are forced to admit that in such cases we have no absolute test for consistency, but only what we may call a *relative consistency proof*. The axiom system Σ' may be one in whose consistency we have great confidence, and then we may feel that we achieve a high degree of plausibility for consistency, but in the final analysis we have to admit that we are not *sure* of it.†

As we shall see later, other tests for consistency are being explored by the methods of formal logic. But, until such methods are successfully developed, the use of models, even of an "ideal" character, will have to suffice.

3 Independence of axioms

In the first paragraph of this chapter we mentioned "independence" of axioms. By "independence" we mean essentially that we are "not saying too much" in stating our axioms. For example, if to the five axioms of the system Γ (I 2.2) we added a sixth axiom stating "There exist at least four points," we would provide no new information inasmuch as the axiom is already implied by Γ (see Theorem 3 of I 3.7). Of course the addition of such an axiom would not destroy the property of consistency inherent in Γ.

3.1   In order to state a formal definition of independence, let Σ denote an axiom system and let A denote one of the axioms of Σ. Let us denote some denial of A by $\sim$A, and let $\Sigma - $ A denote the system Σ with A deleted. If S is any Σ-statement, $\Sigma + $ S will mean the axiom system containing the axioms of Σ and the statement S as a new axiom. Then we define:

3.1.1   Definition. If Σ is an axiom system and A is one of the axioms of Σ, then A is called *independent* in Σ, or an independent axiom of Σ, if both Σ and the axiom system $(\Sigma - $ A$) + \sim$A are satisfiable.

3.2   Just which of the many forms of $\sim$A is used is immaterial. Thus Axiom 5 is independent in Γ (I 2.2) if Γ is satisfiable and if the first four axioms of Γ together with a "non-euclidean" form of the axiom constitute a satisfiable system. For example, for a denial of Axiom 5 take the statement: "There exist a line L and point p not on

† In one well-known case, the system Σ' is a *subsystem* of Σ; viz., the Gödel proof (Gödel [G]) of the relative consistency of the axiom of choice (III 6.3) when adjoined to the set theory axioms.

L, such that there does not exist a line containing p and parallel to L." To show that the system Γ with Axiom 5 replaced by this statement forms a satisfiable system, let us take a collection of *three* coins, let "point" mean a coin of this collection, and "line" mean any pair of points of this collection. Then we have an interpretation of the new system, showing it to be satisfiable. We have already ascertained (2.2) that Γ is satisfiable, and so we conclude that Axiom 5 is independent in Γ.

3.3   The reader will probably gather by this time that the reason for specifying the satisfiability of Σ, in Definition 3.1.1, is to insure that some $\sim$A is not a *necessary* consequence of the axioms of $\Sigma - A$; for, if it were, we would not wish to call A "independent." And, as the definition is phrased, it insures that neither A nor any denial, $\sim$A, of A is implied by the system $\Sigma - A$, so that the addition of A to $\Sigma - A$ is really the supplying of new information.

3.4   Actually, however, we do not place the same emphasis on independence as we do on consistency. Consistency is *always* desired, but there may be cases where independence is *not* desired. Examples of this arise in the teaching of mathematics. Frequently we develop a subject by stating axioms and proving theorems—so that the axiomatic method assumes thereby a pedagogical role. Now it sometimes happens that an early theorem is extremely difficult to prove. Then the theorem may be stated as one of the axioms. Later, when the students have gained sufficient maturity and familiarity with the subject, it may be disclosed to them that the "axiom" is not really independent and a demonstration of its proof from the other axioms of the system may be given. Generally speaking, of course, it is preferable to have all axioms independent; but, if some axiom turns out not to be independent, the system is not invalidated.

As a matter of fact, some well-known and important axiom systems, when first published, contained axioms that were not independent (a fact unknown at the time to the authors, of course). An example of this is the original formulation of the set of axioms for geometry given by Hilbert [H₁] in 1899 (already referred to in I 1.4 and I 1.5). This set of axioms contained two axioms which were later discovered to be implied by the other axioms.† This in no way invalidated the system; it was only necessary to change the axioms to theorems (sup-

---

† See E. H. Moore [a], A. Rosenthal [a, b, c], S. Weinlös [a, b], and Lindenbaum [a]. Also see the footnotes to the first chapter of Hilbert [H₂].

plying the proofs of the latter, of course). Other cases could be cited.†

3.5   Types of independence other than that defined in 3.1.1 have been proposed. For example, E. H. Moore [Mo₁; 82] defined what he called "complete independence":

3.5.1   A system of axioms, Σ, is called *completely independent* if, for every subsystem A_i, A_j, $\cdots$, A_k of the axioms, both Σ and $(\Sigma - A_i - A_j - \cdots - A_k) + {\sim}A_i + {\sim}A_j + \cdots + {\sim}A_k$ are consistent. Here A_i, A_j, $\cdots$, A_k are axioms of Σ and ${\sim}A_i$, ${\sim}A_j$, $\cdots$, ${\sim}A_k$ are denials of A_i, A_j, $\cdots$, A_k respectively. If we take "consistent" to mean "satisfiable," this definition is evidently a generalization of Definition 3.1.1. We shall not go further into this notion, however.

3.6   Before leaving the notion of independence, it might be interesting to consider its relation to the *number* of axioms in a system. If a consistent system of axioms, Σ, contains twelve axioms, say, and one of them is discovered to be not independent, then the system is reducible to only eleven axioms. The system may then be said to be "simplified by this reduction"; the concept "described" by Σ can now be "described" in fewer words. However, this line of thought is illusory, for it does not take much reflection to convince one that mere *number* of axioms is no measure of simplicity. An axiom system may, in a valid sense, be said to be simplified if an axiom is split up into several axioms. Sometimes one decides that an axiom has said too much; so much in fact that it becomes difficult to digest its meaning. The difficulty may be removed by giving instead several axioms, each of a simply understood character, and in toto saying what the original axiom stated.

There is no general rule to guide one in these respects. It is a case of "the same thing can be said in many ways," and consequently one uses his best judgment as to how he will accomplish "simplicity." One can put too much into a single axiom; as an extreme, all axioms of a system can be lumped together in a series of conjunctions (called a "logical product") into one big axiom—thus achieving independence neatly—or one can split an axiom to the point of triteness. (See 4.10.)

† For example, a well-known and for many years widely used (for teaching purposes) system of eight axioms for plane topology due to R. L. Moore [a] was found by the present author [a] to contain a non-independent axiom. In this case the suspicion that the axiom was not independent arose from the fact that the independence proof given for the axiom was not valid, and search for a new proof proved fruitless.

An amusing example is given by Helmer [a] which we may transfer to the system Γ (I 2.2) as follows: Consider Axiom 3 of Γ. For the sake of brevity let us denote the combination of words "If p and q are distinct points, then the number of lines containing both p and q" by the symbols "$\varphi(p, q)$." Then Axiom 3 can be replaced by the axioms: (a) $\varphi(p, q)$ is odd; (b) $\varphi(p, q)$ is less than 8; (c) $\varphi(p, q)$ is not 7; (d) $\varphi(p, q)$ is not 5; (e) $\varphi(p, q)$ is not 3. Axiom 3 may be replaced by these *five* axioms if preferred! In the same article, incidentally, Helmer gives a simple axiom system that is easily seen to consist of independent axioms, and to be not completely independent.

4. Completeness of an axiom system

It was pointed out in I 2.6 that the system Γ would not yield *all* theorems of plane geometry; and, as we have seen, Γ actually has a model containing only a finite number of points; this could not be the case if Γ were adequate as a foundation for euclidean plane geometry. In plane geometry we would wish to be able to assert, for example, that between two points on a line there is a third point (the "bisecting" point for example), which is certainly not assertable on the basis of Γ (cf. the model consisting of four coins!).

4.1   Now, a priori, there is no reason to believe that it is even possible to give an axiom system that would imply *all* theorems of plane geometry. Presumably we could hardly hope to set down all possible theorems of plane geometry, so that we might easily judge that it would be equally impossible to set down a system of axioms that would *imply* all theorems of plane geometry.† Assuming, however, that it *is* possible to set down such a system of axioms, how shall we phrase an explicit definition of the sort of "completeness" which we have in mind here, and, after this, how can we ascertain the fact that a given system is complete?

4.2   In order to fix ideas, let us suppose that we have given an axiom system Σ which was derived from some concept C, using a collection T of undefined terms. (Thus Σ might be the system Γ (I 2.2), C the concept of plane geometry, and T the collection of terms "point," "line.") Now Σ might be inadequate as a system of axioms for C in that there are not enough axioms; more explicitly, in that the axioms do not contain enough assertions to imply all the theorems we want.

† When we speak of "all theorems" we do not, of course, include "false" theorems. And we are tacitly ruling out the trivial fact that by logical manipulation (see IX 3.5.3 for instance) it is possible to prove all theorems ("true" or "false") by the simple device of introducing contradictory axioms. We therefore tacitly assume throughout the discussion of completeness that the axiom systems discussed are consistent.

On the other hand, Σ might be insufficient in the sense that T does not contain enough undefined terms. For example, for plane geometry, not only might the system Γ be lacking in axiomatic assertions, but also it may be necessary to add new terms (as for instance "congruent") to T before we could get all the theorems of plane geometry. It may also occur to the reader that in addition to inadequacies that the axioms, and the collection T, may have, there may also be defects in our *logical apparatus*—the "universal terms" and the logical processes themselves. Each of these possibilities will be considered; the first two in the present section, and the third in Part II (see also III 6.8).

4.3   Definition of completeness

Let us first consider incompleteness due to inadequacy of the axioms themselves. If we revert to the idea of completeness that is based on the notion of a system being sufficient to "imply all theorems," we might say that, if we can find a theorem which can neither be proved nor "disproved" (i.e., no denial of it is provable), then we see that if such a theorem exists it becomes a candidate for a new axiom. This leads to the following definition (recall that a Σ-statement must be phrasable in terms of T):

4.3.1   Definition. An axiom system Σ is *complete* if there is no Σ-statement A (not already in Σ) such that A is an independent axiom in the system $\Sigma + A$.

Loosely speaking, according to 4.3.1 a system Σ is complete if it is impossible to add to it a new independent † axiom (always bearing in mind that we are keeping T fixed, of course).

For example, let Σ be the system Γ (I 2.2), and let A_6 be the statement "There exist at most four points." Both $\Gamma + A_6$ and $\Gamma + \sim A_6$ are satisfiable; the former because of the four-coin interpretation, the latter because of the usual euclidean geometry interpretation (there exist other interpretations of $\Gamma + \sim A_6$ consisting of only a finite number of points; cf. Problem 1 at the end of Chapter I). Thus Γ is not complete according to Definition 4.3.1.

How about the system $\Gamma + A_6$; is this complete? Let us denote $\Gamma + A_6$ by Γ_6. For reasons given later, we would search in vain for a Γ_6-statement, A' (not already in Γ_6), such that A' is independent in the system $\Gamma_6 + A'$. But failure to find such an A' after any finite

---

† So far as our discussion is concerned, the importance of the notion of "independence" is due almost solely to its use in connection with completeness!

number of trials would hardly *prove* Γ_6 complete in the sense of 4.3.1. This fact reveals that Definition 4.3.1 is subject to the same short-coming that Definition 1.1 has, namely, the seeming impossibility of *proving* the property defined when it may actually be possessed by an axiom system. And, as in 1.1, where we gave as "working definition" the Definition 1.3, that of *satisfiability*, we shall here also give a "work-ing definition" as an alternative to 4.3.1. And, just as in 1.1, where we had to interpolate a new notion, that of "interpretation" of an axiom system, before we could give the alternative definition, we shall here also have to precede the new definition by the introduction of a new notion.

4.4   (1-1)-correspondence; isomorphism

The new notion, that of "1-to-1 correspondence," will seem clearer and more natural if we recall the four-coin interpretation of Γ, which we shall call interpretation I_1 for present purposes, and the "ghost town" Z containing only four persons which we described in I 2.5. In the latter case, "person" was to serve as the meaning of "point," and "pair of persons" as the meaning of "line"; assigning these mean-ings constitutes an interpretation I_2 of Γ. Now in what ways do the models $\mathfrak{M}(I_1)$ and $\mathfrak{M}(I_2)$ differ? For the sake of brevity, let us de-note $\mathfrak{M}(I_1)$ by $\mathfrak{M}_1$, $\mathfrak{M}(I_2)$ by $\mathfrak{M}_2$.

This may seem like a trivial question since a collection of four *coins* and a collection of four *persons* differ so obviously in so many ways! But let us consider only those properties of $\mathfrak{M}_1$ and $\mathfrak{M}_2$ that have *significance for* Γ_6. Then the obvious differences, such as the fact that a coin is metallic whereas a person is organic, are not to be taken into account. Only properties and relations having to do with *point* and *line* have any significance so far as Γ_6 is concerned. And, with regard to these, $\mathfrak{M}_1$ and $\mathfrak{M}_2$ have no differences whatsoever. In order to make this more precise, we first introduce the following notion:

4.4.1   Definition. If C_1 and C_2 are two collections, then by a (1-1)-*correspondence between the elements of C_1 and the elements of C_2*, we mean a collection $C_{1,2}$ of pairs (x_1, x_2) in which x_1 and x_2 are ele-ments of C_1 and C_2 respectively, and such that each element of C_1 occurs in a pair (x_1, x_2) exactly once as an x_1, and each element of C_2 exactly once as an x_2. The order in which x_1 and x_2 occur in a pair is not important (unless specifically stated); thus (x_2, x_1) and (x_1, x_2) are the same pair provided that x_1 is an element of C_1 and x_2 an ele-ment of C_2.

As we shall see later (Chapter IV), (1-1)-correspondence is the basis for ascertaining whether two collections have the same number of elements. Thus, two collections C_1 and C_2 have the same number of elements if and only if there is a way of pairing off their elements in the manner described above.

4.4.2   If (x_1, x_2) is an element of $C_{1,2}$, then we shall say that x_1 corresponds to x_2, and vice versa; or that x_1 and x_2 are *corresponding elements;* or that x_2 is the element corresponding to x_1, etc., in the correspondence $C_{1,2}$.

4.4.3   The collections C_1 and C_2 may have common elements; in fact, one of the most important cases, as we shall see later (III 4.9.1) is that in which one of these collections is a part (subcollection) of the other. Of great importance, as a matter of fact, is the *identity correspondence* in the case where C_1 and C_2 are the *same* collection; this is the (1-1)-correspondence consisting of the collection of pairs (x, x), in which there is one pair (x, x) for each element x of $C_1(= C_2)$.

Now $\mathfrak{M}_1$ and $\mathfrak{M}_2$ have four "points" each, and, in each, every pair of "points" constitutes a "line." Considering $\mathfrak{M}_1$ and $\mathfrak{M}_2$ collections of points and lines, it is easy to see that there is a (1-1)-correspondence $\mathfrak{M}_{1,2}$ between the elements of $\mathfrak{M}_1$ and the elements of $\mathfrak{M}_2$ such that (1) if x_1 is a point in $\mathfrak{M}_1$, then the corresponding element in $\mathfrak{M}_2$ is a point; and (2) if x_1 and y_1 constitute a line in $\mathfrak{M}_1$, then the corresponding elements x_2 and y_2 constitute a line in $\mathfrak{M}_2$; and vice versa.† Moreover, any true statement about the points and lines of $\mathfrak{M}_1$ is also a true statement about $\mathfrak{M}_2$ if the special points and lines mentioned in the statement are replaced by the corresponding points and lines of $\mathfrak{M}_2$. For example, if the statement "The lines L_1 and L_1' have the point p_1 in common" is a true statement about $\mathfrak{M}_1$, then the statement "The lines L_2 and L_2' have the point p_2 in common" is a true statement about $\mathfrak{M}_2$ if L_2, L_2', p_2 correspond respectively to L_1, L_1', p_1. Consequently we call $\mathfrak{M}_{1,2}$ a (1-1)-correspondence between $\mathfrak{M}_1$ and $\mathfrak{M}_2$ with *preservation of* Γ_6-*statements.* And we define:

4.4.4   Definition. Two models $\mathfrak{M}_1$ and $\mathfrak{M}_2$ of an axiom system Σ are called *isomorphic with respect to* Σ if there exists between the elements of $\mathfrak{M}_1$ and the elements of $\mathfrak{M}_2$ a (1-1)-correspondence with preservation of Σ-statements.

† That *any* (1-1)-correspondence between the points of $\mathfrak{M}_1$ and the points of $\mathfrak{M}_2$ gives an isomorphism is an accident due to the simplicity of the models. If the system Γ had been augmented by an axiom stating "There exist 16 and only 16 points," then an isomorphism between two models would probably have to be set up with great care to make lines correspond to lines.

4.5   Categoricalness

With the notion of isomorphism thus defined, we **a**re ready to state the "working definition" of completeness, which is embodied in the notion of *categoricalness:* †

4.5.1   Definition.   An axiom system Σ is called *categorical* if *every* two models of Σ are isomorphic with respect to Σ.

4.6   Proof that categoricalness implies completeness in the sense of Definition 4.3.1 ‡

Suppose that an axiom system Σ is categorical.   Now, if Σ were not complete in the sense of 4.3.1, there would exist a Σ-statement A such that both $\Sigma + $ A and $\Sigma + \sim$A are satisfiable systems.   Let I_1 be an interpretation of $\Sigma + $ A and let I_2 be an interpretation of $\Sigma + \sim$A. Since Σ is categorical, there is a (1-1)-correspondence $\mathfrak{M}_{1,2}$ between the elements of $\mathfrak{M}(I_1)$ and the elements of $\mathfrak{M}(I_2)$, with preservation of Σ-statements.   But this is impossible, since A is a Σ-statement, true of $\mathfrak{M}(I_1)$ and false of $\mathfrak{M}(I_2)$!

4.7   Let us indicate why the axiom system Γ_6 is categorical, and hence complete by 4.3.1:   By Theorem 3 of I 3.7 and Axiom A_6 every model of Γ_6 has exactly four points.§   By Axiom 3 (I 2.2), if p and q are points, there is one and only one line containing p and q; and it follows from Axioms 4 and 5 and Theorem 2 (I 3.6) that this line cannot contain any other point (if there exist only four points—and this is the case with Γ_6).   Thus there exist, in any model of Γ_6, exactly six lines, each of these consisting of one of the six possible pairs of points in the model.   To set up an isomorphism $\mathfrak{M}_{1,2}$ between two models $\mathfrak{M}_1$ and $\mathfrak{M}_2$ of Γ_6, with preservation of Γ_6-statements, we need only set up a (1-1)-correspondence between the points of $\mathfrak{M}_1$ and the points of $\mathfrak{M}_2$, and a (1-1)-correspondence between the lines of $\mathfrak{M}_1$ and the lines of $\mathfrak{M}_2$ such that if x_1, y_1 are points of $\mathfrak{M}_1$ corresponding respectively to points x_2, y_2 of $\mathfrak{M}_2$, then the line of $\mathfrak{M}_1$ containing x_1 and y_1 corresponds to the line of $\mathfrak{M}_2$ containing x_2 and y_2.   We leave the remainder of the proof to the reader.‖

† The term *categorical* seems to have been introduced by O. Veblen [a], who states that it was suggested by John Dewey.   As a test for completeness, however, the notion was used earlier; see Huntington [a] for instance.

‡ We recall that our definition of independence, 3.1.1, is in terms of satisfiability.

§ Appeal to Theorem 3 here is justified on the basis of 2.2.1.

‖ For another example of a "finite geometry" (containing exactly seven points and seven lines) and proof of categoricalness of the corresponding axiom system, see Veblen and Young [V-Y, pp. 2–7].   One of the axioms in this system is "Any two lines have at least one point in common."

Also see Richardson [R; II § 8 and XVII §§ 157–159].

4.8   Completeness of Hilbert's geometry

In Γ_6 we have, then, an example of an axiom system that is complete. But Γ_6 is not, it must be admitted, a very interesting system, its chief virtue being its simplicity and consequent adaptability to purposes of exposition. The reader may still feel that, when it comes to mathematically "rich" concepts, such as the usual euclidean geometry, with their seemingly unlimited number of theorems, completeness may not be so easily attained. Fortunately this is not necessarily the case, although the *proofs* of completeness are not, as a rule, so easily attained as the above. In the case of plane euclidean geometry, a number of categorical axiom systems have been given. The system of Hilbert for the geometry of the plane and three dimensions ("solid" geometry) achieved completeness in a way that excited considerable discussion. As originally set up by Hilbert, the system included the following statement, which he called "Completeness Axiom": †

"The elements (points, straight lines, planes) form a class of objects, which under the set of all previously made assumptions, is not capable of further extension."

This meant that no new points, lines, or planes could be added to the collection of points, lines, and planes satisfying the other axioms without rendering at least one of these other axioms false.

Clearly this is a peculiar type of axiom in that it almost seems to achieve completeness for the system by boldly *asserting* it; and its reference to "all previously made assumptions" smacks of an element of "higher caste" in a "hierarchy" of axioms. It is intimately related, moreover, to its predecessor, the "Archimedean axiom," which, roughly speaking, assures that the lines of the geometry shall be "long enough" without being "too long." Possibly it was this that led P. Bernays to the discovery that the axiom can be stated as a theorem, being replaced in the axiom system by the following "Axiom of Linear Completeness":

"The points of a line form a system which under the set of previously given axioms is not capable of further extension." ‡

4.9   For other systems of axioms for geometry, the reader is referred to the "Suggested Reading" at the end of this chapter.

† The English translation given here is derived from Young [Y]; quoted by permission of The Macmillan Co. Hilbert did not include this axiom in the first edition of his *Grundlagen* [H₁]; it did appear in the second and later editions, and was modified in the seventh edition [H₂].

‡ This axiom (the above is not a literal translation) appears in the seventh (1930) edition of Hilbert's book. See Hilbert [H₂; 30].

Axiomatic treatments of other mathematical concepts (in arithmetic, algebra, analysis, etc.) will be referred to later.

4.10   Incompleteness due to T

What effect does the selection of T, the collection of undefined technical terms, have on the completeness of an axiom system Σ? Hilbert's system used five undefined terms: point, line, plane, between, congruent. The system of Pieri, published the same year (1899) as Hilbert's system, used only two undefined terms (point, motion), as did also the system of Veblen [a] (point, order).

Veblen also uses fewer (12) axioms than Hilbert, and one of these was shown by R. L. Moore [b] to be unnecessary if one of the remaining axioms is changed slightly. However, as we pointed out above (3.6), the *number* of axioms is no criterion of simplicity. By using more undefined terms and more assumptions, Hilbert is able to make his geometry more "elementary" and closer to the spirit of the geometry of Euclid. Veblen's system is a more penetrating system in that it starts "lower" in the geometric scale and does not arrive at the type of theorem to be found in the usual high school text so soon as Hilbert's.

Just how the selection of undefined terms affects the achievement of completeness seems not to have been seriously studied. The concept C being fixed, we may expect that the selection of T will have some effect, if only because of the influence on the statements selected as axioms.†

One thing may be stated, and this is of importance in the sequel (Chapter VII), namely, that a complete axiom system employing a collection T of undefined technical terms will generally fail to be complete when a collection T' consisting of T augmented by new terms is employed. This is trivial since, if new undefined terms are added to T and nothing is stated in terms of them, then the new system can hardly be complete! We assume here, of course, that the new terms in T' are not definable in terms of T. Consequently, given a complete system of axioms, Σ, with collection T of undefined terms, we may increase the number of terms in T to form a new collection T', in terms of which we may now state new independent axioms, possibly achieving a new complete system Σ'! An example of this would be the case in which Σ is a set of axioms for *plane* euclidean geometry and Σ' an

† So far as we know, there is no system of axioms for geometry based on *point* and *line* alone, nor any discussion as to whether completeness could be achieved in these terms alone.

enlarged system for "solid" euclidean geometry. We shall see other examples in the sequel (VII 2.7.1, for instance).

4.11 Completeness and the Law of the Excluded Middle

Before leaving this discussion of completeness, we shall make another remark regarding the applicability of the Law of the Excluded Middle (cf. 2.1). If an axiom system Σ is not categorical, and if A is a Σ-statement such that both $\Sigma + A$ and $\Sigma + \sim A$ are consistent, it would not be permissible to state, on the basis of the system Σ alone, either "A holds" or "A does not hold." It would, however, be correct to state "Either A holds or A does not hold."

We frequently use this principle in proving theorems. For example, in the system Γ we may wish to prove some theorem T, and are able to show that (1) if every line contains at most 4 points, then T holds; and (2) if there exists a line which contains more than 4 points, then T holds. Since either every line contains at most 4 points or not every line contains at most 4 points, we would now consider theorem T proved.

4.12 Desirability of completeness

Some comment regarding the desirability or undesirability of completeness should also be made at this point. When we wish to define a concept allowing a wide variety of interpretations, or a large range of application to different fields of mathematics or physics, then completeness will usually not be achieved or even desired. We shall see instances of this later in the axioms for *simple order*, *group*, etc. In such concepts we see one of the great advantages of the axiomatic method, what we might call the "economy aspect." For, as we have pointed out in Section 1, one is at liberty to make any interpretation he pleases, and the theorems which have been proved in the system of axioms become true statements about the model resulting from the interpretation. The "economy" involved here consists of the proving, once for all, of statements about a large number and variety of (seemingly unrelated) fields of study. Thus, when we come to study the notion of group, we shall notice that examples of groups (i.e., models of the group axioms) abound in mathematics (and other fields), and the theorems proved on the basis of the group axioms are immediately available for use in all such cases! And it is a common mathematical device to prove, of a given concept, that it contains a model of some already known and developed axiom system, so that the theorems of the system may be made available for use in the study of the given concept. It is interesting to note (as a sort of converse!), too, that it has not infrequently happened that mathematicians, working in different branches of mathematics, have duplicated one another's work; the only difference between their results being that of language —each speaking in terms which could be made the common terminology of some axiom system. Naturally, this is one of the things that *leads* to the invention of axiom systems, i.e., the discovery that the same "abstract notions" are operating under various guises in different branches of mathematics.

So far as a concept like that of plane euclidean geometry is concerned, the object is usually to set down, as Hilbert did, a complete set of axioms. We shall see an example of the same sort of thing in other cases, as for instance in the definition of the "mathematical continuum" which lies at the basis of analysis. It is of the very nature of such special concepts that their "definition," or *characterization* (to use the term most frequently employed), leads to complete systems of axioms. As we shall see later, we can so specialize the *order* and *group* concepts, mentioned above, as to attain completeness in describing them axiomatically, somewhat as we specialized the system Γ to obtain Γ_6.

5   The logical basis

In our discussion of consistency, we mentioned (2.1) the Law of Contradiction and the Law of the Excluded Third; that we place a great degree of confidence in their applicability is evidenced in 2.2.1 and 2.2.2. Independence was defined (3.1.1) in terms of satisfiability, so that the same "laws" are involved in this notion.

Definition 4.3.1 makes completeness, in turn, dependent on the notion of independence, and hence of satisfiability. The definition (4.5.1) in terms of isomorphism, as we saw, "implies" the former definition in the sense that, when a system is categorical, then it is complete according to 4.3.1. Now, aside from the assumption of the "laws" of classical logic, there is the interpretation—not always clear, as we have noticed (I 3.4 for instance)—placed on the "universal" terms of that logic. The average person's only contact with geometry is in the high school course, and no mention by name is made there of the "Aristotelian logic" as a rule. The logical apparatus employed (justifiably, for pedagogical reasons) is usually a "taken-for-granted" or "rule-of-thumb" logic. Its value probably lies in its naturalness, and as such it undoubtedly forms a good basis for the study of "formal logic" in college, if the student goes this far and happens to "elect" a course in the latter.

This "natural" logic tacitly assumes the Law of Contradiction and the Law of the Excluded Third; witness the "reductio ad absurdum" type of proof which is such a favorite in high school geometry. No attention at all is paid to logical terminology, such as the use of the terms "collection," "all," "not" (again justifiably).

It is not surprising, therefore, that the axiomatic method, originally derived from the axiom-postulate method of Euclid, proceeded on the same logical basis, employing a "taken-for-granted" logic. However, as we shall see, concurrently with the development of the axiomatic method during the latter part of the past, and the beginning of the present, centuries, this "natural" logic was beginning to be attacked. The first criticism was directed, not so much at the "laws" of the logic, as at the *terms* themselves, in particular at the notion of "collection." And, in our return to this subject in the sequel, it will be to this notion of collection that we first direct our attention. For not only does the consistency of an axiom system depend on our assumption of the logical "laws," but also all the attributes of an axiom system discussed above, including completeness, are determined to a greater extent than we realize by the way in which we use the so-called "universal" terms of logic.

6   Miscellaneous comment

It was emphasized above (I 5) that in setting up an axiom system Σ we have some concept C in mind that we are actually describing. The concept C is not only the source of our axioms, but, if it is a valid model of Σ, also *predetermines* the consistency of Σ. Moreover, if C possesses the requisite sort of uniqueness, then the axiom system Σ will be categorical if it is sufficiently descriptive of C.

6.1   Now there are cases where, instead of C preceding Σ, we have Σ preceding C! This happens whenever Σ is derived from a previously existing axiom system Σ' by alteration (such as by denying or deleting an axiom). For example, if from the concept C of euclidean geometry we derive a complete axiom system Σ' that includes the "parallel axiom" (Axiom 5 of the system Γ above), we might derive a non-euclidean geometry Σ from Σ' by replacing the "parallel axiom" by a denial of the same—and then look for a concept which Σ' might describe. Historically, this is essentially what happened in non-euclidean geometry.† And we duplicate this process whenever we prove independence of an axiom A in an axiom system Σ, since we

† Cf. Bell [B₁; 40–46] for instance.

first set up the system $(\Sigma - A) + \sim A$ and then look for an interpretation of the latter.

Of course the derivation of new axiom systems from old can degenerate into a game. But frequently the "game" turns out to be sufficiently interesting to justify itself, and is often found useful in both mathematics and its applications.† Many important concepts are developed in modern algebra, which makes great use of the axiomatic method, through the investigation of "altered" axiom systems.

6.2 Advantages of the axiomatic method

Certain advantages of the axiomatic method have already been alluded to above. For example, we mentioned (4.12; also see I 1.5, I 3.2) the "economy" achieved when an axiom system Σ has many models in the same or different branches of mathematics. A single theorem in Σ yields a theorem in each interpretation; but the latter requires no special proof so long as the theorem was proved in the system Σ. An excellent example of this, mentioned in 4.12, is the axiom system for a *group*, which we shall study in the sequel; this notion, defined axiomatically, is one of the most outstanding "labor-saving devices" in modern mathematics. Other examples will be given in Sections 7 and 8 below. And, obviously, once we have recognized, in some branch of mathematics, that a certain setup or situation constitutes a model of a previously known axiom system Σ, then we are likely to see many new possibilities opening up because of the knowledge already embodied in the study (previously made) of Σ! In this way, the axiomatic method not only achieves economy but also throws new light wherever interpretations of known axiom systems are possible.

We have also just pointed out that, by the alteration of existing axiom systems, new mathematical concepts may be generated—not always fruitful concepts, to be sure, but nevertheless frequently of sufficient importance to justify their study.‡ In this manner, new branches of mathematics may be created, and the method becomes (as in modern algebra) a useful research tool.

Another distinct advantage of the method that deserves special mention is its character of implicit "definition." Although the genesis and development of a mathematical concept may proceed along sev-

---

† Cf. Bell [B₁; 36–40].

‡ We recognize that some of the above commentary is probably productive of questions in the reader's mind such as, "What is a *fruitful* concept?" We prefer to delay the discussion of such matters, with the assurance that we shall discuss them later.

eral entirely different lines, once the concept has matured, so to speak, the axiomatic characterization of it may prove extremely advantageous. For example, the development of the real number system, which forms the foundation of modern analysis, was a slow evolution over many centuries. Today, as we shall see, we can give it a precise axiomatic definition and study its properties by means of the theorems based on the axioms. The like may be stated of many other mathematical concepts.

An advantage, related to the above, which may or may not have occurred to the reader while we were proving theorems on the basis of the system Γ, is that of "placing the responsibility where it belongs." Frequently a mathematics student exclaims, "I could work this problem, I think, if I only knew what I could assume!" This is an oft-heard complaint. For, if he is not certain about just what assumptions he can make, how is he to proceed with a proof? However, if one presents a student with an axiom system Σ and wishes him to prove a certain Theorem A, he can say, "Here is a Σ-statement, A. Prove A"; one has thus given a specific direction to the student, and the latter knows exactly what his "point of departure" is! For this reason, the axiomatic method forms a useful pedagogical device in the teaching of mature students.

6.3   Disadvantages of, and objections to, the axiomatic method

"Nothing is perfect," and the axiomatic method turns out to be no exception! Most of the criticisms of the method, as it is commonly employed and as we have described it, are too complicated to permit simple exposition in the compass of a single section, and will have to be allowed to emerge as we progress through the succeeding chapters. For not the least of the disadvantages of the axiomatic method as it is usually employed are related to its utter dependence on logic—not only the Aristotelian "laws," but also the assumed "universality" of the logical terms. If it should turn out that the logical machinery itself reveals flaws, then what faith can be placed in the reliability of the theorems deduced?

Some mathematicians object to the highly formal character of the method; particularly its foundation in undefined terms, basic assumptions (axioms) in terms of these, and logical deduction capable of being carried through without any interpretation in mind whatsoever! They feel that formality is quite good and entirely justified in some instances, but that it can be carried too far, especially when it is used, for instance, to treat the ordinary integers 1, 2, 3, $\cdots$, as *undefined* terms! (See the Peano axioms in III 5.1; also see the criticism by Russell [R_1; I] in that connection, and Klein [Kl; 14–15].) Clearly the method is not for the immature mind. Most mathematicians and pedagogues are agreed that in teaching geometry to high school students it is much better to allow the student to take for granted as "obvious" all those fundamental notions whose formalization would only seem a waste of time to him.

There are mathematicians, to be sure, who will maintain that all mathematics should be placed on an axiomatic basis. This does not mean that they ask that a *single* axiom system should be given for all of mathematics. This would certainly be impossible, and tantamount to a *definition* of *mathematics*—something which, as we shall see, it would be almost a miracle to get as many as five † mathematicians to agree upon. But it is asserted by many that each branch or portion of mathematics should be axiomatized. At the other extreme are mathematicians who will have nothing to do with axioms; whose conception of mathematics is such that formalization immediately squeezes the *mathematical* substance out of the material formalized.

7 Axioms for simple order

Before leaving the study of the axiomatic method, let us describe two very simple examples of concepts which appear in various guises in mathematics, and which were axiomatized and studied for their own sake in order that the "economy" feature of the method (application to many different models) might be utilized. One of these is the concept of *simple order* (frequently called *linear order*). It is probably unnecessary to demonstrate to the reader that "ordered" collections abound in mathematics. The points of a line, the integers 1, 2, 3, ··· used in counting (these we shall call the *natural numbers* ‡), are two of the most common examples of ordered collections. And the notion is of such a fundamental character that it is abundantly exemplified in our physical surroundings; we order our streets, our books on shelves, soldiers in file, and so on.

What common element is involved in all such cases? Simply that, if p and q are distinct elements of any one of these collections, then either p precedes q or q precedes p. In the case of points on a line, "precedes" may mean "is to the left of"; in the case of the natural numbers, "2 precedes 5" means "2 is smaller than 5"; in the case of streets running "north and south," "precedes" may mean "is to the west of"; and so on. Consequently we make "precedes" the basic

---

† Perhaps "two" would be correct here, but we would rather allow a little margin for error!

‡ Some writers include 0 among the natural numbers.

term which receives meaning according to the nature of the collection ordered; that is, *precedes* is adopted as an undefined technical term. And, as the objects that occur in ordered collections also vary from one collection to another, we adopt some undefined term for these; *point* is as good as any.

So far as the axioms themselves are concerned, we naturally start with the property that we have already noticed is common to all ordered systems, namely, "If p and q are distinct points, then either p precedes q or q precedes p." Now is this all we need state? Suppose p and q are not distinct points; shall we let p precede q or vice versa? Since this is clearly not the case in any of the examples that we have scanned, we ought to rule it out by an axiom: "If p precedes q, then p and q are distinct points." And now do we have all we need by way of axioms? To see that we do not, we need only point out that, if we would avoid circular or "cyclical" order, we need to say more. Let p, q, r be the vertices of an equilateral triangle inscribed in a circle C, and let "x precedes y" mean that x and y are distinct and that the arc from x to y on C in a clockwise direction is less than a semicircle. Then, if p, q, r occur in the order stated in a clockwise direction around C, p precedes q, q precedes r, and r precedes p. This example is a model of the system formed by the two axioms already stated, and, if we wish to restrict ourselves to defining *linear* rather than *cyclical* order, it should be ruled out. This may be done by stating "If p precedes q and q precedes r, then p precedes r." In all the examples previously stated this is a true statement, but it fails in the example of cyclical order just given.

It is not obvious, of course, that the three statements fixed upon above suffice to describe exactly what we mean by linear order. This becomes apparent only when we see what the three statements imply. For certainly we are not looking for a *complete* axiom system—an ordered collection may contain any number of "points," and consequently not every two models of the axioms we decide on are going to be isomorphic! If we are interested in defining a linearly ordered *triple*, we would of course add the statement "There exist three and only three points," and we could then show, without much labor, that the collection of four statements forms a categorical axiom system; whereupon it would be apparent that we had made enough basic assumptions to accomplish our purpose (i.e., of defining a linearly ordered triple).

The three statements about order can be presented succinctly in the following way: Let C be any collection whose elements we call *points* and which are denoted by small letters x, y, z, a, b, $\cdots$; and let there be given a "binary relation" † between the points of C which we denote by $<$ and call "precedes." Then C is called *simply ordered*, or *linearly ordered*, relative to $<$, if the following axioms (cf. Huntington [Hu; 10]) hold:

(1) If x and y are distinct points of C, then $x < y$ or $y < x$.‡

(2) If $x < y$, then x and y are distinct.

(3) If $x < y$ and $y < z$, then $x < z$.

On the basis of these axioms we can now prove such theorems as "If x and y are points of C, then not both $x < y$ and $y < x$ hold"; "If n is a natural number such that C contains exactly n points, then symbols x_1, x_2, $\cdots$, x_n can be so assigned to these points as to make the relations $x_1 < x_2$, $x_2 < x_3$, $\cdots$, $x_{n-1} < x_n$ all hold." Note that the latter statement goes a long way toward justifying the feeling that (1)–(3) above imply all that we wish concerning linear order, assuming that we want to keep sufficient "incompleteness" to allow many different interpretations. Let us call the above axiom system O.

(The reader may like to establish the independence of the axioms of O.)

7.1   The statement "$(C, <)$ is a simply ordered system" may be used as an abbreviation for the statement "C is a set and $<$ is a binary relation between elements of C such that C is simply ordered relative to $<$."

8   Axioms defining equivalence

One of the most used (and abused) notions in mathematics is that of *equivalence relation*. Like the notion of simple order, it is also exemplified in our social and physical environment. Wherever *classification* occurs, one finds what the mathematician calls *equivalence*. One merely agrees to call all those things in the same class "equivalent." For example, if in a given city one classifies all people according to their church membership, placing in a single class all those belonging to the same church (and in a single class all those not belonging to any church), then there is established an equivalence with respect to church membership; all Catholics would be considered "equivalent," all Baptists would be "equivalent," etc. Or one might classify them

---

† Here we treat "relation" between two things as a universal logical notion (cf. 6.3 "Disadvantages . . ."). For analysis of the notion in terms of classes, see VIII 8.2.7.1; in terms of propositional functions, see IX 5.2.2.

‡ We always use "or" in the sense of "and/or." Thus, so far as Axiom (1) is concerned, both "$x < y$" and "$y < x$" might hold. However, the combined Axioms (1)–(3) will rule out this possibility.

according to age, two persons being then "equivalent" if they are of the same age in years. Thus two persons, x and y, might be equivalent in the sense of church membership, and not equivalent with respect to their ages. Similarly, in a college, two students may be equivalent with respect to their status as freshmen, sophomores, etc.

8.1   Without pausing to attempt an analysis of their origin (see Peano [P_1; 9]) or to justify the particular choice of statements, we give the usual axioms for equivalence as follows: Let S be any collection whose elements we denote by small letters x, y, $\cdots$, and $\approx$ a binary relation between elements of S. (We avoid the symbol $=$ since it has too many connotations, such as "identity.") Then $\approx$ is called an equivalence relation in S if the following axioms hold:

(1) If x is an element of S, then $x \approx x$.
(2) If $x \approx y$, then $y \approx x$.
(3) If $x \approx y$ and $y \approx z$, then $x \approx z$.

Note that (3) is the same as (3) of the system O of Section 7, if the difference in symbols denoting the relations is ignored—this property of a binary relation is called *transitivity*—and that it holds for both $<$ and $\approx$ is expressed by stating that both these relations are *transitive*. Similarly, (1) is called *reflexiveness* and (2) *symmetry*. Thus the relation $\approx$ is *reflexive, symmetric,* and *transitive*. Let us call this axiom system E.

8.2   In the examples cited above, statements (1) and (2) appear trivial perhaps. Thus, in the classification according to age, that a person is of the same age as himself appears too trivial for mention! And of course, if x is the same age as y, then y is the same age as x! The necessity for stating these properties as axioms becomes apparent as soon as one begins the "justification process"; that is, showing that the axioms imply all that one wishes to have implied (without implying too much!). And, if x is of the same age as y, and y of the same age as z, then x is of the same age as z. Evidently in any decomposition of a collection into classes, where no two classes overlap, the meaning "x is in the same class as y" for "$x \approx y$" constitutes an interpretation of the axiom system E. The system is, incidentally, consistent, in view of the interpretations stated above. The reader will find it amusing to establish the independence of the axioms in E. [In connection with axiom (1), note that it is never essential in a case where for each element x of the collection S there is some element y of S such that $x \approx y$, since in this case $x \approx x$ will follow from (2) and (3). In general, however, (1) is independent.]

8.3   Now the use of equivalence relations in mathematics is usually of a sort that is the direct converse of the manner in which we have presented the notion above. Instead of starting with a collection S which is already split into non-overlapping classes, and getting the corresponding equivalence relation, the mathematician notices the presence of an equivalence relation and then sets up the classes! A simple illustration of this is furnished by the collection of natural numbers, with "$x \approx y$" meaning "x differs from y by a multiple of 3" (0 is a multiple of 3—the 0th multiple!). This is obviously an equivalence relation, and, if we decompose the collection of natural numbers into classes, putting into the same class two numbers that differ by a multiple of 3, we get three classes of numbers: (1, 4, 7, $\cdots$), (2, 5, 8, $\cdots$), and (3, 6, 9, $\cdots$).

8.4   A better example, and one of great interest in connection with the subject of this chapter, is furnished if we notice that *isomorphism* forms an equivalence relation. Specifically, if Σ is an axiom system, $\mu(\Sigma)$ is the collection of all models of Σ, and if $\mathfrak{M}$ and $\mathfrak{N}$ are models of Σ, let "$\mathfrak{M} \approx \mathfrak{N}$" mean "$\mathfrak{M}$ and $\mathfrak{N}$ are isomorphic with respect to Σ." Note that the axioms of E become true statements with this meaning for "$\approx$," so that we get an interpretation of E. In this case, if we decompose $\mu(\Sigma)$ into classes, placing two models in the same class if and only if they are isomorphic, we notice that *categoricalness of* E *corresponds exactly to the case where only one class results*. In the case of non-categoricalness there might be any number of classes. In a way, the number of such classes serves as a "measure of completeness" of an axiom system; the fewer the number of classes, the greater the amount of completeness present!

8.5   We notice then that, corresponding to any collection S and an equivalence relation $\approx$ in S, there always exists a unique decomposition of S into classes, called *the class decomposition of S corresponding to* $\approx$. We shall leave to the reader the proof of this on the basis of the axiom system E. He may accomplish this by using the following outline:

Definition.   If x is an element of S, let $S(x)$ denote the collection of all elements y of S such that $x \approx y$.

Theorem 1.   If x is an element of S, then $S(x)$ is not empty; in particular, x is an element of $S(x)$.

Corollary.   Every element x of S is in some $S(x)$.

Theorem 2.   If $x \approx y$, then the classes $S(x)$ and $S(y)$ are the same.

Corollary.   A class $S(x)$ is completely determined by any one of its elements.

Theorem 3.   If two classes $S(x)$ and $S(y)$ have a common element z, then they are the same class.

Theorem 4.   The classes $S(x)$ constitute a unique decomposition of S into non-overlapping classes; we call this *the class decomposition of S corresponding to* $\approx$.

SUGGESTED READING

Birkhoff [Bi; I]
Hilbert [H₃; §§ 8–12]
Hilbert and Bernays [H-B; § 1]
Huntington [Hu; II]

Richardson [R; XVI, 448–457]
Veblen [a]
Veblen and Young [V-Y; Intro.]
Young [Y; IV–V, VII]

PROBLEMS

Consider the following axiom system, which we shall designate by O′. This consists of the axiom system O of Section 7 augmented by the following axiom:

Axiom 4.   There exist two and only two distinct points in C.

1. Show that the system O′ is satisfiable.

2. Is the system O′ consistent according to Definition 1.1?

3. Show that Axiom 3 is independent in the system O′. Hence, show that the axiom system obtained by deleting Axiom 3 from O′ is not a categorical system.

4. Show that, if in the axiom system O′ we replace Axiom 3 by the axiom "Not both $x < y$ and $y < x$ hold," then the resulting axiom system is categorical.

5. Is the system O′ categorical? Is it complete according to Definition 4.3.1?

6. Show that, if we augment the axiom system O of Section 7 by the axiom "There exist three and only three points," then the resulting system O₃ of axioms is categorical.

7. Let O₃′ denote the system O₃ of Problem 6 augmented by some axiom of the form, "If a, b, c, d are four distinct points, then . . ." Is this axiom independent in O₃′?

8. If C is any collection and $\leq$ a binary relation between elements of C, then C is called *partially ordered with respect to* $\leq$ if the following axioms hold:

(1) For every element x of C, $x \leq x$.

(2) If $x \leq y$ and $y \leq x$, then x and y denote the same element of C.

(3) If $x \leq y$ and $y \leq z$, then $x \leq z$.

[Note that (1) and (3) are reflexiveness and transitivity of $\leq$. The property of the binary relation stated in (2) is called *anti-symmetry*.]

Denote this axiom system by P. Prove P consistent and non-categorical; establish independence of each of its axioms.

9. If Σ_1 and Σ_2 are axiom systems having the same set, T, of undefined terms, define $\Sigma_1 \approx \Sigma_2$ to mean that the collections $\mu(\Sigma_1)$ and $\mu(\Sigma_2)$ (see 8.4) are the same. Is this relation $\approx$ an equivalence relation in the collection of all axiom systems based on T (i.e., having T as their sets of undefined terms)?

10. If Σ_1 and Σ_2 are two axiom systems based on T (cf. Problem 9), define $\Sigma_1 \leq \Sigma_2$ to mean that $\mu(\Sigma_1)$ contains $\mu(\Sigma_2)$ as a subcollection. Is the collection of all axiom systems based on T partially ordered with respect to this relation "$\leq$"? (Cf. Problem 14.)

11. Let Σ_1 and Σ_2 be axiom systems as in Problem 10. Define $\Sigma_1 \Rightarrow \Sigma_2$ to mean that the axioms of Σ_2 are provable (as theorems) in the axiom system Σ_1 (we may read "$\Sigma_1 \Rightarrow \Sigma_2$" as "$\Sigma_1$ implies Σ_2"). Show that $\Sigma_1 \Rightarrow \Sigma_2$ implies that $\Sigma_2 \leq \Sigma_1$ (the latter as defined in Problem 10). Discuss the converse.

12. With Σ_1, Σ_2, etc., as in Problem 11, define $\Sigma_1 \Leftrightarrow \Sigma_2$ to mean that both $\Sigma_1 \Rightarrow \Sigma_2$ and $\Sigma_2 \Rightarrow \Sigma_1$ (the latter may also be written $\Sigma_1 \Leftarrow \Sigma_2$, if preferred). Show that $\Leftrightarrow$ is an equivalence relation in the collection of all axiom systems based on T.

13. Let P' denote the axiom system obtained by replacing axiom (1) of the system P (Problem 8) by the axiom "If x and y are elements of C, then $x \leq y$ or $y \leq x$." If, in P', we replace "$\leq$" by "$<$ or identical with," what relation is there between the resulting axiom system and the axiom system for simple order (Section 7)?

14. Show that the classes, elements of the class decomposition of the collection of all axiom systems based on T, corresponding to the relation $\Leftrightarrow$ defined in Problem 12, form a partially ordered system with respect to $\leq$, if the latter is defined to mean that $C_1 \leq C_2$ provided that, for each axiom system in class C_1 and each axiom system in class C_2, $\Sigma_1 \leq \Sigma_2$. (Compare Problem 10.)

15. If Σ is an axiom system, define a Σ-question to be a question of the form 'Does A hold?" where A is a Σ-statement. Then define Σ to be complete if it implies an answer to every Σ-question. Show that this definition is equivalent to Definition 4.3.1.

16. Discuss the "reductio ad absurdum" type of proof (as used in proving theorems in elementary geometry for instance) in terms of the logical "laws" of contradiction and excluded third.

17. If $\mathfrak{S}$ is a collection whose elements are themselves collections (for example, $\mathfrak{S}$ might be a collection of libraries, each library being itself a collection of books), and A, B are elements $\mathfrak{S}$, let $A \leftrightarrow B$ mean that there exists a (1-1)-correspondence between the elements of A and the elements of B (cf. Definition 4.4.1). Show that $\leftrightarrow$ is an equivalence relation in the collection $\mathfrak{S}$.

18. Show that, if two simply ordered sets A and B have the same number, n, of elements, then they are isomorphic relative to the simple order axioms.

Problems 19–23 will be based on the following axiom system: †

Let S be a collection, of which certain subcollections are designated as *m-classes*. By definition, two such m-classes are called *conjugate* if they have no element in common. The following axioms are to hold (we denote elements of S by small letters x, y, z, $\cdots$):

(1) If x and y are distinct, there is one and only one m-class containing x and y.
(2) For every m-class, there is one and only one conjugate m-class.
(3) There exists at least one m-class.
(4) No m-class is empty.
(5) Each m-class contains only a finite number of elements of S.

19. Show that every m-class has at least two elements.
20. Show that S contains at least four elements.
21. Show that S contains at least six m-classes.

---

† See Problem 2894 in the *American Mathematical Monthly*, vol. 29 (1922), pp. 357–358, for solutions as well as a discussion by Professor O. Veblen of the origin of this axiom system in his class.

22. Show that no m-class has more than two elements.

23. Prove that the given axiom system is categorical.

24. Show that the axiom system on which Problems 19–23 are based is equivalent (as in Problem 12) to the system Γ_6 of Section 4.3, if elements of S are called *points*, and *line* is substituted for m-class.

25. Compare the following definition of isomorphism with that given in Sections 4.4.3 and 4.4.4:

Let Σ be an axiom system. Then a Σ-statement may be denoted by a symbol $S(v_1, v_2, \cdots; R_1, R_2, \cdots; t_1, t_2, \cdots)$, which may be abbreviated to $S(v_i; R_j; t_k)$, where the v_i, R_j, and t_k represent variables, relations, and undefined terms of Σ. If $\mathfrak{M}_n$ is a model of Σ, then a Σ-statement becomes an I_n-Σ-statement $S(v_i{}^n; R_j{}^n; t_k{}^n)$ upon substitution (according to the interpretation I_n that produced $\mathfrak{M}_n$) in S of "values" $v_i{}^n$ for some or all of the variables v_i, etc. Then two models $\mathfrak{M}_1$ and $\mathfrak{M}_2$ are isomorphic with respect to Σ if there exists a (1-1)-correspondence $\mathfrak{M}_{1,2}$ between the elements of $\mathfrak{M}_1$ and the elements of $\mathfrak{M}_2$ such that all corresponding I_1-Σ-statements and I_2-Σ-statements of $\mathfrak{M}_1$ and $\mathfrak{M}_2$ are simultaneously true or false.

26. As a means to possible generalizations of the " $\Rightarrow$ " and " $\Leftrightarrow$ " of Problems 11 and 12, discuss (and criticize) the following: If Σ_1 and Σ_2 are axiom systems based respectively on collections T_1 and T_2 of undefined technical terms, let $\Sigma_1 \Rightarrow \Sigma_2$ mean that the elements of T_2 may be so defined in terms of the elements of T_1 as to make the axioms of Σ_2 provable theorems in the axiom system Σ_1.

III

Theory of Sets

In Chapter I, Section 2, we gave an example of a simple geometric axiom system. The first axiom of this system stated: "Every line is a collection of points." The corollary to Theorem 1 (I 3.3) stated: "Every line contains at least one point"; i.e., the collection of points constituting a line is never empty. It will be recalled that in connection with this corollary some justification was given for the use of the notion of *empty collection*, and it was remarked that, although "collection" was one of the supposedly "universal" logical terms, we found it necessary to explain, in part at least, just how or in what sense we were using the term. In the same connection it was also remarked that we were touching upon a question that has caused considerable concern to mathematicians and logicians, viz., *What is a collection?*

Of course, we can look up the word "collection" in a dictionary, but if we do we find such definitions as "a group of collected objects or individuals," "an aggregation," "accumulation." These will hardly be of much help. And the mathematician uses "definition" in a different sense from that of the dictionary. When a mathematician gives a definition, it is intended that it will be not a mere synonym (such as "aggregation" for "collection") which the reader may happen to know the meaning of, but a criterion for identifying; a *characterization* of the thing defined.† If the "definition" is not of this kind, it is of no use to the mathematician.

During the past fifty years, there have been proposed almost as many "definitions" of the term "collection" as there have been of the

† Incidentally, this kind of definition is probably one of the most difficult notions to get over to the student of mathematics. Try as one will, it sometimes seems impossible to convince a student that, if he wants to know whether something is a certain type of mathematical entity which has previously been defined, he should *see if it satisfies the criterion given in the definition*. This sounds trivial, probably, to one who has never *taught* mathematics, but I am sure that any teacher of mathematics will understand!

term "mathematics" itself (we shall come to the latter in due time!). And none has yet met the criterion that it serve satisfactorily to identify the notion. Let us look into the reasons for this state of affairs concerning a notion that must seem so trivial to anyone who has never looked into it before!

1 Background of the theory

In the first place, let us straighten out the synonyms for "collection"! This chapter is labeled "theory of sets" because the American mathematician uses the word "set" more frequently than "collection"; this is probably because of its brevity, for mathematicians like abbreviations. However, our English colleagues seem to prefer "aggregate"; an Englishman would have entitled this chapter "theory of aggregates." On the other hand, our American colleagues who teach philosophy, including a course in logic, would probably label it "theory of classes." And mathematicians have frequently employed the terms "family," "system," and "group," although these words are usually reserved for more special types of collections.† It is probably safe to say that in the United States mathematicians prefer the terms *set, collection, class*, in that order.‡

Since some readers may wish to consult French or German works, we might interpolate here the remark that the French term for "collection" is "ensemble," and the German term is "Menge." (In French the title of this chapter would become "Théorie des ensembles;" of course the Germans have combined it into one word, "Mengenlehre"!). In French texts the letter E (with or without an index as in E_i) is almost invariably used to denote a set, and in German texts the letter M is used.§

Of course collections have been used in mathematics since the very beginnings of the subject, by the Greeks for instance. The modern theory of sets is usually considered to have begun with Georg Cantor (1845–1918), who devised the first numbers for infinite sets (i.e., *transfinite numbers*) during the latter part of the nineteenth century.‖ It

† For example, a mathematician would be very unlikely to use the term "group" instead of "set" or "collection" if he actually meant the latter, because of the special use (see Chap. VII) for which the term "group" is reserved today.

‡ Undoubtedly a "collection of sets" sounds better, to many, than "a set of sets." One never seems to see the term "a set of collections."

§ In the early part of the present century, when so many American mathematicians went abroad for their doctoral or post-doctoral work, one could usually detect which foreign influence was dominant, on their return, by the preference for E or M to denote a collection.

‖ Fortunately Cantor's two most authoritative papers (see Cantor [C; 282ff]) are available in an English translation by Jourdain; Cantor [C₁].

is revealing to read the "definition" of set given by Cantor. The first sentence of the first of the papers just cited is (translated): "By a 'set' we shall understand any collection into a whole, M, of definite, distinguishable † objects m (which will be called 'elements' of M) of our intuition or thought." This was written by a first-class mathematician, who clearly did not know the word "set" was "loaded" (as did nobody else at the time).

1.1   Enlightenment was not long in forthcoming. As a matter of fact, it was virtually ready not long after Cantor published his ideas, as a result of the announcement ‡ by an Italian logician, Burali-Forti, of a fundamental difficulty with one of Cantor's basic definitions. Unfortunately Burali-Forti misinterpreted the definition, so that his insight did not at first win recognition (for the objection he raised was just as valid when opposed to the correct interpretation). Soon after, Russell announced his famous "antinomy," described below, and this time there was no attempt to avoid the difficulty by subterfuge or otherwise, and the problem of "what to do?" had to be met head on. Once the dam was broken, the flood was on, and the construction of contradictions and paradoxes became almost a mathematical "indoor sport."

1.2   Notice that we said "contradictions and paradoxes." The examples constructed were generally of two kinds: those that were bona fide contradictions, and those that were only "apparent contradictions" without actually being contradictory. The former are frequently given the technical name *antinomy;* the latter we do not worry about, although we frequently use them for amusement or instructional purposes (as for instance in the case of the "proof" that all triangles are isosceles cited in I 3f). We shall describe both the (amended) Burali-Forti and Russell examples, since they are real contradictions.

The Burali-Forti contradiction we shall defer until a later section (V 3.2.3), however, since it requires an acquaintance with the notion of "ordinal number." The Russell antinomy involves no such technicalities, and for our future purposes we shall state it in the following form:

† In his translation (Cantor [C₁]), Jourdain says "definite and separate." However, it seems likely that by "bestimmten wohlunterschiedenen Objekten," Cantor meant to imply that the objects are distinguishable from one another in some sense.

‡ Evidently Cantor was already aware of the difficulty, however; see V 3.2.3f.

2   The Russell contradiction

Consider any collection S. Its elements are to be thought of as individual objects—each a "unit." However, in general the elements will themselves be sets if we care to "dissect" them. Thus a collection of books has, for each element, a single, individual book. But, if we wish, we can consider a book not as an individual, indivisible object, but as an (ordered) collection of printed words; and in turn each word as an (ordered) collection of letters.

Since, generally, the elements of S may be sets themselves, the possibility (not probability!) arises that S may happen to be an element of itself! For example, someone (the name has escaped us) has suggested the set of all abstract ideas; such a set is certainly an element of itself if we grant (and who wouldn't!) that it is itself an abstract idea. If the notion seems rather far-fetched, however, there is no need to worry about it, since the Russell antinomy involves only sets that do *not* have themselves as elements. Such sets we may call *ordinary* sets. Thus, the set of natural numbers is ordinary—and most sets that we use are ordinary.

2.1   Now suppose that we collect all ordinary sets in one collection $\mathfrak{U}$. Then the elements of $\mathfrak{U}$, by definition, are ordinary sets, and every ordinary set is an element of $\mathfrak{U}$. Using exactly the same type of reasoning that we used in high school geometry, we prove the following two theorems:

Theorem A.   *The set $\mathfrak{U}$ is an ordinary set.*
Proof.   For suppose $\mathfrak{U}$ is not an ordinary set. Then $\mathfrak{U}$ is an element of itself.
But the elements of $\mathfrak{U}$ are all ordinary sets. Hence, as $\mathfrak{U}$ is an element of $\mathfrak{U}$, it is an ordinary set.
Thus the supposition that $\mathfrak{U}$ is not ordinary leads to the conclusion that $\mathfrak{U}$ is ordinary, hence to a contradiction. We must conclude that our supposition is false, hence that $\mathfrak{U}$ is ordinary.   Q.E.D.

Theorem B.   *The set $\mathfrak{U}$ is not an ordinary set.*
Proof.   For suppose $\mathfrak{U}$ is an ordinary set. Then $\mathfrak{U}$ is not an element of $\mathfrak{U}$, by definition of "ordinary."
But *all* ordinary sets are elements of $\mathfrak{U}$. Hence, if $\mathfrak{U}$ is not an element of $\mathfrak{U}$, it is because $\mathfrak{U}$ is *not* ordinary.
Thus the supposition that $\mathfrak{U}$ is ordinary leads to the conclusion that $\mathfrak{U}$ is not ordinary, hence to a contradiction. We must conclude that our supposition is false, hence that $\mathfrak{U}$ is not ordinary.   Q.E.D.

2.2   Theorems A and B plainly contradict one another. And we have obtained this contradiction by purely logical deduction. Furthermore, if "set" is to be regarded as a logical notion, the whole affair, from the definition of the set $\mathfrak{U}$ to the end of the proof of Theorem B, is purely logical.

> The set $\mathfrak{U}$ is often called "the Russell set." Actually, in view of the above, it cannot be admitted as a set if we are to continue to hold fast to the Law of Contradiction. Some have also called $\mathfrak{U}$ a "self-contradictory set."
>
> An amusing (except to philosophers, who can substitute the word "mathematicians" for "philosophers" below) formulation of Russell's contradiction was given by Grelling [Gr; pp. 44–49] in a "proof" that "the set of all philosophers is a camel."

It is not surprising, then, that the first reaction of some mathematicians to this matter was that it concerned "logicians," not "mathematicians," so let the logicians find what was wrong and set their house in order! But this attitude was short-lived, since, if mathematics is to use logic, any defect of logic is of concern to mathematics —especially when the defect is found in a concept of logic that is so frequently used in mathematical definition and proof! The natural result was a movement among mathematicians, slow at first but accelerating in recent years, toward the study of logic. And, whereas logic was traditionally a cut-and-dried rehash of the work of Aristotle—with great concentration on the syllogism, etc.—it has today become a live and growing field of investigation, known under the name of *symbolic logic* or *mathematical logic*.

> 2.3   Two comments should be made here. In the first place, symbolic logic itself had its beginnings long before the discovery of contradictions such as the one just described above. For evidence of this, the reader may glance at the bibliography of symbolic logic compiled by Church [a, b]; the works cited cover a period beginning with the year 1666. There can be little doubt, however, of the great impetus given to its development by the logical contradictions. Secondly, and related to the preceding sentence, the breadth of the modern interest, and extent of research, in symbolic logic is evidenced in the formation of the Association for Symbolic Logic, Inc., and the founding of a journal, *The Journal of Symbolic Logic;* the latter began publication in 1936 and has now (1950) reached its fourteenth volume.
>
> It is of interest also to remark that "border-line" interests such as have been exemplified for so long among the mathematical physicists are paralleled among the "mathematical logicians." And, just as the former may be found in either the mathematics or the physics department (or both) of a university, so may the latter be found in either the mathematics or the philosophy department. (Probably because it was developed by the Greek philosophers, logic has traditionally been taught in the philosophy department—a distinction of significance only in the modern university where the departmentalization due to the tremendous growth of

the sciences, etc., has been made necessary.) That breaking down of barriers between fields of learning in our universities, implored and exhorted by so many educators but opposed by budgetary officers, will probably be brought about by forces within the fields themselves! In the introduction to his bibliography, Church [a] was moved to state "It has been the intention to confine the bibliography to symbolic logic proper as distinguished from pure mathematics on the one hand and pure philosophy on the other. The line is, of course, difficult to draw on both sides, . . ."

3   Basic relations and operations

Deferring any attempt to explain the above contradiction—it was introduced at this point only to show the necessity for a closer analysis of the term "set"—let us consider some of the elementary parts of so-called "set theory," illustrating them with important examples of sets basic in mathematics. We shall not begin with a definition of "set," but will proceed, as before, as though we are dealing with a logical "universal," with the idea of becoming more familiar with its meaning and application in mathematics before attempting further analysis.

First let us introduce a few symbols, not because we wish to become "technical," but for the sake of brevity and simplification. Probably anyone who has "taken" high school algebra thinks of symbols when the word "mathematics" is mentioned. If the course was satisfactorily (1) taught by the teacher and (2) absorbed by the pupil, then the pupil must have realized the gain accomplished in the introduction of "$x, y, z, \cdots$" and operations (addition, equating, transposition in an equation, etc.) with them. Anyone unconvinced of this should see what efforts were involved in the solution of simple problems before the introduction of modern algebraic techniques (for that matter, imagine having to add, multiply, or divide numbers in the Roman symbols: MXVI $\times$ XLVII for instance). †

3.1   Relations between sets

If S is a set, and x is an element of S, then we express this by the symbols

(3a) $$x \, \varepsilon \, S,$$

which may be read "x is an element of S" or "x is contained in S." In special instances, but rarely, we may wish to reverse (3a),

(3a') $$S \ni x;$$

† There is in existence a letter to an Italian of the Middle Ages advising that he send his son to the German universities because long division was taught there!

in general, however, we shall use (3a). The negation of (3a) is denoted by the symbols $x \notin S$. We may abbreviate the relations $x_1 \varepsilon S$, $x_2 \varepsilon S$, $\cdots$, $x_n \varepsilon S$ to x_1, x_2, $\cdots$, $x_n \varepsilon S$.

3.1.1   Notice that in 3.1 we used different types of symbols for the element and the set: a lower-case x and capital S. Generally we shall adhere to this custom. It can become complicated, of course, if we start "pyramiding" sets. Thus, if x, S are already introduced, and S is in turn an element of a "still larger" set, we shall resort to German capitals: $S \varepsilon \mathfrak{S}$ for instance. Greek capitals may be used for higher types: $\mathfrak{S} \varepsilon \Sigma$, etc. (See Problem 4.)

3.1.2   A set A is called a *subset* of a set B if $x \varepsilon A$ implies $x \varepsilon B$ for all x; in words, A is a subset of B if every element of A is also an element of B. The relation is expressed symbolically by the symbol $\subset$:

(3b) $A \subset B,$

which may also be reversed:

(3b′) $B \supset A.$

Since, by definition, $A \subset A$ for every set A, we express the fact that $A \subset B$ and A is not identical with B by the statement that A is a *proper subset* of B (sometimes the term "true subset" is used).

3.1.3   That the sets A and B are identical, i.e., have the same elements, is expressed by the equality sign:

(3c) $A = B.$

Evidently *a necessary and sufficient condition that $A = B$ is that both $A \subset B$ and $B \subset A$ hold.* This is the basis of one of the most frequently employed methods for establishing the identity of two sets. It should be noticed, too, that the equality relation $=$ is an equivalence relation (II 8) in any collection of sets whatsoever. In particular, in any collection of sets there can be at most one empty set, and it is usually denoted by a "zero" symbol, "0," or a modification thereof such as "∅." We shall generally use the latter. The empty set is frequently called *the null set*.

3.1.4   *If $\mathfrak{S}$ is any collection of sets and $\emptyset \varepsilon \mathfrak{S}$, then for every $S \varepsilon \mathfrak{S}$,*
           $\emptyset \subset S$
[The logical equivalent of "$x \varepsilon A$ implies $x \varepsilon B$" is "$x \notin B$ implies $x \notin A$"; the reader may prefer the latter form of the definition of "$A \subset B$" in proving that $\emptyset \subset S$.]

Negations of $\subset$, $\supset$, and $=$ are denoted by $\not\subset$, $\not\supset$, and $\neq$, respectively.

3.2   A symbol for defining special sets

An especially useful symbol for the defining of individual sets is the formula "$\{\ \mid\ \}$," which is applied as follows: Suppose that we have the combination of symbols:

(3d) $A = \{x \mid x \text{ is a human being}\}.$

Then (3d) would be read

(3d')   "A is the set of all things x such that x is a human being."

In other words, A is the set of all human beings. In (3d) the braces $\{\ \}$ are used to denote the set of all things denoted by whatever is enclosed by the braces, and the "$\mid$" may be read "such that."

To get a better idea of the use of this symbol, suppose that we wish to define the set, S, of all points that lie within the unit square of the coordinate "xy-plane" (such as is used in the subject of "graphs" in the elementary algebra or analytic geometry courses), which is bounded by the two coordinate axes and the lines, parallel thereto, one unit to the right of the y-axis and one unit above the x-axis respectively. This set [within the framework of the subject matter, so that the meaning of (x, y) is understood], may be defined as follows:

$$S = \{(x, y) \mid 0 < x < 1, 0 < y < 1\}.$$

Certainly this is more specific and easily understood, as well as more economical of symbols, than the definition in words which precedes it.

In cases where the "such that" is superfluous, we use the braces $\{\ \}$ within which the elements are named instead of $\{\ \mid\ \}$. Thus, $\{2, 4\}$ denotes the set whose elements are the numbers 2 and 4; $\{2\}$ denotes the set whose single element is 2 (we shall wish to distinguish this *set* from the *number* 2 incidentally).

[An exception which has evolved in practice occurs when, given a set S and $x \in S$, one frequently writes $S \cup x$ instead of $S \cup \{x\}$, or $S - x$ instead of $S - \{x\}$ (the operations $\cup$ and $-$ are defined in 3.3.1 and 3.3.2). However, when standing alone, the symbol $\{x\}$ *must* be used to distinguish between the *set* whose single element is x, and x itself. This is particularly important when x is itself a set, since then $\{x\}$ has only *one* element whereas x may have many elements.]

3.2.1   The proposal of the symbol $\{\ |\ \}$ suggests that the notion of "property" might be made basic instead of the notion of "set." For, just as in (3d) the set A is defined by the property of "being a human being," so in general one would expect that some property distinguishes the elements of any given set. If so desired, it would be feasible to build a theory of sets on this basis.

3.3 Operations with sets

In the classical set theory, the basic operations are *addition* and *multiplication*. As might perhaps be inferred from its connotation in ordinary use, to *add* sets is merely to combine their elements to form one set. Thus, if A is the set of all even natural numbers, and B the set of all odd natural numbers, then $A + B$ would be the set, N, of all natural numbers. If A were also to have all prime numbers—2, 3, 5, 7, etc.—as elements, $A + B$ would still give N, since the occurrence of 3, say, in both A and B, does not "double" its occurrence in $A + B$. As another example, using points in the coordinate xy-plane again, we can write:

(3e) $\{(x, y)\ |\ 0 < x < 1, 0 < y < 1\} + \{(x, y)\ |\ 0 \leqq x < 2, 0 < y < 1\}$

$$= \{(x, y)\ |\ 0 \leqq x < 2, 0 < y < 1\}.$$

In relation (3e), the second term has "swallowed" the first; in general, if $A \subset B$, then $A + B = B$. If sets A_i are given, where the index i ranges over some "index set" I, then $\Sigma_i A_i$, or $\Sigma_{i\,\varepsilon\,I} A_i$ denotes the set of all elements that belong to at least one of the sets A_i. For example, if A_1, A_2, A_3 are sets, then $A_1 + A_2 + A_3$ may be replaced by $\Sigma_{i\,\varepsilon\,I} A_i$, where I is the set of integers $\{1, 2, 3\}$; in this case, however, the symbol $\sum_{n=1}^{3} A_n$ is used more frequently, n being an almost universally employed generic symbol for a natural number (compare "n-dimensional space" for example).

3.3.1   The symbols $+$ and Σ are today frequently replaced by the symbols $\cup$ and $\bigcup$, especially where the $+$ symbol is being used for other purposes (as in algebra for instance). The symbols $\cup$, $\bigcup$, which may be called "union," "join," or "cup," are derived from the symbol v used commonly in symbolic logic to denote "and/or." In fact, $\cup$ may be defined in terms of v by the expression

(3f) $A \cup B = \{x\ |\ (x\,\varepsilon\,A) \mathbin{\mathsf{v}} (x\,\varepsilon\,B)\};$

in words, "$A \cup B$ is the collection of all those things x such that x is an element of A and/or x is an element of B." Similarly, $\Sigma_i A_i$ is replaced by $\bigcup_i A_i$. We shall give preference to the new symbols $\cup$, $\bigcup$ in the sequel, reserving $+$ for its traditional role in arithmetic and algebra.

3.3.2   The *difference*, $A - B$, is defined by the expression

(3g) $A - B = \{x \mid (x \, \varepsilon \, A) \ \& \ (x \notin B)\}$,

which can be read "$A - B$ is the collection of all those things x such that x is an element of A but not an element of B." In (3g) we use the symbol $\&$ instead of the symbol $\cdot$ ordinarily used in symbolic logic to denote "and," preferring to restrict $\cdot$ to such uses as algebraic multiplication. In (3g) it is not necessary that B be a subset of A. Thus, if $A = \{x \mid x$ is a prime number$\}$ and $B = \{x \mid x$ is an odd number$\}$, then $A - B$ is the set whose only element is the number 2; in symbols, we write $A - B = \{2\}$. When B is a subset of A, then $A - B$ may be called the *complement* of B in A.

3.3.3   To "multiply" sets A and B is to give the *product $A \cdot B$*, in the classical terminology; or, for a collection of indexed sets A_i, the product is indicated by $\prod_i A_i$ or more specifically $\prod_{i \, \varepsilon \, I} A_i$, where I is the index set. Today $\cdot$ and $\prod$ are frequently replaced by $\cap$ and $\bigcap$ respectively, which may be called "intersection," "meet," or "cap." The definitions are:

(3h) $A \cdot B = A \cap B = \{x \mid (x \, \varepsilon \, A) \ \& \ (x \, \varepsilon \, B)\}$

(3h′) $\prod_{i \, \varepsilon \, I} A_i = \bigcap_{i \, \varepsilon \, I} A_i = \{x \mid x \, \varepsilon \, A_i \text{ for every } i \, \varepsilon \, I\}$.

An expression such as $\bigcap_{n=1}^{k} A_n$ indicates $\bigcap_{i \, \varepsilon \, I} A_i$, where $I = \{1, 2, \cdots, k\}$; $\bigcap_{n=1}^{\infty} A_n$ is an intersection of sets A_n where, for every natural number n, A_n is a given set. We shall prefer the symbols $\cap$, $\bigcap$.

3.4   At this point we can augment the argument given in I 3.4 for the empty set, $\emptyset$. Suppose that A and B are sets having no element whatsoever in common. Then we can express this fact, using the $\emptyset$ symbol, by the symbols

$$A \cap B = \emptyset.$$

Or, if $A \subset B$, then

$$A - B = \emptyset.$$

This use of $\emptyset$ may be compared with the use of zero in $3 - 3 = 0$. The reader familiar with the history of mathematics will recall the antagonism to the introduction of zero as a *number;* † an analogous antagonism is felt, by many who are unfamiliar with set theory, to the introduction of the null set!

3.5   Parentheses are used, as in elementary algebra, to indicate operations that are to be performed before removal of the parentheses. Thus, $S = (A - B) \cup C$ indicates that the set S is the union of (1) the set $A - B$ and (2) the set C. On the other hand, the set $A - (B \cup C)$ is the set of all elements of A that are in neither B nor C. We see that the use of parentheses in a union of sets—such as $(A_1 \cup A_2) \cup A_3$— is unnecessary, if we refer to the definition in 3.3.1. However, it is sometimes clarifying, when the union of A_1 and A_2 is of special significance, to enclose their union in parentheses.

3.6   If $A \neq \emptyset$, then A is called *non-empty* or *non-vacuous*. If A has more than one element, then it is called *non-degenerate*. If $A \cap B = \emptyset$, then A and B are called *disjoint* sets. And, more generally, if $\{A_\nu\}$ is any collection of sets A_ν, where ν runs over some set of indices or marks, such that for every two different indices ν' and ν'', $A_{\nu'} \cap A_{\nu''} = \emptyset$, then we shall again call the A_ν disjoint sets.

4   Finite and infinite sets

One of the most important distinctions in mathematics, from any standpoint (be it methodological or philosophical), is that between finite sets and infinite sets. If we wish to give them explicit definitions, we usually define one or the other and arbitrarily place all sets not satisfying the definition in the other category. Thus, we may define finite set, and then infinite set as any set that is not finite; or we may define infinite set, and then finite set as any set that is not infinite. In either case, we divide any collection A of sets into two categories, each set in the collection falling definitely in one category or the other.

It would seem more natural, surely, to define finite set and then infinite set as "not finite," rather than the reverse, inasmuch as our everyday experience seems to involve encounters only with "finite" sets (sets of people, sets of books, etc.). Furthermore, it is only in comparatively recent years that there has been developed any respectable theory of infinite sets.

† The author has frequently illustrated, for his students, the difference between "0" and "nothing" by pointing out that a "0" in the grade book opposite a student's name indicates that the student actually handed in an assignment, whereas nothing opposite the name indicates no work handed in; in the former case, "good intention" is indicated on the part of the student at least!

In defining "finite" we shall presume that the reader is familiar with the sequence of natural numbers—1, 2, 3, ····.† However, there may be no serious objection to this, as it means, virtually, that we presuppose familiarity with the ordinary counting process. As we define the term, a set is finite if, roughly speaking, *its elements can be counted.* We say "roughly" because, practically speaking, we can hardly say that the set of all grains of sand on the earth allows of its elements being counted! The trouble here, however, is that we are thinking of counting as a *physical* process, hence a time-consuming process.

4.1   In order to avoid this difficulty, we revert to the notion of (1-1)-correspondence defined in II 4.4.1. Let us denote by N the set of all natural numbers, and by N_n the set defined by the expression

(4a) $N_n = \{x \mid (x \varepsilon N) \,\&\, (1 \leqq x \leqq n)\}.$‡

Then we may define "finite" as follows:

4.1.1   Definition. A set S is *finite* if either it is empty, or there exists a natural number n such that between the elements of S and the elements of the set N_n there exists a (1-1)-correspondence.

Note that, for a non-empty finite set, the pairs in the (1-1)-correspondence are of type (x, k), $x \varepsilon S$, $k \varepsilon N_n$, and consequently we may denote uniquely the element x in the pair (x, k) by x_k. Thus the set of all states in the United States is finite, since between its elements and the elements of N_{48} there exists a (1-1)-correspondence; the set of all moons of the earth is finite since between its elements and the elements of N_1 there exists a (1-1)-correspondence; the set of all present-day kings of France is finite, since it is empty. In the case of the set G of all grains of sand on the earth, we do not know the corresponding N_n, since we cannot count them; but, by virtue of simple physical facts, and the properties of the set N (we go fully into these later), it is not difficult to show that the required N_n exists (at a given time, because, owing to erosion, etc., there is no reason to think that G is a fixed set).

4.2   Having defined "finite" as above, we define *infinite* as *not finite.* Thus N itself is not finite, although this has to be proved of course; the set of all points on a euclidean line or euclidean plane is not finite; etc.

4.3   In order to differentiate between the above definitions of finite and infinite and those given below, let us agree to call them the *ordi-*

† Regarding alternative definitions of "finite," see 4.10.

‡ Whenever we use symbols $<$ and $=$ in connection with natural numbers, we shall, unless otherwise stated, mean $1 < 2$, $2 < 3$, and so on, and $=$ denoting "equals" in the ordinary sense of logical identity ($2 = 2$, $3 = 3$, etc.). The set N is simply ordered relative to this relation $<$ (II 7) in what we may call its *natural order.*

nary finite and *ordinary infinite* (if for no other reason than that they probably represent what we ordinarily think of as the meanings of these terms).

4.4   The alternative definitions, which are due to Dedekind, will seem more natural if we recall the classic example † of the (1-1)-correspondence between the set N of all natural numbers and the set N_e of all even numbers. The pairs in this case are of the type $(n, 2n)$, where $n \varepsilon N$, $2n \varepsilon N_e$; in detail, the pairs are (1, 2), (2, 4), (3, 6), (4, 8), and so on.

4.5   Although we made the convention (Definition II 4.4.1) that the order of the terms in the pairs of a (1-1)-correspondence is not of importance so far as the *correspondence* is concerned, it is frequently convenient, in particular cases, to attach a significance to the order, especially where the two sets in question have elements in common. Thus, in the present case, the numbers 2 and 4 in the pair (2, 4) happen to be elements of both N and N_e, and it is convenient to have a rule to tell us that in this pair, however, 2 is to be considered an element of N, and 4 an element of N_e. An alternative rule in the present case is to notice that the smaller of the two numbers in a pair is always an element of N and the larger of N_e. In the general case, however, when we need to have a way of recognizing which set an element belongs to, we shall make use of the order of the terms in the pair, remembering, however, that this is not significant so far as the (1-1)-correspondence (which is a *symmetric* equivalence relation between sets) is concerned but merely a symbolic device for recognizing the set to which an element belongs.

4.6   A more elementary example, perhaps, is the (1-1)-correspondence between the elements of N and the elements of the set $N - \{1\}$ (the latter being the set of all natural numbers except the number 1; cf. 3.3.2). The pairs representing the (1-1)-correspondence are of the type $(n, n + 1)$, where $n \varepsilon N$, $n + 1 \varepsilon N - \{1\}$. We shall make use of this example in the sequel (5.3).

4.7   The reader should note, incidentally, that in each of these examples the "law" or "rule" for the (1-1)-correspondence is explicitly stated. Up to now we have avoided mentioning the significance of the term "there exists" as used in Definition II 4.4.4, for instance. The "rule" $(n, n + 1)$ tells us explicitly what are the elements of the (1-1)-correspondence between the elements of N and the elements of $N - \{1\}$, and is one of the ways in which we fulfill the requirement "there *exists* a (1-1)-correspondence. . . ." We shall consider this matter more fully later. It is possible, for instance, that we may sometimes be satisfied with a logical proof of the "existence" of a (1-1)-correspondence, without knowing any such explicit definition of it such as is given above.

4.8   If we denote the set of all odd numbers by N_o, then there exists a (1-1)-correspondence between N_e and N_o whose elements are of the type $(2n, 2n - 1)$, where n is a natural number. This example

† Galileo evidently was aware of such examples; see Bell [B₃; 272ff].

differs from the two above in that here the sets involved (N_e and N_o) are disjoint, whereas in each of the above two cases one of the sets was a proper subset of the other. In this example we evidently need no rule to tell us to which set the respective elements belong.

4.9   Dedekind's definition of infinite is suggested by observation of such correspondences † as that between N and N_e, in which one of the sets (N_e) is a proper subset of the other (N). Such a circumstance, Dedekind observed, must be *characteristic* of what we intuitively recognize as "infinite" sets:

4.9.1   Definition (Dedekind).   A set S is *infinite* if it has a proper subset S_1 such that between the elements of S and the elements of S_1 there exists a (1-1)-correspondence.

Thus the set N is infinite according to Definition 4.9.1. (It is interesting to notice that it is much easier to prove this than to prove N infinite by the ordinary definition; see below.)

Of course we may now call a set finite if it is not infinite. And to distinguish this definition from that (4.1.1) of the ordinary finite, we call it the *Dedekind finite;* and similarly we call the "infinite" defined in 4.9.1 the *Dedekind infinite.*

4.10   In the foreword to the second edition (1893) of [D₂], Dedekind proposed a non-negative definition of "finite" as follows:

"A set S is called *finite* if there exists a mapping ‡ of S into itself such that no proper subset of S is mapped into itself."

He predicted that it would be very difficult to develop a theory on the basis of this definition unless the sequence of natural numbers is assumed. However, in an unpublished note (see [D₃; LXIII]) he developed some of the properties of sets that are finite by the new definition; and in 1932 Cavaillès [a] continued the investigation, showing how to develop the fundamental properties of finite sets (such as the finiteness of all subsets of a finite set, the mathematical induction property, etc.). None of this necessitates any use of the Choice Axiom (see Section 6).

An extensive investigation of possible definitions of "finite" and of their interrelations was made by Tarski [a]; the reader is referred to his work for further details and citations to earlier investigations.

---

† As Dedekind observed ([D₂; 2nd ed.], or the *Werke*), both Cantor and Bolzano had called attention to the property of infinite sets which he (Dedekind) made the basis of his definition; however, neither elevated it to the rank of a *defining* characteristic.

‡ See IV 3.2.3.1.

5 Relation between the ordinary infinite and the Dedekind infinite

When we have two definitions of the same term, here "infinite," we should investigate the relationship between them. The ordinary finite and infinite presuppose a knowledge of the set, N, of natural numbers; the Dedekind definitions of finite and infinite presuppose only the concept of (1-1)-correspondence. We have defined what we mean by a (1-1)-correspondence; but up to now we have used the set N as a universally known concept, just as we suppose that its elements, such as the number 2, are universally known in the context of such axiom systems as are set up for geometry.

In attempting to compare the two definitions of infinite given above, we shall come face to face with the fact that the set N has certain associated properties † which are necessary for a solution of the problem, and which we do not encounter in the concept of any individual number, such as 2. For example, associated with the set N is the "mathematical induction principle," which the reader may or may not have studied in freshman college algebra, but which has no significance for the individual number. A knowledge of individual numbers, and how to use them in counting, by no means implies a knowledge of the induction principle, as every instructor who has tried to teach it is well aware. This principle is used as an axiom in the famous axiomatic definition of N as a set of *numbers* (undefined term), due to Peano: ‡

5.1 Peano's definition of the natural number system

Peano gave a system of axioms concerning a collection, N, of undefined elements called *numbers*, and an undefined binary relation, s, between numbers. If x and y are elements of N, then $x \, s \, y$ is read "x is a successor of y." The axioms are:

(1) N contains a number, 1, such that $1 \, s \, x$ holds for no $x \, \varepsilon \, N$.

(2) If $x \, \varepsilon \, N$, there exists a unique $y \, \varepsilon \, N$ such that $y \, s \, x$; y is called the *successor* of x.

(3) If $y \, s \, x$ and $y' \, s \, x'$, and y is the same number as y', then x and x' are the same number.

(4) (Mathematical induction principle.) If G is a subset of N such that: (i) $1 \, \varepsilon \, G$ and (ii) if $x \, \varepsilon \, G$ and $y \, s \, x$ then $y \, \varepsilon \, G$; then $G = N$.

---

† These associated properties are not properties of N as a *set*, any more than is the fact that $2 \times 2 = 4$ is such a property. They are associated with the fact that the elements of N have a "natural order," 1, 2, 3, and so on. Cf. 4.1f.

‡ See Peano [P₂]; also arithmetical portions of Peano [P₃], as for instance [P₃; II, § 2, 1]. Also compare Dedekind [D₂; § 6].

If N is identified with the set of all natural numbers, and 1 with the natural number 1, and *successor* of a natural number n identified with the natural number $n + 1$, then an elementary knowledge of the natural numbers suffices to convince one that axioms (1), (2), and (3) hold for them. It is usually necessary to give some arguments, however, to convince one that axiom (4) holds. And, for this, the instructor † resorts to some such subterfuge as asking the class to imagine the natural numbers represented by blocks standing in juxta-position so that a forward push on the block representing the number n forces it to knock over the block representing $n + 1$; ‡ the block rep-resenting 1 is pushed over and in its fall knocks over the block repre-senting 2; the latter, in turn, falls against the block representing 3 and knocks it over; and so on, all the blocks being knocked over as a result of the pushing over of the first block. The analogy, of course, is that G is the set of blocks that actually fall; if it contains 1, as in axiom (4), and if for each number in G the successor is in G (and hence ready to be knocked over!), then *all* the blocks fall; that is, G is the whole set of blocks, the set N. This is *not* a proof, of course.

5.2   Proof that a set which is Dedekind infinite is ordinary infinite

Now let S be a set which is Dedekind infinite. Then S has a proper subset S' such that between the elements of S and the elements of S' there exists a (1-1)-correspondence.

Either S is ordinary finite or ordinary infinite, since we defined ordi-nary infinite as "not ordinary finite," and it will be sufficient to show that S is not ordinary finite. If S were ordinary finite, there would exist a set N_k, as defined above (4.1.1), such that between the elements of S and the elements of N_k there exists a (1-1)-correspondence.§

Now *if, in general, A and B are sets, and A' is a proper subset of A such that* (1) *between the elements of A and the elements of A' there exists a (1-1)-correspondence, and* (2) *between the elements of A and the ele-*

† If he is the traditional "drill" type of instructor, he may not attempt the convincing process, but will ram it down the student's throat as a *fact* to be assimi-lated without justification. Perhaps this is just as well; who knows!

‡ Just as children frequently stand dominoes in this fashion, so that a push on the first domino in line is sufficient to knock over *all* the dominoes.

§ It must be emphasized that we are here assuming a knowledge of the natural numbers just as in Section 4 (especially in terms of $<$ as in 4.1), including a knowl-edge of the mathematical induction principle. We are not, therefore, proceeding by the axiomatic method as described in Chapters I and II, basing our theorems on the Peano axioms. See Problem 22.

ments of B there exists a (1-1)-correspondence, then we can assert that there exists a proper subset B' of B such that there exists a (1-1)-correspondence between the elements of B and the elements of B'. To prove this, denote the pairs constituting the (1-1)-correspondence between elements of A and elements of B by (a_ν, b_ν). Then the set $\{b_\nu \mid (b_\nu \in B)$ $\&((a_\nu, b_\nu)$ is a pair for some $a_\nu \in A')\}$ is the desired set B'.

Consequently, if A, B, and A' are replaced by S, N_k, and S' respectively, we can assert that there exists a proper subset N_k' of N_k such that there exists a (1-1)-correspondence between the elements of N_k and the elements of N_k'. We shall show that this is impossible.

5.2.1   Theorem. *There exists no set N_k such that there exists a (1-1)-correspondence between the elements of N_k and the elements of a proper subset of N_k.*

Proof. Consider the set N_1. As its only proper subset is $\emptyset$, there exists no (1-1)-correspondence between the elements of N_1 and a proper subset of N_1. Hence, if we let G denote the set of all natural numbers k for which the theorem is true, $1 \in G$. Also, if a number $n \in G$, then $n + 1 \in G$. For suppose not. Then the set $N_{n+1} = N_n \cup \{n + 1\}$ is in a (1-1)-correspondence T with a proper subset N_{n+1}' of itself. In N_{n+1}', let r denote the element paired with $n + 1$ in T, and let $R = N_{n+1}' - \{r\}$. Now, if $n + 1 = r$, it follows that $N_n \supset R$ and there exists a (1-1)-correspondence between N_n and R obtained from T by leaving out the pair $(n + 1, r) = (n + 1, n + 1)$. This is impossible since $n \in G$ and R is a proper subset of N_n.

However, if $n + 1 \neq r$ and $n + 1$ is not in R, we again have an impossible case since R is again a proper subset of N_n. But, if $n + 1 \neq r$ and $n + 1 \in R$, we cannot say this. However, let us interchange r and $n + 1$ in the respective elements $(n + 1, r)$, $(t, n + 1)$ of T—so that these pairs are replaced by $(n + 1, n + 1)$, (t, r). We get a new (1-1)-correspondence T which reduces to the case shown impossible in the preceding paragraph. As we have now considered all possible cases, we must conclude that $n + 1 \in G$.

By the mathematical induction principle, $G = N$. That is, no set N_k is in (1-1)-correspondence with a proper subset of itself.

Corollary.   *The set N is ordinary infinite.*

The above type of argument (without the mathematical induction) can be adapted to prove:

5.2.2   Theorem. *If S is a set such that there exists no (1-1)-correspondence between the elements of S and the elements of any proper subset* of S, and S is augmented by a new element e, then the set $S \cup \{e\} = S_1$ has a like property.

[In the above terminology, if S is not Dedekind infinite then $S_1 = S \cup \{e\}$ is not Dedekind infinite.]

5.2.3 Corollary. If a set S is Dedekind infinite, and $x \, \varepsilon \, S$, then $S - \{x\}$ is Dedekind infinite.

5.3 Proof that a set which is ordinary infinite is Dedekind infinite

We consider now the converse problem: Is a set which is ordinary infinite also Dedekind infinite? The proof that it is leads to a new principle, encountered here for the first time in our development of the foundations.† First, let us consider the following argument:

Let S be a set which is ordinary infinite, i.e., not ordinary finite. Then S is not empty, and we can select an element x_1 of S. Again, $S - x_1$ is not empty; for otherwise $S = \{x_1\}$, and the pair $(x_1, 1)$ constitutes a (1-1)-correspondence with N_1 rendering S ordinary finite. So we can select an element x_2 of $S - x_1$.

Continuing in this way, suppose that we have selected elements $x_1, x_2, \cdots, x_k$ of S. Then we argue that $S - x_1 - x_2 - \cdots - x_k$ is not empty; for otherwise $S = \{x_1, x_2, \cdots, x_k\}$, and the pairs $(x_1, 1)$, $(x_2, 2)$, $\cdots$, (x_k, k) would constitute a (1-1)-correspondence between S and N_k, rendering S ordinary finite. So we can select an element x_{k+1} of $S - x_1 - x_2 - \cdots - x_k$.

In this manner, we have shown how to select an element x_n of S for every natural number n (by virtue of the mathematical induction principle; see Problem 9 at the end of the chapter). Let S_1 denote the collection of all such elements x_n, and let $R = S - S_1$ (R may or may not be empty—we do not care). Let $S' = S - x_1$. Then between the elements of S and the elements of its proper subset S' there exists a (1-1)-correspondence T whose pairs are: (1) the pairs of type (x_n, x_{n+1}), where $x_n \, \varepsilon \, S_1$ and $x_{n+1} \, \varepsilon \, S'$; (2) the pairs of type (r, r), where $r \, \varepsilon \, R$ (there will not be any pairs of this type if R is empty; note that R is a subset of both S and S'). Hence S is Dedekind infinite.

Notice that part (1) of the (1-1)-correspondence T is the exact analogue of the (1-1)-correspondence between the elements of N and the elements of $N - \{1\}$ set up in 4.6 above.

† Historically, it was first noticed in another connection, which will be encountered later.

5.3.1   Comment on the above proof

We said above that "we have shown how to select an element x_n of S for every natural number n," and no two such elements are the same. But have we? We "select" x_1, then x_2, then x_3, and so on. We don't give any *rule* for these selections—they seem to be the result of free choice. But how are we to make an infinite set of free choices, one after the other (the collection x_1, x_2, x_3, $\cdots$ is infinite in either the ordinary or Dedekind sense)?

5.3.1.1   An example may make the above criticism clearer. If we have a die with faces numbered 1 to 6, we can consider a decimal number $0.a_1$ obtained by one throw of the die; if 1 comes up, let $a_1 = 1$ and we have the number 0.1; or, if 6 comes up, we have 0.6. We can also consider a number $0.a_1a_2a_3$ obtained from three throws of the die, letting the digits a_1, a_2, a_3 be the numbers successively obtained in the three throws. To be sure, the number is not determinate from our definition; thus, $0.a_1$ may be any one of six different numbers. We would not talk then of *the* number so obtained until *after* we threw the die; and then the number is quite definite. But, *before* the throw, its definition is not precise enough to fix it. In what sense, then, could we possibly speak of the number $0.a_1a_2 \cdots a_n \cdots$, where there is a digit a_n for each $n \, \varepsilon \, N$, to be obtained by a throw of a die? In this case we cannot even complete the throws of the die and hence make the number precise.

The objection can now be raised that there is no sense in mixing numbers, which are a mathematical notion, with physical concepts such as throwing of dice, and with time (which is used up in throwing and which consequently renders the number $0.a_1a_2 \cdots a_n \cdots$ indefinable in any precise sense). This objection may be met by pointing out that it is the indeterminacy, the free choice, of a_n that is the root of the difficulty, and that this is present in the above proof which utilizes no physical concepts. For some sets S we could get around the difficulty by eliminating free choice. Thus, if S is the set of all ordinary fractions between 0 and 1 ("proper fractions"), we could *specify* $x_1 = \frac{1}{2}$, $x_2 = \frac{1}{4}$, and in general, having x_n, let $x_{n+1} = \frac{1}{2}x_n$ (i.e., $(\frac{1}{2})^{n+1}$). But in the above proof we don't know enough about the nature of S to make any such specifications.

Very well, we may counter-object, don't say "select"; just say, *let x_1 be an element of S*, then *let x_2 be an element of $S - x_1$*, and, in general, having obtained x_n, *let x_{n+1} be an element of $S - x_1 - x_2 - \cdots - x_n$*. The word "select" implies a selector, whereas the "let x_n be $\cdots$" formula avoids such a connotation.

We can let the argument rest here; either let us admit that the "let x_n be $\cdots$" formula solves the difficulty, or let us not admit it. There seems to be no *logical* way of settling the matter. We encounter a question of what might be called *mathematical method* or *mathematical existence* (depending on the point of view), rather than something that can be handled by appeal to the classical Aristotelian logic. Notice, however, that except for this aspect of it, the above proof that an ordinary infinite set is Dedekind infinite is evidently quite acceptable. Specifically, there is evidently no objection to the proof, contained in the above, that

5.3.2   *If a set S has a subset S_1, such that between the elements of S_1 and the elements of the set of natural numbers, N, there exists a (1-1)-correspondence, then S is Dedekind infinite.*

6   The Choice Axiom

The difficulty we encountered in the preceding section—the question of the existence of the set S_1 of 5.3—may be handled by appeal to what is ordinarily called the "Choice Axiom" (or the "Zermelo Postulate"; see 6.3 and 6.7). This statement must not be construed to mean that we are going to *eliminate* the difficulty; far from it. From the point of view of one who insists that generally no such set S_1 exists, we are only going to attribute the difficulty to a "principle" which will, as we shall see, serve as a haven for all sorts of such difficulties. It is convenient to have a single principle to which we can bring such matters and not be forced to leave a lot of seemingly unrelated special problems lying about unattended!

6.1   To introduce the principle referred to, suppose that we consider the set of forty-eight states of the United States, where each state is considered not a geographical entity, but a collection of its individual citizens. And, for convenience, let us assume that no person is a citizen of more than one state. Question: Does there exist a set, R, consisting of one and only one citizen from each state? This must seem like a trivial question, for certainly such a set must exist. For instance, each state has two senators, already selected, and all we need do is make up a set by selecting one senator from each pair representing a state.

6.2   Now, imagine that, instead of forty-eight states, we have an example of a "nation" whose states are in (1-1)-correspondence with the elements of N; denote the state that is paired with $n \, \varepsilon \, N$ in this correspondence by S_n. Can we still assert the existence of the set R?

If so, R consists of one and only one person, p_n, from each state S_n. But how is p_n to be selected? Even if, as in the case of the forty-eight states, there is a senate comprised of two senators from each state, we would still have to select p_n from the pair of senators from state S_n. If in every case one senator is definitely older than the other, we could select p_n, for all n, by the rule that he is to be the older senator from S_n. If the rule does not apply, some other characteristic may serve; if not, we shall have to resort simply to asserting the existence of R, and in this case we would be making an application of the principle known as the Choice Axiom:

6.3   Definition (Choice Axiom).   *If $\mathfrak{S}$ is a collection of disjoint non-empty sets S_ν, then there exists a set R which has as its elements exactly one element x_ν of each S_ν.*

The element x_ν is called the *representative element* of S_ν; and R may be called a *representative set* for $\mathfrak{S}$.

On the basis of the Choice Axiom we can prove:

6.4   *If $\mathfrak{S}$ is a collection of non-empty sets S_ν, disjoint or not, then there exists a set $\mathfrak{R}$ whose elements are pairs (S_ν, x_ν) in which $x_\nu \, \varepsilon \, S_\nu$, and such that each S_ν occurs in one and only one pair.*

6.5   If in 6.4 the elements of $\mathfrak{S}$ are disjoint, then the set $R = \{x_\nu \mid x_\nu \, \varepsilon \, (S_\nu, x_\nu)\}$ is the same type of set as the set R of 6.3, each x_ν being considered the representative element of S_ν. Thus 6.4 implies 6.3. To see that 6.3 implies 6.4, we may form, for each ν, the set $\mathfrak{A}_\nu$ of all pairs $(S_\nu, x_{\nu\mu})$, where now *every* element $x_{\nu\mu}$ of S_ν occurs in a pair. Then the collection, Γ, of all sets $\mathfrak{A}_\nu$, is a collection of disjoint, non-empty sets, so that by 6.3 there exists a set $\mathfrak{R}$, which has as its elements exactly one element $(S_\nu, x_{\nu\mu})$ of each $\mathfrak{A}_\nu$.

6.6   We may continue to call the elements x_ν, which occur in pairs $(S_\nu, x_\nu) \, \varepsilon \, \mathfrak{R},$† the *representative elements* of the sets S_ν, except that we realize that a given x_ν may be the representative element of more than one S_ν. This might be the case, for example, if an S_ν and an $S_{\nu'}$, elements of $\mathfrak{S}$, were such that $S_\nu \subset S_{\nu'}$; in such a case the element x_ν is necessarily an element of $S_{\nu'}$, and it may happen that $x_\nu = x_{\nu'}$.

Before discussing the Choice Axiom further, however, let us see how it applies to Section 5.3:

6.7   Let S be a set which is not ordinary finite. We apply 6.4 as follows: The sets S_ν are the non-empty subsets of S; that is, $\mathfrak{S}$ is the

---

† As each S_ν occurs only once in a pair $(S_\nu, x_\nu) \, \varepsilon \, \mathfrak{R}$, we may drop the μ used in the $x_{\nu\mu}$ of the proof for the case where S_ν appears once with each $x_{\nu\mu}$.

collection of all non-empty subsets † of S. In the set $\mathfrak{R}$, whose existence is asserted by 6.4, there is one and only one pair in which S (which is a subset of itself, and hence an "S_ν") occurs; denote it by (S, x_1). Also, since the set $S - x_1 = S_2$ is a subset of S, it occurs in a pair (S_2, x_2). And having assigned symbols x_1, x_2, $\cdots$, x_n for any $n \, \varepsilon \, N$, denote by (S_{n+1}, x_{n+1}) the pair in which $S_{n+1} = S - x_1 - x_2 - \cdots - x_n$ occurs.

The set, A, of all such elements x_n is exactly of the type of the set S_1 in 5.3.2. Hence the proof that an ordinary infinite set is Dedekind infinite may be based on the Choice Axiom.

6.8 Comment on the Choice Axiom

As we shall have occasion later to comment on the further implications of the Choice Axiom, we shall be content with a few general observations at this point.

In the first place, why call it an *axiom* or *postulate* (as in "Zermelo Postulate")? As we have presented it, it is not part of an axiom system involving undefined terms (and other axioms) subject to various interpretations. Rather it seems to be a basic principle, of a more absolute character than an axiom system for geometry which can be applied to certain models, perhaps, but about whose truth or falsity we would hardly (at least *today*) argue. It is possible, to be sure, to devise axiom systems in which the Choice Axiom occurs as one of the axioms (see VIII 8). But the term "axiom" in this case is not due to such uses of the principle; rather it seems to have derived from the ancient and traditional conception of an axiom as a "universal truth," or "a self-evident proposition, requiring no formal demonstration to prove its truth, but received and accepted as soon as mentioned."‡ The Choice Axiom must seem, at first sight, to fulfill these qualifications. For what is more natural than to assume, if a collection of disjoint non-empty sets be given, that there exists a set containing one element of each set of the collection?

In particular, if we are given a single set S, we do not hesitate to think of a set $\{e\}$ consisting of a single, unique element e of S! And we probably would not hesitate to assume the existence of a representative set for the collection of forty-eight states, even if there were not senators all ready to be named (cf. 6.2). As a matter of fact, commencing with the premise that it is permissible to select an element from

---

† The use of this collection may be avoided by using the collection of all ordinary finite subsets of S. See Sierpinski, [S₁, 116–117].

‡ This quotation is from Huntington [a; footnote †, p. 264].

a given set, it is easy to show by mathematical induction that for every natural number n the Choice Axiom holds for any collection of n non-empty sets.

It is perhaps clear from the discussion given previously (5.3.1.1 for instance), that much of the objection to the Choice Axiom stems from the *lack of precise definition* of the representative set. An often quoted (see Sierpinski [S$_1$; 125] for instance) example of Russell, modified to suit our purposes, may throw further light on this aspect of the matter. Imagine a world in which there exists an infinite collection of pairs of shoes! Does there exist a set S consisting of one shoe from each pair? We may say that the answer is affirmative, since we can *define S* to consist of the *left* shoe from each pair. But suppose that this imaginary world also contains an infinite collection of pairs of socks; does a corresponding set S exist for this collection? Unfortunately socks are manufactured in pairs of identical form, it being impossible to distinguish a left sock from a right sock, so that we have no way of defining a representative set S.† Despite this lack, we may still feel justified in asserting that such a set exists; but to do so is to employ the Choice Axiom, whereas in the case of the boots no appeal to such an "axiom" is necessary.

This example brings out the fact that it is precisely in cases where there is insufficient information regarding the character of the sets in question that appeal must be made to the Choice Axiom. It suggests that as mathematics has grown, reaching out to concepts of a greater degree of abstraction, it has become necessary to add new principles that are not available in the classical logic (which was not devised as a tool for dealing with the infinite as we conceive of it today); and the Choice Axiom is one of these new principles. (Compare the remark in II 4.2 regarding possible inadequacy of the logical apparatus.)

This may all seem like a "tempest in a teapot" at the present stage of our discussion, but we shall ask the reader to suspend judgment until we have been able to present more of the *consequences* of the Choice Axiom. After all, who pays any regard to the blaze of a match until it starts a forest fire!

SUGGESTED READING

Birkhoff and MacLane [B-M; XI]
Cantor [C$_1$]
Grelling [Gr; 1–15, 40–44]
Hobson [Ho; §§ 1–5]

Kamke [Ka$_1$; 1–5]
Peano [P$_3$; II § 2, pp. 1–4]
Richardson [R; XIV]
Sierpinski [S$_1$; 1–12, 103–117]

Young [Y; VI]

† Someone has suggested that if each pair were being *worn* we would!

PROBLEMS

1. Compare the following (due to Grelling, 1908) to the Russell antinomy: Divide all adjectives into two classes, calling those that describe themselves autological, and those that do not heterological. Thus "English" and "short" are autological, and "French" and "long" are heterological. Is the adjective "heterological" either autological or heterological?

2. Do likewise with the heron-fish fable: The heron, having caught a fish, tells the fish that if he cannot tell the heron what he is going to do with him, then he, the heron, will eat the fish; otherwise, he will let him go. The fish answers "You are going to eat me." What can the heron do with the fish?

3. And likewise with the barber fable: A barber in a certain town shaved everyone who did not shave himself, and only those. Who shaved the barber?

4. In a given university, let $\mathfrak{C}$ denote the set of all sections (mathematics sections, history sections, etc.) in session at a given time, $\mathfrak{G}$ the set of all graduate sections, $\mathfrak{M}$ the set of all sections in graduate mathematics, C a section in graduate mathematics, and p a student in C. Set up the "ε" and "$\subset$" relations between $\mathfrak{C}$, $\mathfrak{G}$, $\mathfrak{M}$, C, and p. Explain the choice of symbols (cf. 3.1.1).

5. Prove that N is not ordinary finite.

6. Prove Theorem 5.2.2 and its corollary (5.2.3).

7. Young [Y, 63] gives the following argument for 5.2.3: S has a proper subset S' such that there exists a (1-1)-correspondence T between the elements of S and the elements of S'. Let x' be the element of S' paired with x in the correspondence T. The set $S_1' = S' - \{x'\}$ is then a proper subset of $S_1 (= S - \{x\})$ such that there exists a (1-1)-correspondence between the elements of S_1 and the elements of S_1'. The set S_1 is, therefore, Dedekind infinite.

What is missing from this argument?

8. In the same connection, Young states "an infinite class cannot be exhausted by removing its elements one at a time."

But suppose that, between 12:00 noon and 12:30 P.M., 1 is deleted from N; between 12:30 and 12:45, 2 is deleted from N; during the next $\frac{1}{8}$ hour 3 is deleted; during the next $\frac{1}{16}$ hour 4 is deleted; and so on. What is left of N at 1:00 P.M.? Discuss the statement of Young.

9. Supply the argument by mathematical induction which was omitted in the fourth paragraph of 5.3.

10. Prove the converse of 5.3.2. [Hint: Let S' be a proper subset of S and let $\{(x, f(x))\}$ be a (1-1)-correspondence such that $x \varepsilon S$, $f(x) \varepsilon S'$. Let $x_1 \varepsilon S - S'$, and for each natural number $n > 1$ let $x_n = f(x_{n-1})$. Then $S_1 = \{x_n\}$ is the desired subset of S.]

11. In an imaginary world W, a man starts from his home at 12:00 noon to walk to a post office. He walks at a uniform rate, reaching the post office at 1:00 P.M. He leaves home with 1 cent, intending to buy a stamp. However, between 12:00 and 12:30 a friend offers him a brighter coin than the one he has, and, intrigued by it, he trades his original coin for it. Between 12:30 and 12:45 a similar event occurs, so that at 12:45 he has a still different coin. During the next $\frac{1}{8}$ hour a similar exchange occurs; during the next $\frac{1}{16}$ hour another occurs; and so on. Assuming that W allows such unlimited possibilities, does the man have a coin at 1:00 o'clock to buy the stamp that he set out to buy? [In case the pennies are all different, a logical conclusion is possible; but, if the same two pennies are involved throughout, no conclusion is possible.]

12. Use the $\{ \ | \ \}$ symbol to define the following sets: (a) the set of all points in the coordinate plane that lie interior to the unit circle with center at the origin; (b) the set of points defined in (a) with those having negative abscissas deleted; (c) the set $(A \cap B) \cup C$ where A, B, and C are sets; (d) the set $A \cap (B \cup C)$; (e) the set $A - (B \cup C)$; (f) the set $(A - B) \cup C$.

13. Prove the following "distributive laws":

$$A \cap (B \cup C) = (A \cap B) \cup (A \cap C),$$

$$A \cup (B \cap C) = (A \cup B) \cap (A \cup C).$$

14. Let the complement of a set A relative to a set S be denoted by $\mathcal{C}_s A$, or, briefly, by $\mathcal{C}A$. Then prove:

$$\mathcal{C}(A \cap B) = \mathcal{C}A \cup \mathcal{C}B,$$

$$\mathcal{C}(A \cup B) = \mathcal{C}A \cap \mathcal{C}B.$$

15. In the notation of Problem 14, notice that $\mathcal{C}(\mathcal{C}A) = A$. Use this to derive the second formula in Problem 14 from the first.

16. Show by mathematical induction (on the number, n, of set symbols, counting repetitions) that, if M is an expression composed of set symbols A_1, A_2, $\cdots$, A_n and the symbols $\mathcal{C}$, $\cap$, $\cup$, but containing no $\mathcal{C}(\ )$, then $\mathcal{C}M$ is the expression obtained by replacing, in M, each A_i, $\mathcal{C}A_i$, $\cap$, and $\cup$ by $\mathcal{C}A_i$, A_i, $\cup$, and $\cap$ respectively.

17. If $M = (A \cup \mathcal{C}B) \cap (A \cup C)$, find $\mathcal{C}M$.

18. Prove that, if $A \subset N$ (N the set of all natural numbers), then A has an element a which precedes ($<$) every other element of A in the natural order (4.1, footnote) of N.

19. Some have insisted that the only type of set allowable in mathematics is one such that it is determinate of everything whether it is an element of the set or not. Criticize this criterion.

20. The following problem is attributed to Tarski: Let N denote the set of all natural numbers, and for any two natural numbers m and n let "$m = n$" mean "m is identical to n." Consider any set S_1 having only one natural number as an element. Obviously, if $m,n \ \varepsilon \ S_1$, then $m = n$. Suppose it has been shown that, for any set S_n having exactly n natural numbers as elements, the relation $m,n \ \varepsilon \ S_n$ implies $m = n$. Consider any set S_{n+1} having exactly $n + 1$ natural numbers as elements; let us denote its elements by x_1, x_2, $\cdots$, x_n, x_{n+1}. As the set $S_{n+1}' = S_{n+1} - x_{n+1}$ has exactly n natural numbers as elements, the relation $m,n \ \varepsilon \ S_{n+1}'$ implies $m = n$; in particular, $x_1 = x_n$. Now consider the set $S_{n+1}'' = S_{n+1} - x_n$. Since S_{n+1}'' contains exactly n natural numbers, the relation $m,n \ \varepsilon \ S_{n+1}''$ implies $m = n$; in particular, $x_1 = x_{n+1}$. But, if $x_1 = x_n$ and $x_1 = x_{n+1}$, then $x_n = x_{n+1}$, and it follows that all elements of S_{n+1} are identical. Hence we have proved, in particular, that all natural numbers are identical! What is wrong with this "proof"?

21. Consider the accompanying figure. It consists of:

(1) Two parallel line segments L_1 and L_2 of unit length one unit distance apart. On L_1, p_1, p_2, $\cdots$, p_n, $\cdots$ are points such that p_n is at a distance $1/(n + 1)$ from the base of L_1; and, on L_2, q_1, q_2, $\cdots$, q_n, $\cdots$ are points such that q_n is at a distance $1/(n + 1)$ from the top of L_2.

(2) The line segment p_1q_1, on which r_1, r_2, $\cdots$, r_n, $\cdots$ are points such that r_n is at a distance $1/(n + 1)$ from q_1.

(3) A broken line $p_2s_1r_1t_1q_2$ as shown.

(4) In general, a broken line $p_{n+1}s_nr_nt_nq_{n+1}$ as shown. Let a *path* from L_1 to L_2 consist of *any* broken line—$p_2s_1r_1r_6t_6q_7$ for instance—made up of segments of the given broken lines, but with only its endpoints, p_2 and q_7 in the instance cited, on L_1 and L_2 respectively. Let two paths be called *different* if they have no point in common.

Show that, for every natural number n, there exist n different paths from L_1 to L_2. Show also that there does not exist an *infinite* number of different paths from L_1 to L_2. What general "moral" can be drawn from this example in regard to existence theorems provable by mathematical induction?

22. Define the relation $<$ in terms of the successor relation $x \, s \, y$ of 5.1, so that it will correspond to the natural order as defined in 4.1f.

23. Carry out the mathematical induction argument to prove the Choice Axiom for finite sets, as suggested in the third paragraph of 6.8.

IV

Infinite Sets

In the preceding chapter we discussed the general notion of set and noticed how certain debatable principles (Choice Axiom) and contradictions (Russell antinomy) may be encountered in the theory of sets. In the present chapter we shall set forth sufficient material regarding infinite sets—especially with regard to the "numbers" that may be used in handling them—to give us a basis for further definition of basic notions, as well as to uncover other principles and possible contradictions. Some basic mathematical entities, as for example the "real number continuum," cannot be fully appreciated without some knowledge of this sort. And we shall encounter mathematical problems which, like that of showing that the ordinary infinite implies the Dedekind infinite, cannot be solved without appeal to principles that have never been encountered in the classical logic.

As the reader may know, until modern times the infinite was simply "the infinite"; something represented by a symbol like a figure eight lying on its side: ∞. The "number" of natural numbers was "∞," the number of real numbers "∞," the number of points in a coordinate xy-plane, ∞^2 [since ∞ x's together with ∞ y's can give ∞^2 pairs (x, y) —although the *doubly ordered* character of the pairs (x, y) was undoubtedly the inspiration for the symbol ∞^2]. Curious results followed from the use of this symbol (such as attempts to include it in arithmetic—$2 \times \infty = \infty$ for instance—although any competent mathematician would warn of the dire consequences of such attempts!).

With Cantor's invention of the theory of transfinite numbers, a new perspective opened up. Actually infinite numbers and an arithmetic for them were developed. What might at first have seemed to be adventures in fantasy turned out to have important applications in mathematics; as a matter of fact, it was certain applications that led Cantor to his studies in the infinite. Some of these we shall see in the sequel.

1　Countable sets; the number $\aleph_0$

We saw in III 5.2 that N is ordinary infinite. As we shall presently see, it represents the simplest type of infinite set—as a consequence of which, we might remark, we used its subsets N_k as criteria for defining the ordinary finite and infinite.

1.1　Let us consider another infinite set, i.e., the set F of all real fractions, technically called *rational numbers;* a real fraction being any number which can be put in the form p/q, where p is any integer (positive or negative) and q any natural number. (Thus $\frac{1}{2}$, $\frac{17}{12}$, $\frac{32}{8}$, $-\frac{8}{7}$, $\frac{\frac{2}{3} + \frac{6}{7}}{4}$, etc., are all real fractions; and every natural number is a real fraction, since, for example, $2 = \frac{2}{1}$.) Obviously there are "more" elements in F than there are in N—although a mathematician would at first be startled by such a statement; it is all a matter of the meaning to be attributed to "more than." And anyone who has never heard of a "transfinite number" will probably admit that, if to any set (such as N) we *add* new elements to obtain a new set (such as F), then the latter has *more* elements than the former. And this is quite true, unless by "more than" we mean "a greater cardinal number †than," in which case it is quite false! Again we see the necessity of making the conventions regarding the meanings of words clear, since to one group of people they mean one thing and to another they mean something else (as any traveler knows).

The reason for the above "misunderstanding" is that, if A and B are sets such that between the elements of A and the elements of B there exists a (1-1)-correspondence, then the mathematician thinks of A and B as having the *same number* of elements; and that he is inclined to interpret the statement "A has more elements than B" as meaning (in a sense to be made precise below) that "the number of elements in A is greater than the number of elements in B." In the next breath, however, he will admit that, if B is a *proper* subset of A, then A has more elements than B, since the new connotation of "more" is implied by "B is a *proper* subset of A." The latter is exactly what was intended by the use of "more than" in the preceding paragraph. However, the mathematician should not be taken to task for this inconsistency, since he never uses "more than" as a technical term, and in his professional work would never be found guilty of this inconsistency. He will be the first to admit, moreover, that the above is simply an example of the necessity for precise definition of terms.

† To be defined below

In the case of F and N, F does have more elements than N in the sense that N is a proper subset of F. But, in the "number" sense, F does not have "more" elements than N, since there does exist a (1-1)-correspondence between the elements of N and the elements of F.

1.2   (1-1)-correspondence between N and F

The easiest way to see that such a (1-1)-correspondence exists (although perhaps not the most preferable!—see Section 5) is to notice that the elements of F can be arranged in an order like that (1, 2, 3, $\cdots$) of the natural numbers when these are placed in their "natural" order. To do this, we first split the elements of F into finite sets, and then we arrange these finite sets in the desired order.

For the first step, that of splitting F into finite sets, recall the definition of the elements of F; a number is an element of F if it can be put in the form p/q, where p is any integer and q is a natural number. Let us imagine each element of F, then, as already in such a form, and moreover in its "lowest terms" (i.e., so that p and q have no common factor greater than 1; "two-thirds" is then written as $\frac{2}{3}$, not $\frac{4}{6}$, for example); the number zero will be represented by $\frac{0}{1}$ only. Define the *index* of p/q as $|p| + q$ (where, as usual, $|p|$ is the absolute or numerical value of p); thus the index of $\frac{0}{1}$ is 1; of $-2\left(=\frac{-2}{1}\right)$ is 3; of $3\left(=\frac{3}{1}\right)$ is 4; etc. Then we place in the same set all elements of F that have the same index.

Now the set of numbers with index 1 has only 0 as its element; the set of numbers of index 2 has -1 and 1 as its elements; and so on. Let us agree to order the elements of a set of given index in pairs according to absolute value, each pair consisting of a negative and positive number of equal absolute value, the relative order between pairs being determined by numerical magnitude; for example, according to this rule the set of index 5 will be ordered as follows:

$$-\tfrac{1}{4}, \tfrac{1}{4}, \ -\tfrac{2}{3}, \tfrac{2}{3}, \ -\tfrac{3}{2}, \tfrac{3}{2}, \ -4, 4.$$

Next we arrange these finite sets according to the size of their indices. The ordering of elements of F then turns out like this:

$$(F) \quad 0, \ -1, 1, \ -\tfrac{1}{2}, \tfrac{1}{2}, \ -2, 2, \ -\tfrac{1}{3}, \tfrac{1}{3}, \ -3, 3, \ -\tfrac{1}{4}, \tfrac{1}{4}, \ -\tfrac{2}{3}, \tfrac{2}{3}, \ \cdots.$$

We call this "sequence" (F). Since every element of F has a definite index and a uniquely determined position in the set of that index, it will have a definite position in (F). And to get a (1-1)-correspondence between N and F, let the nth number in (F), starting from the left, be denoted by f_n, and make the pairing (n, f_n), $n \, \varepsilon \, N$, $f_n \, \varepsilon \, F$.

1.3   (1-1)-correspondence between N and A

We can, as Cantor showed, go even further with the above process. Specifically, let A be the class of all real roots of ordinary algebraic equations of the type

(1a) $$a_0 x^n + a_1 x^{n-1} + \cdots + a_{n-1} x + a_n = 0,$$

where n is a natural number, a_i an integer, $i = 0, 1, \cdots, n$, and $a_0 > 0$. The elements of A are called *algebraic numbers*. The elements of F all belong to A—$F \subset A$—since p/q is a root of the equation

(1b) $$qx - p = 0.$$

But F is a *proper* subset of A since the equation

$$x^2 - 2 = 0$$

has roots $\pm \sqrt{2}$, and it is not difficult to show that $\sqrt{2}$ cannot be put in the p/q form which elements of F can assume. So A is a "larger" set than F. Yet, surprisingly enough, there still exists a (1-1)-correspondence between the elements of N and the elements of A.

To show this, we proceed very much as we did in Section 1.2; we first split the elements of A into finite ordered sets, and then order these sets. To get the finite sets, let us define the index of an equation such as (1a) as the number

$$a_0 + |a_1| + \cdots + |a_{n-1}| + |a_n| + n.$$

As the a's and n are integers, the index is always a natural number. There exists no equation of index 1, since both n and a_0 are at least 1. The only equation of index 2 is $x = 0$, and the only root of equations of index 2 is the number zero. The only equations of index 3 are $2x = 0$, $x \pm 1 = 0$, $x^2 = 0$, yielding roots 0, -1, 1. Thus for each index there exists only a finite number of equations and hence a finite number of roots corresponding; of the latter we reject the non-real roots (thus $x^2 + 1 = 0$ affords no real numbers for us) and order the remainder by the same rule that we used in the finite sets for F, except that we reject any number that was a root of an equation of lower index.

As in the case of F, we finally arrange the sets according to the size of their indices. The sequence A then starts off like this:

$$(A) \quad 0, -1, 1, -\tfrac{1}{2}, \tfrac{1}{2}, -2, 2, -\tfrac{1}{3}, \tfrac{1}{3}, -\tfrac{1}{2}\sqrt{2}, \tfrac{1}{2}\sqrt{2}, -\sqrt{2}, \sqrt{2}, -3,$$
$$3, \cdots.$$

1.4   Non-existence of (1-1)-correspondence between N and R

Now A is itself a subset of a still larger class, namely the class of all *real numbers*, which we shall denote by R. We have to be specific about what we mean by a real number here, just as we were in regard to the elements of F and A. For present purposes, then, a *real number* is any number which can be represented by an unending decimal, in the ordinary decimal system, of the form

$$(1c) \qquad\qquad \pm k_1 k_2 \cdots k_m.a_1 a_2 \cdots a_n \cdots$$

where each k and each a are one of the digits $0, 1, \cdots, 9$; $k_1 k_2 \cdots k_m$ is the "integral" part of the number; $a_1 a_2 \cdots a_n \cdots$ is the "decimal part," also called a *decimal fraction;* and no n exists such that all digits $a_n, a_{n+1}, \cdots$ are zero (with the single exception that the number zero is represented by $0.a_1 a_2 \cdots a_n$, where *all* a_n are zero). For instance, the number $122\tfrac{1}{3}$ is an element of R, since it is represented by $k_1 = 1$, $k_2 = k_3 = 2$ (*m* being 3 here), and all a's are 3: thus, $122.33 \cdots 3 \cdots$. Similarly, $\sqrt{2}$ is real, since here $k_1 = 1$ (*m* being 1 in this case), $a_1 = 4$, $a_2 = 1$, $a_3 = 4$, etc.; and it is impossible that all $a_n, a_{n+1}, \cdots$ be zero for some n, since this would imply that $\sqrt{2}$ is an element of F. Also, the natural numbers are real numbers, since, for example, 2 can be represented by letting k_1 be 1 (*m* being 1), and letting all a's be 9; thus, $1.99 \cdots 9 \cdots$ (see Problem 2 at end of the chapter).

Now Cantor discovered that there does not exist any (1-1)-correspondence between the elements of N and the elements of R. For suppose such a correspondence did exist. Let the real number paired with each natural number n in this correspondence be denoted by r_n. Also denote the digit in the nth decimal place of r_n by $a_n{}^n$. Then we can define a real number $r = 0.a_1 a_2 \cdots a_n \cdots$ such that, for each n, $a_n = 1$ if $a_n{}^n \neq 1$, and $a_n = 2$ if $a_n{}^n = 1$. Since $r \, \varepsilon \, R$, it must be an r_n itself, say r_i. But r_i has $a_i{}^i$ as the ith decimal digit, whereas r has a different digit a_i! Because of this contradiction we must conclude that no (1-1)-correspondence of the supposed type exists.

1.4.1   The reader, if entirely unfamiliar with the above type of argument, may wish to explore some of the details more closely. For this purpose, it may help to imagine the digits of the numbers r_n arranged in a square array, obtained by setting the numbers down in a vertical sequence (omitting the integral parts since they do not influence the result) thus:

$$r_1: \quad .a_1{}^1 a_2{}^1 \cdots a_n{}^1 \cdots$$
$$r_2: \quad .a_1{}^2 a_2{}^2 \cdots a_n{}^2 \cdots$$

. . . .

$$r_n: \quad .a_1{}^n a_2{}^n \cdots a_n{}^n \cdots$$

. . . .

To get the number r, follow the main diagonal of the array beginning at the upper left-hand corner, and write down a digit $a_1 \neq a_1{}^1$, $a_2 \neq a_2{}^2$, $\cdots$, $a_n \neq a_n{}^n$, $\cdots$ according to the rule given above. For example, if the array started like this:

$$r_1: \quad .4146 \cdots$$
$$r_2: \quad .9999 \cdots$$
$$r_3: \quad .1019 \cdots$$
$$r_4: \quad .2682 \cdots$$

. . . .

then r would look like .1121 $\cdots$; and we already see that r will not be one of the numbers r_1, r_2, r_3, r_4.

1.5   The countable sets

It appears, then, in view of 1.4, that, by using the notion of (1-1)-correspondence, we can make a distinction between certain infinite sets. Thus we already see that N and R can be distinguished from one another in this way. And, indeed, if $\mathfrak{S}$ is any collection of sets whatsoever, we can decompose $\mathfrak{S}$ into disjoint classes, using the fact that (1-1)-correspondence between elements of two sets is an equivalence relation (see II 8.5). If $\mathfrak{S}$ has as its elements just the sets N, F, A, and R, for example, then the class decomposition of $\mathfrak{S}$ corresponding to (1-1)-correspondence consists of a class $\mathfrak{S}_1$ whose elements are N, F, A, and a class $\mathfrak{S}_2$ whose *single* element is R.

Now, if $\mathfrak{S}$ is any collection of finite sets, and $\mathfrak{S}$ contains a finite set, S, having exactly 15 elements, say, then the class containing S would contain *all* the elements of $\mathfrak{S}$, each of which has exactly 15 elements. And, if there were a set consisting of exactly 3 elements, then the class containing this set would also contain *all* elements of $\mathfrak{S}$ each of which has exactly 3 elements, and only these. That is, (1-1)-correspondence as an equivalence relation induces a class decomposition of $\mathfrak{S}$ such that each class consists of all sets having a certain fixed number of elements. It is natural, therefore, to think of any two sets whose elements can be put in (1-1)-correspondence as "having the same number" of elements. Accordingly, Cantor made the definition:

1.5.1 Definition. If A and B are two sets such that there exists a (1-1)-correspondence between the elements of A and the elements of B, then we shall say that A and B *have the same cardinal number*.

> Cantor used the term "have the same power (*Mächtigkeit*)." Notice, incidentally, that we have *not* defined "number" or "cardinal number," but only the term "have the same cardinal number." A definition of "cardinal number" follows below.

If two (ordinary) finite sets have the same cardinal number, then they have the same "number" of elements in the usual sense; if one has 15 elements, then the other has 15 elements, etc. And, as we showed above, the sets N, F, and A all have the same cardinal number, but N and R do not; we say that N and R have "different cardinal numbers." And, although we have not yet defined "cardinal number," we can introduce, by analogy with the natural numbers, the numbers $\aleph_0$ ("aleph-null") and c: When we say that "a set S has $\aleph_0$ elements," or, alternatively, that "its cardinal number is $\aleph_0$," we mean that between its elements and the elements of N there exists a (1-1)-correspondence. In particular, N, F, and A each has $\aleph_0$ elements. And if there exists a (1-1)-correspondence between the elements of a set M and the elements of R, then we say "M has c elements," or alternatively, that "its cardinal number is c." The symbols "$\aleph_0$" and "c" would come, with practice, to have the same significance for us as the number 15 for example; for we never have defined the latter and we never *define* any of the natural numbers in the primary schools, since by the time a child enters school he has usually been introduced to the counting process and he "*knows*" what we mean if we say, "You may have only *two* pieces of candy."

The following terms will be useful in the sequel:

1.5.2 Definition. If a set has $\aleph_0$ elements, then we call it *denumerable*. If a set is either (ordinary) finite or denumerable, then we call it *countable*.

> The reader should be warned that, although these *terms* are standard, their *meanings* vary in use. Thus "denumerable" is sometimes used to mean "countable," as we have defined the latter (English authors commonly use the term "enumerable," incidentally). The only safe way, when these terms are encountered in a mathematical work, is to ascertain explicitly the author's use of the terms. The usual German and French terms are "abzählbar" and "dénombrable." Bourbaki, for example, uses the latter in the sense of "countable" as defined above, and "infini dénombrable" in the sense of "denumerable" as defined above; see Bourbaki [B₁; 40]. On the other hand, Sierpinski [S₁; 41] uses "dénombrable" in the sense of denumerable as defined above.

1.5.3   A set which is not countable is called *uncountable*. [Many authors use the term "non-denumerable." For example Sierpinski (loc. cit.) uses the French "non-dénombrable."] Thus R is an uncountable set. And we may, a priori, divide sets generally into two categories, the countable and the uncountable. The proof (III 5.3) that an ordinary infinite set is also Dedekind infinite devolved to showing that every ordinary infinite set contains a denumerable subset; III 5.3.2 may be restated: "If a set has a denumerable subset, then it is Dedekind infinite." And, if we grant the use of the Choice Axiom, we can state (as a result of III 6.7):

1.5.4   *Every infinite* † *set contains a denumerable set.*

2   Uncountable sets

Thus far the only example of an uncountable set that we have introduced is the set R. In this section we shall give other examples, although we shall reserve some standard examples for later purposes. In particular, we give first some examples of sets that have the same cardinal number as R.

2.1   The simplest of these is *the set, E, of all points on a euclidean straight line.* Anyone who has studied *analytic geometry* will recall that the basic frame of reference was the "coordinate axes." For *plane* analytic geometry, these were the "x-axis" and "y-axis": two straight lines usually perpendicular to one another, on each of which were "marked off" numbers starting from zero at the intersection of the axes (the "origin"), with positive numbers in one direction, negative in the opposite. It was *assumed* that to each point on the x-axis (and similarly on the y-axis) there corresponded a "number" and conversely that to every "number" there corresponded a point on the axis. In the terminology introduced above, it was assumed, then, that there exists a (1-1)-correspondence between the elements of R and the points of the axis; ‡ that is, the set of points on each axis has the cardinal number c. No proof is given in the analytic geometry, as a rule, that this assumption is valid. However, on the basis of a complete set of axioms for euclidean geometry the assertion is prov-

---

† Since we make this statement on the basis of the Choice Axiom, we need not specify "ordinary" or "Dedekind" here, the two being equivalent in this case (III 5).

‡ In addition, it is assumed that this correspondence is "order-preserving," but this does not concern us here. The assertion of this correspondence is sometimes called the "Cantor axiom."

able † in the sense that the set of all points on any straight line whatsoever has the cardinal number c. Moreover, if L is such a line, and
S a *segment* of L, then the set of points on S again has the cardinal
number c (see Problem 8 at the end of the chapter).

2.2   That two line segments (considered as collections of points) have the same
cardinal number may be demonstrated by construction: Let abc be any plane
triangle, and d a point between b and c. To show that the set of points on bc has the
same cardinal number as the set of points on dc, let $b'd$ be a segment parallel to
ac with its endpoint b' on ab. Then let $b'c'$ be a segment parallel to bc with endpoint
c' between a and c. Consider any point x of bc. The line ax meets $b'c'$ in a point x';
and in turn a line through x' parallel to $b'd$ meets dc in a point x''. The collection
$\{(x, x'') \mid x \,\varepsilon\, bc\}$ constitutes a (1-1)-correspondence between the points of bc and the
points of dc. Since bc and dc can have arbitrary lengths, so long as dc is not longer
than bc, this construction is readily adapted to proving the desired theorem.

2.3   That the set of points on a euclidean straight line segment is *uncountable* is
frequently proved as follows: Let ab be a segment of a straight line L; we may take
the length of ab to be 1 unit. Then let us assume that the points of ab form a
countable—hence denumerable (since they do not form a finite set)—collection.
From the (1-1)-correspondence that exists between the points and the natural numbers, which follows from the assumption, we derive symbols x_n just as in III 4.1.1,
so that each point of ab can be "named" x_n, $n = 1, 2, 3, \cdots$, no two points being
assigned the same "name." Now, for each n, let I_n be an interval of length $(\frac{1}{2})^{n+1}$
with center x_n. Then the intervals I_n cover the segment ab. (That is, every point
of the interval is in at least one I_n.) Consequently their lengths should add up to
1, at least, since ab has unit length. But the sum of the series whose general term
is $(\frac{1}{2})^{n+1}$ is only $\frac{1}{2}$. Thus the assumption that the points of ab form a countable
collection leads to contradiction.

[If one is familiar with the "Borel theorem," according to which a *finite* number of
the segments I_n must cover ab, then the justification (omitted above) for using the
infinite series $\frac{1}{4} + \cdots$ is avoided. Note that the above type of argument shows
that any countable set of points on a line L can be covered by a set of intervals
whose total length is as small as we please; we merely use intervals I_n of length
$c/2^{n+1}$, where c is whatever (fixed) length we please.]

2.4   *The set of all points in the euclidean plane has the cardinal number* c. In the general remarks at the beginning of this chapter we recalled that the symbol "∞^2" was frequently used to designate the
"doubly ordered" array of points in a plane, with the unfortunate
connotation that somehow there is a "larger infinity" of points in the
plane than on the line. It is not surprising, then, that it was antici-
pated by some mathematicians that the Cantor theory of cardinal
numbers would provide a means of distinguishing *two*-dimensional
space from *one*-dimensional space. Actually, however, the set E^2 of

† We refer here to such a system as that of Hilbert [H₂] (see H; 36–37) or Veblen
[a; 383] for example. The Birkhoff [a] system makes the assertion an axiom.

all points in a euclidean plane has the cardinal number c; i.e., the sets R and E^2 have the same cardinal number.†

The proof is very simple.‡ It will be sufficient to show that the set E^1 of real numbers x such that $0 < x \leqq 1$ and the set E^2 of all points in the coordinate plane defined by

$$E^2 = \{(x, y) \mid (0 < x \leqq 1) \,\&\, (0 < y \leqq 1)\},$$

have the same cardinal number (see Problem 8 at the end of the chapter). As $E^1 \subset R$, each element of E^1 is representable in the form $0.a_1 a_2 \cdots a_n \cdots$ as in 1.4. We divide the array $a_1 a_2 \cdots a_n \cdots$ into "blocks"; the following example illustrates what we mean. Consider a number such as $0.32046008 \cdots$. The successive "blocks" are 3, then 2, then 04, then 6, then 008, and so on; i.e., each "block" contains one digit different from 0, and this its last digit. We then construct an ordered pair $(0.a_1^1 a_2^1 \cdots, 0.a_1^2 a_2^2 \cdots)$ such that $a_1^1 = 3$, $a_1^2 = 2$, $a_2^1 = 04$, $a_2^2 = 6$, $a_3^1 = 008$, and so on—$(0.304008 \cdots, 0.26 \cdots)$. That is, we assign the blocks alternately to the two coordinates of a point of E^2. Since this process can be reversed, it provides a (1-1)-correspondence between the elements of E^1 and the elements of E^2. (See Problems 3–6 at the end of the chapter.)

2.5   *The set, $I = R - F$, of all irrational real numbers has the cardinal number c.* To prove this, we first prove:

2.5.1   Lemma.§ *If A and B are countable sets, then $A \cup B$ is countable; and, if either is denumerable, then $A \cup B$ is denumerable.*

Proof. If A and B are both finite, then $A \cup B$ is finite (see III 5, Theorem 5.2.2 for example). If A is denumerable, and B is finite, then, as in III 4.1.1, let the elements of A be assigned symbols x_n. If B is empty, then $A \cup B = A$; otherwise its elements are representable by symbols $y_1, y_2, \cdots, y_k$, where $k \,\varepsilon\, N$. Change the symbol x_n

---

† The problem of distinguishing between different dimensions is satisfactorily solved in that branch of mathematics known as Topology (cf. VII 3.5.8).

‡ The proof given in Young [Y; 167ff] is not valid. The construction which Young gives is that of Hilbert's "space-filling continuous curve," which sets up a many-one correspondence (see 3.2.3.1 below), not a (1-1)-correspondence (the latter being *impossible* in the case where the elements of E^2 are to lie on a continuous curve given by the correspondence).

§ As we use the term "lemma," it is a statement which will be an aid in proving theorems but is not of itself of sufficient importance to be called "theorem" (because of its being a very special case of a later theorem, for instance, or not being of great import for the general theory under development). Not infrequently, however, a "lemma" proves to be more important than the theorem for whose proof it was designed.

to y_{n+k}; then all elements of $A \cup B$ are assigned symbols y_m, $m \, \varepsilon \, N$. If *both* A and B are denumerable, let the symbols for elements of A be x_n as before, and for B let them be y_n, $n \, \varepsilon \, N$. Change x_n to z_{2n-1} and y_n to z_{2n}.

2.5.2   Theorem. *If S is a Dedekind infinite set and S' is a countable set, then $S \cup S'$ has the same cardinal number as S.*

Proof. As S is Dedekind infinite, it has a denumerable subset S_1 (cf. Problem III 10). Let $S - S_1 = M$; then $S = M \cup S_1$, where M and S_1 are disjoint sets.

Now $S \cup S' = (M \cup S_1) \cup S' = M \cup (S_1 \cup S')$, and by Lemma 2.5.1, $S_1 \cup S'$ is denumerable. As S_1 is also denumerable, there is a (1-1)-correspondence T_1 between the elements of $S_1 \cup S'$ and the elements of S_1; let T_2 be the identity correspondence (II 4.4.3) between the elements of M and the elements of M. The union $T_1 \cup T_2$ gives a (1-1)-correspondence between the elements of $S \cup S'$ and the elements of S.

2.5.3   Corollary. *The set I of all irrational real numbers has the cardinal number c.*

[For $R = I \cup F$, and, by 1.2, F is denumerable.]

2.5.4   The elements of $R - A$ are called *transcendental numbers*. And, since in 1.3 we showed A to be denumerable, we also have

2.5.5   Corollary. *The set of all transcendental numbers has the cardinal c.*

2.5.6   Remark. Lemma 2.5.1 is usually considered the basis of a proof of the *existence of transcendental numbers.* For, if $R - A$ were countable, then, in view of 1.3, $(R - A) \cup A = R$ would be countable, contradicting 1.4. It is to be noted that we thus have a proof of the existence of an *uncountable* set of numbers, *not one of which have we exhibited or pointed out in any way!* (See 3.1.9 however.) We can, of course, exhibit such numbers—we give an example below—but the above argument has the feature of revealing the *uncountable* character of their totality. It was remarked by Sierpinski [S₁; 64] that, in the same year (1873) in which Cantor announced this result, Hermite demonstrated the transcendence of e, the base of natural logarithms, and ten years later Lindemann demonstrated the transcendence of π (from which follows the impossibility of "squaring the circle" with ruler and compass).

3   Diagonal procedures and their applications

The proof of the uncountability of R given in 1.4 (see particularly 1.4.1) introduces a method commonly called "Cantor's diagonal method" or "diagonal procedure." As we shall see later, some mathematicians do not admit the existence of an uncountable set of real numbers as a legitimate consequence of the argument given in 1.4. However, it is generally admitted that the diagonal procedure itself, as it was used to construct the number r from the numbers r_n in 1.4, is a valid method for constructing numbers.   (See 3.1.1.)

3.1   Construction of irrational and transcendental numbers

We showed in 1.2 how to arrange the set F of all real fractions (i.e., *rational numbers*), in a sequence:

$$(F) \quad 0, \ -1, \ 1, \ -\tfrac{1}{2}, \tfrac{1}{2}, \ -2, \ 2, \ -\tfrac{1}{3}, \tfrac{1}{3}, \ -3, \ 3, \ -\tfrac{1}{4}, \tfrac{1}{4}, \ -\tfrac{2}{3}, \tfrac{2}{3}, \ \cdots.$$

From this sequence let us select the numbers which lie in order of magnitude between 0 and 1:

$$(F_1) \qquad\qquad \tfrac{1}{2}, \ \tfrac{1}{3}, \ \tfrac{1}{4}, \ \tfrac{2}{3}, \ \cdots.$$

If now we express these numbers in the decimal form prescribed for the elements of R in 1.4, and imagine them forming a square array as in 1.4.1, we get

$$0.4999 \cdots$$
$$0.3333 \cdots$$
$$(F_1) \qquad\qquad 0.2499 \cdots$$
$$0.6666 \cdots$$

$$\cdot \quad \cdot \quad \cdot \quad \cdot \quad \cdot$$

The application of the rule for obtaining r in 1.4 gives a number $0.1111 \cdots$; let us denote this number by r_ω. Evidently r_ω is a well-defined number since the order of the terms in (F), and hence in (F_1), was explicitly given and the rule of 1.4 is quite explicit; we can calculate r_ω to as many decimal places as we wish.

3.1.1   It is sometimes protested that r_ω cannot be well-defined, since it is defined in terms of an infinite set of numbers [the elements of (F_1)], each of which is itself an infinite decimal. This ignores the fact, however, that, so far as determining r_ω is concerned, not a single element of (F_1) is needed in its *infinite* decimal form; all that is needed of each number in (F_1) is a knowledge of a *single one* of its digits, namely, the digit on the main diagonal of the above array. The digits constituting r_ω are as well-defined, for instance, as are those of $\sqrt{2}$, whose digits are obtainable only by means of algorithms, such as the process taught in the grade schools for extracting square roots. As a matter of fact, the digits of r_ω are *better known* than those of $\sqrt{2}$, if we use, instead of the rule given in 1.2, a rule (Section 5) which enables us to find *directly* (without first setting down the preceding terms) the 100th term, for instance, of the sequence, hence the 100th digit of r_ω *without prior computation of the preceding 99 digits of r_ω*—something we cannot do for $\sqrt{2}$!

3.1.2   Let us now form a new array by placing r_ω at the head of
(F_1):

$$0.1111 \cdots$$

$$0.4999 \cdots$$

(F_2) $0.3333 \cdots$

· · · · ·

and again apply the diagonal procedure. This time we get a number
(whose first five significant digits we already know): $0.21111 \cdots$
[since the terms on the main diagonal of (F_2) are 1, 9, 3, 9, 6, $\cdots$].
Let us denote this number by $r_{\omega+1}$.†

We may repeat the above procedure for finding $r_{\omega+1}$ by placing
$r_{\omega+1}$ at the head of (F_2), thus forming a new array (F_3); application
of the diagonal procedure to (F_3) yields a number $0.121111 \cdots$, which
we denote by $r_{\omega+2}$.

3.1.3   For *every* natural number n we can now *define by induction*
a number $r_{\omega+n}$ as follows: Having defined $r_{\omega+n-1}$ from an array (F_n),
we place $r_{\omega+(n-1)}$ at the head of (F_n) to form a new array (F_{n+1}).
Application of the diagonal procedure to (F_{n+1}), using the rule of 1.4,
gives a new number which we denote by $r_{\omega+n}$. The number $r_{\omega+n}$ is
different from all numbers in the array (F_{n+1}), since it differs in at
least one digit from each of the numbers forming this array. In particular, then, $r_{\omega+n}$ is not an element of F and is therefore an irrational
number.

With the definition of r_ω ($= r_{\omega+0}$) and the general rule for finding
$r_{\omega+n}$, for any natural number n, as given in the preceding paragraph,
we have given *by induction* a definition of an infinite sequence r_ω,
$r_{\omega+1}, \cdots, r_{\omega+n}, \cdots$ of irrational numbers, all different from one another (3.1.2 is actually superfluous, then, except as explanatory ma-
terial introducing the general definition of 3.1.3).

3.1.4   It is possible to go further, however. If we follow the device
used in the proof of Lemma 2.5.1 for the case where A and B are denumerable, we may form a *single* array (F_ω) from the elements of (F_1)
and the elements of the collection $\{r_{\omega+n}\}$; the order from the top of
the array down will correspond to $\frac{1}{2}, r_\omega, \frac{1}{3}, r_{\omega+1}, \frac{1}{4}, r_{\omega+2}, \cdots$. And
by the diagonal procedure we obtain from (F_ω) a number that we de-

---

† The origin of the subscripts that we are using will be clear when we introduce
the ordinal numbers; part of our present purpose is to introduce these (ordinal)
numbers in a natural fashion.

note by $r_{\omega \cdot 2}$. Then, from arrays $(F_{\omega+1})$, $(F_{\omega+2})$, etc., obtained by placing $r_{\omega \cdot 2}$ at the head of (F_ω), etc., we can again set down a definition by induction of a set of numbers $\{r_{\omega \cdot 2+n}\}$, all different from those in (F_ω) and from one another.

3.1.5   It is not difficult to set down a definition by induction of a general array, $(F_{\omega \cdot k+n})$, for every natural number pair k, n, and hence a number $r_{\omega \cdot k+n+1}$ obtained from $(F_{\omega \cdot k+n})$ by the diagonal procedure (using the rule of 1.4). Note that this defines a *denumerable set of denumerable sets* of numbers: r_ω, $\cdots$, $r_{\omega+n}$, $\cdots$; $r_{\omega \cdot 2}$, $\cdots$, $r_{\omega \cdot 2+n}$, $\cdots$; $\cdots$; $r_{\omega \cdot k}$, $\cdots$, $r_{\omega \cdot k+n}$, $\cdots$; $\cdots$. But we can go further! First we prove:

3.1.6   Theorem.†   *If* $\{S_n\}$ *is a denumerable* ‡ *collection of denumerable sets* S_n, *then the set* $\{x \mid x \, \varepsilon \, S_n$ *for some* $n\}$ *is denumerable.*
    Proof.   For each n, denote the elements of S_n by symbols x_{nk}, $k = 1, 2, 3, \cdots$. Assign the index $j = n + k$ to each x_{nk}. Then for a given natural number j there exists only a finite number of elements x_{nk} (allowing both n and k to vary) of index j. (Thus, for $j = 3$, only x_{12} and x_{21} qualify.) We may, then, arrange the symbols x_{nk} in groups according to index, and order them within the group according to the first subscript n:

$$x_{11}, \ x_{12}, \ x_{21}, \ x_{13}, \ x_{22}, \ x_{31}, \ \cdots.$$

Finally, we pair each x_{nk} with the natural number that corresponds to its position in the above linear order, thus: $(x_{11}, 1)$, $(x_{12}, 2)$, $(x_{21}, 3)$, $\cdots$. The desired (1-1)-correspondence follows immediately.

3.1.7   With the aid of Theorem 3.1.6, we may set up a (1-1)-correspondence between N and the set formed by the union of (F_1) and all irrational numbers defined above by induction. Denoting the elements of (F_1) by $r_1, r_2, r_3, \cdots$, and using the symbols of 3.1.5, we have the ordering $r_1, r_2, r_\omega, r_3, r_{\omega+1}, r_{\omega \cdot 2}, \cdots$. From this follows the desired (1-1)-correspondence with the elements of N, and *we may begin all over again*, as in 3.1, to construct entirely new irrational numbers. (The first of these we could denote by r_{ω^2}, the second by r_{ω^2+1}, etc.)

† Compare with Lemma 2.5.1. Unless a (1-1)-correspondence *is given* for each n, between the elements of S_n and N, as is the case to which we shall apply this theorem below, then we can maintain that the Choice Axiom is needed in order to *assign* the correspondence to each S_n. Cf. Sierpinski [S_1; 124ff].

‡ We may say "countable" here if we wish, but we prefer to treat only one case; the more general case will follow immediately as soon as we study the "order" relations of cardinal numbers.

3.1.8   Remarks.   By this time the reader should have become rather fatigued by the above procedures, and perhaps be inclined to ask: "How long can this go on?"   Analysis of Sections 3.1.1 to 3.1.7 suggests the answer "Just so long as the numbers defined form a denumerable set."

But here we need to use extreme care.   In 3.1.1 we elaborated on the "well-defined" character of the number r_ω, pointing out that we possess an algorithm, i.e., a well-defined finite procedure, which enables us to state exactly what any particular digit of r_ω is—whether it is 0, or 1, or 2, $\cdots$, or 9.   In this sense, we are able to *exhibit* r_ω. And the same remark holds for each and every one of the numbers defined above (even $r_{\omega^2} = 0.112121 \cdots$ is quickly calculated to 6 decimal places from the information given above).   We have *effectively* defined, or given an *effective* definition of, each of these numbers. And the definition involved *effective* definitions of the way in which the numbers already defined at any stage can be put in (1-1)-correspondence with the natural numbers; in the latter case we say that the sets of these numbers (previously defined) were *effectively countable* or *effectively denumerable*.   It is preferable, then, that we say in answer to the above question "Just so long as the set of numbers already defined forms an effectively denumerable collection."   For the very essence of what we have done above is *to give a definite process* for obtaining the numbers.   It will aid in understanding the significance of this if we interpolate the following:

3.1.8.1   Fallacious theorem.   *Any collection, H, of numbers definable by continuing as far as possible the process commenced above in* 3.1.1–3.1.7 *is uncountable.*

Proof.   For suppose that such a collection H is countable.   Then its elements form a denumerable collection to which the diagonal procedure may be applied to define a new number, r, which is different from all numbers in H.   But this implies that the process can be continued, and the assumption that H is countable leads to a contradiction.

3.1.8.2   What is wrong here?   The proof is entirely analogous to that of 1.4; however, in that case we were discussing a set, R, of supposedly *already existing* numbers.   Very well, one may counter, why is not H a set of already existing numbers?   For one thing, we do not have a satisfactory description of H.   What do we mean by "continuing as far as possible the process commenced in 3.1.1–3.1.7?"   In 3.1.7 we had to *redefine* the (1-1)-correspondence with the natural numbers before we could carry on with the diagonal procedure; we had accumulated so many numbers at this stage ("a denumerable set of denumerable sets") that this became necessary. Clearly, then, "continuing" the process "commenced in 3.1.1–3.1.7" involves *redefinition* at successive critical points in the process. And, until the necessary definitions have been specifically given, H is not itself really defined.

Thus, the process may be continued as long as *we* are able to define new ways (at the critical points of the process) of setting up (1-1)-correspondences between the numbers already defined and the natural numbers; and these definitions have to be, by the very nature of the process, *effective definitions* which enable us to exhibit or calculate the number thereafter defined. What we *can* say, then, is that, as long as the set of numbers already defined at any point in the process is *effectively denumerable*, then the process may be continued.

3.1.8.3   The "we" at the beginning of the previous paragraph was italicized in order to emphasize the contrast in the points of view which may be taken here. *Effective* definition depends on someone *effecting*, i.e., giving, the definition. However, one may take the point of view that a definition may exist without anyone actually *giving* it. The "hard-boiled realist" would ask "Where?" In justice to the idealist, however, we may say that he could take the position that, given a dictionary D, one may consider the set $\mathfrak{D}$, of all possible finite arrangements, repetitions allowed, of words from that dictionary. Some of these will form definitions which, if "discovered" by someone, will become effective definitions adaptable to continuing the (possibly heretofore stopped for lack of effective definition) above process. For the sake of argument, one might call these *potential definitions*. And then one could ask, what is the character of a set H of potentially definable numbers obtained by continuing the above process?

Unfortunately the question is still inexact, since at no stage of the process is the manner of continuing *unique*. The diagonal procedure is itself precisely defined, but the ways of setting up the (1-1)-correspondence with the natural numbers at each stage are "unlimited." [Even in 3.1.2, we could begin by placing r_ω *after* the first element of (F_1) instead of at the head of (F_1)!] In order to get rid of this difficulty, let us set up a (1-1)-correspondence between the elements of N and the elements of $\mathfrak{D}$.

3.1.8.4   Ordering of all "sentences" using a dictionary D. This may be done as follows: The elements (words and symbols) of D are already (alphabetically) ordered. If each such element is considered an arrangement of words, they form an ordered subset $\mathfrak{D}_1$ of $\mathfrak{D}$. Then the arrangements of elements of D, two at a time, can be ordered in obvious ways to form an ordered subset $\mathfrak{D}_2$ of $\mathfrak{D}$. In general, the arrangements of elements of D, n at a time, can be ordered to form an ordered subset $\mathfrak{D}_n$ of $\mathfrak{D}$. And, since each $\mathfrak{D}_n$ is finite, ordering according to index (each element of $\mathfrak{D}_n$ being of index n) induces an ordering in one array of the elements of $\mathfrak{D}$ (as in the treatment of F and A in 1.2 and 1.3 respectively).

With such a (1-1)-correspondence, we may stipulate that at any point in the above process the new definition of ordering the numbers previously defined shall be the first to occur in the ordered arrangement of $\mathfrak{D}$. In this way, we may conceive of H as a definite class of numbers. And we may then state:

3.1.8.5   Theorem. *The collection H as redefined is not effectively countable.*

The proof is like that of 3.1.8.1, except that we now have that, if H is effectively countable, then there exists an element of $\mathfrak{D}$ constituting a rule for establishing a (1-1)-correspondence between the elements of H and the elements of N and hence a new number definable by the diagonal process.

3.1.8.6   The preceding remarks obviously suffer from inexactness, being largely descriptive. We should be more precise about what dictionary, D, we are using; for instance, it should contain the symbol "ω" used so frequently in 3.1.1–3.1.7, although the word "omega" would do. Also, it should contain other symbols, such as (,), $\cdots$, ., 0, etc.

Having specified D accurately, we could then define an *effective definition* as a potential definition which has been observed and *recorded* so that it has become available for use by anyone. [The "realist" would omit the "potential definition" and say that "an effective definition is one that is expressed (already recorded!) in terms of D."] And a collection would be effectively countable if there existed an effective definition of a (1-1)-correspondence between its elements and those of N.

As we shall see later, we come near, here, to the notion of a *formal system*, and for the present we leave the matter where it stands.

3.1.9   We remarked in 2.5.6 that we had obtained, in Corollary 2.5.5, a proof of the existence of an uncountable set of transcendental numbers without even exhibiting a single such number! If, in 3.1, we commence with the set A instead of F, then r_ω and all numbers later defined are transcendental. And, if we accept the existence of a set H as subsequently defined, one then has a non-effectively countable class of transcendental numbers, for some of which we have effective definitions, and for the remainder only potential definitions (relative to D).

3.2   The general diagonal procedure

We saw in 3.1 how, given an effectively denumerable set M of real numbers, we may effectively define, in terms of M, a real number that is not in M. From the standpoint of the complete totality, R, of real numbers, this is (at least theoretically) possible because R is uncountable.

3.2.1   We are now going to show how, given (1) a set S, and (2) a collection $\mathfrak{S}$ of subsets S_ν of S, such that between the elements of S and the elements of $\mathfrak{S}$ there exists a (1-1)-correspondence, we can effectively define a subset S' of S that is not an element of $\mathfrak{S}$—i.e., not an S_ν. The method we are going to describe constitutes what we may call a "general diagonal procedure."

3.2.1.1   First let us consider a very simple example. Let S be a set having 3 elements, a, b, and c. Let $\mathfrak{S}$ be the following set of three subsets: $\{a, b\}$; $\{b, c\}$; $\{c\}$. Both S and $\mathfrak{S}$ have 3 elements, so that the stipulation of a (1-1)-correspondence between the elements of S and the elements of $\mathfrak{S}$ is satisfied; suppose that we denote the elements of $\mathfrak{S}$, in the order named above, by S_a, S_b, S_c (thus $S_a = \{a, b\}$ for example). Now the *method* is expressed in the following:

(3a)   Rule.   *Form a set S' which contains an element x of S if and only if S_x does not contain it.*

In the present case, S' will be, precisely, the set $\emptyset$, for S_a contains a, S_b contains b, and S_c has c as its only element; so S' does not contain a, b, or c.

3.2.1.2   The general case presents no difference. The rule (3a) is stated in sufficiently general terms if we agree that S_x is to denote the element of $\mathfrak{S}$ that is paired with $x \, \varepsilon \, S$ in the given (1-1)-correspondence. And we shall prove the basic theorem:

3.2.1.3   Theorem. *If S is any set and $\mathfrak{S}$ is the collection of all subsets of S, then S and $\mathfrak{S}$ do not have the same cardinal number.*
    Proof.   Suppose there exists a (1-1)-correspondence T between the elements of S and the elements of $\mathfrak{S}$. Let S_x denote the element of $\mathfrak{S}$ that is paired with $x \, \varepsilon \, S$ in this (1-1)-correspondence. Form the set S' according to (3a). Then S' is a subset of S. But then $S' \, \varepsilon \, \mathfrak{S}$ and accordingly must be an S_x—say S_a. This is absurd, since, by (3a), S' contains a if and only if S_a does not contain a. We must conclude, then, that T does not exist.

3.2.1.4   A corollary of 3.2.1.3 is the well-known elementary formula of arithmetic: $n < 2^n$ for every natural number n. For, if a set S has

n elements, then S has 2^n subsets † (counting the null subset); and clearly $2^n \not< n$, since each element x of S constitutes the element $\{x\}$ of $\mathfrak{S}$. As soon as we have defined "$<$" for cardinal numbers, we shall have a similar inequality for them (Theorem 4.2.4.1).

3.2.2 Cantor's diagonal procedure a special case

To see the relation between the above and Cantor's diagonal procedure, we shall represent real numbers, the elements of R, in the binary scale instead of the decimal.

3.2.2.1 For theoretical work in analysis and function theory, the binary representation has long been used. In recent years, in the development of high-speed computing machines and even in the study of the human nervous system, the binary scale has assumed great importance.

By the binary scale we mean the representation of real numbers on the base 2, using only the digits 0 and 1. Thus, whereas 101.01 is the number $10^2 + 1 + 10^{-2}$ in the decimal scale, in the binary scale it becomes $2^2 + 1 + 2^{-2} = 4 + 1 + \frac{1}{4} = 5\frac{1}{4}$. Other bases may be used, of course; thus, in the *ternary* scale, whose base is 3, the above number denotes $3^2 + 1 + 3^{-2} = 10\frac{1}{9}$ (there exists, incidentally, a society for the propagation of the duodecimal scale, whose base is 12). When more than one base is being used to represent numbers, the base used to represent a number may be indicated by enclosing the number in parentheses followed by a subscript denoting the base. Thus, $(101.01)_2 = 5\frac{1}{4}$ and $(101.01)_3 = 10\frac{1}{9}$. In short, the actual value of a number is computed in powers of the base, the powers being determined by the positions of the digits just as in the decimal system.‡ Note that 10. always denotes the base number.

3.2.2.2 In a manner similar to that given in 1.4, we represent each real number by a form (1c) (Section 1.4), where now, however, each k and each a are either 0 or 1. Since the set

$$E^1 = \{x \mid (x \, \varepsilon \, R) \, \& \, (0 < x \leqq 1)\}$$

has the cardinal number c (see Problem 8), we may restrict ourselves to the case where all k's are zero, i.e., to *binary fractions*. And this time we allow finite binary fractions; indeed, such numbers will be represented by *both* their finite and infinite binary fractions (thus, 0.1 and $0.011 \cdots 1 \cdots$, although both representing $\frac{1}{2}$, will be present). Since the number of finite binary fractions is countable (see Problem

---

† In elementary texts, these are called "selections" instead of "subsets"; thus from a set of 3 things, $2^3 = 8$ selections may be made. In view of the discussion of III 6, we avoid the use of the term "selection" for obvious reasons when dealing with infinite sets.

‡ The arithmetic of the binary scale is extremely simple, and the elementary school child would certainly welcome the adoption of the scale! For example, the only "multiplication table" he would need to learn would be $0 \times 0 = 0$, $1 \times 0 = 0$, and $1 \times 1 = 1$!

16), it follows from Theorem 2.5.2 that the set R' of all such finite and infinite fractions still has the cardinal number c.

Instead of the argument as phrased in 1.4, we proceed as follows: Each binary fraction $.a_1 a_2 a_3 \cdots a_n \cdots$ determines a subset of N, namely, the subset which contains a natural number n if and only if $a_n = 1$. Thus the number $0.11 \cdots 1 \cdots$ in which every a_n is 1 determines the set N itself; the number $0.1011 \cdots 1 \cdots$ in which only a_2 is zero determines the subset consisting of all elements of N except the natural number 2; the subset of N consisting of all odd numbers is determined by the number $0.1010 \cdots$ in which only a_n's with odd subscripts are 1's; etc. Conversely, every subset N' of N determines a binary fraction $0.a_1 a_2 \cdots a_n \cdots$, in which $a_n = 1$ if and only if $n \varepsilon N'$. Thus the cardinal number of R' is the same as that of the set, $\mathfrak{N}$, of all subsets of N.

By Theorem 3.2.1.3, $\mathfrak{N}$ and N do not have the same cardinal number. Hence R' and N do not have the same cardinal number.

3.2.2.3   The appeal to Theorem 3.2.1.3 has concealed the use of the diagonal procedure in the above argument. If we recall the proof of 3.2.1.3, however, we see that the argument depends, as in 1.4, on supposing that there does exist a (1-1)-correspondence between the elements of R' and the elements of N, and, if r_n' is the element of R' paired with n in this correspondence, on choosing 0 or 1 for the nth digit of a new number r according as the nth digit of r_n' is 1 or 0 respectively; the latter is the exact analogue, as explained in 3.2.2.2, of defining a subset N' of N which contains n or does not contain n according as the nth digit of r_n' is 0 or 1, respectively.

3.2.3   An alternative procedure

The use of the binary scale in 3.2.2 suggests an alternative way of presenting the general diagonal procedure. First, however, we introduce the following definitions:

3.2.3.1   Definitions. If S and S_1 are sets (not necessarily disjoint), then a *mapping* of S *into* S_1 is a collection of pairs (x, y), $x \varepsilon S$, $y \varepsilon S_1$, such that each $x \varepsilon S$ occurs in one and only one (x, y); any $y \varepsilon S_1$ may occur in any number of pairs, however. (Such a mapping is also called a *many-one correspondence* between the elements of S and the elements of S_1.) If every $y \varepsilon S_1$ occurs in at least one pair, the collection is called a mapping of S *onto* S_1. A (1-1)-correspondence as defined in II 4.4.1 is a special case of a mapping. The set of *all* mappings of a set S into a set A is usually denoted by the symbol A^S.

In function theory terminology, a mapping of S into S_1 is called a *single-valued function defined over S with values in S_1*, and is denoted by a symbol of type $f(x)$, $x \, \varepsilon \, S$. Instead of the symbol (x, y) for a pair, we write $y = f(x)$, or $f(x) = y$, to indicate that x and y are paired; y is called the *value of $f(x)$ at x*. In the case of the so-called functions of a real variable, both S and S_1 are identical with R (or, more generally, subsets of R); in the case of complex functions, S and S_1 are subsets of the complex number system. For example, using the equations of plane analytic geometry, the function $y = x$ gives a mapping of R *onto* R; the function $y = e^{-x^2}$ gives a mapping of R *into* R and *onto* the set $\{y \mid 0 < y \leqq 1\}$.

3.2.3.2   Now, if S is any set, then a subset S' of S determines, uniquely, a *function $f(x)$*, $x \, \varepsilon \, S$, whose values are in the set S_1 consisting of the numbers 0 and 1. This function is defined as follows: If $x \notin S'$, we let $f(x) = 0$; otherwise $f(x) = 1$. (That is, in the "mapping" terminology, a subset S' determines a mapping of S into S_1; this is a mapping of S *onto* S_1 in every case except when $S' = \emptyset$ or $S' = S$.) If $\mathfrak{F}$ is the set of all such functions (i.e., $\mathfrak{F} = S_1{}^S$), and $\mathfrak{S}$ the set of all subsets of S, then between the elements of $\mathfrak{F}$ and the elements of $\mathfrak{S}$ there exists a (1-1)-correspondence, in which to each S' corresponds the function $f(x)$ defined above, and conversely.

3.2.3.3   Alternative proof of Theorem 3.2.1.3. Supposing that T exists as in the earlier proof of Theorem 3.2.1.3, it follows that there exists a (1-1)-correspondence T' between the elements of S and the elements of $\mathfrak{F}$. Denote the element of $\mathfrak{F}$ that is paired with a given element a of S by $f_a(x)$. But we can now define (diagonal procedure!) a function $f(x)$ such that, for a given element a of S, $f(a) \neq f_a(a)$.† But, as a mapping of S into $S_1 = \{0, 1\}$, $f(x)$ is an element of $\mathfrak{F}$, and hence is an $f_a(x)$. But this is absurd since $f(a) \neq f_a(a)$ and the supposed correspondence T cannot exist.

3.2.3.4   Remark. The substitution of the set $\mathfrak{F}$ for the set $\mathfrak{S}$ as in 3.2.3.2 has led to the use of the symbol 2^S for the set of all subsets of a set S; here the "2" denotes the set $\{0, 1\}$.

4   Cardinal numbers and their ordering

In 1.5.1 we defined what we mean by saying that two sets *have the same cardinal number*. We did not, however, define *cardinal number*. In introducing the symbols $\aleph_0$ and c we remarked that they would come, with practice, to have "the same significance for us as the num-

† That is, $f(a) = 0$ if $f_a(x)$ has the value 1 at $x = a$; otherwise $f(a) = 1$.

ber 15 for example; for we never have defined the latter and we never *define* any of the natural numbers in the primary schools," since by the time a child enters school he has usually learned to count and knows (we sometimes say "knows intuitively") the meaning of the numbers used in counting. That is, the natural numbers already have an "intuitive meaning" for him, and to attempt a definition of them would seem senseless to him.

4.1   It is possible, however, to define these numbers as special cases of what we call cardinal numbers. If we analyze the psychology of the "intuitive meaning" of the number 2, we shall probably conclude that "2 apples" brings up to the mind of the hearer an image of a *pair*, here a pair of apples. A similar remark might hold for the phrase "20 apples"; but it would hardly hold for "200 apples." From the psychological viewpoint, it seems probable that 200 is simply one of the numbers one ultimately gets by starting with the numbers whose mental images are distinct—1, 2, 3—and applying consecutively the operation of adding 1, as taught in the elementary schools. (This is certainly the case with a number like 3,762,147; it is conceivable that, owing to some special circumstances of one's occupation, one's experience with 200 may induce a special intuitive knowledge of 200.) But numbers such as $\aleph_0$ and c are hardly to be attained in any such manner (by adding 1, that is).

If we return to the mental image brought up by "2," we may recognize that it constitutes a sort of abstract *norm*—a *pair* of not any special objects, but what we might call a "pair in the abstract." It was this that we had in mind when we remarked that, through frequent use, the number $\aleph_0$ would come to have a similar significance for us, possibly like the abstract image of the natural numbers in their natural order—which is probably our usual concept of N (it being difficult to dissociate the individual numbers from the *order* induced by the counting process). Similar remarks might be made about the number c. The Frege-Russell definition,[†] which we give below, probably stems from such considerations:

(4a)   Definition. The *cardinal number* of a set M is the set $\overline{\overline{M}}$ of all sets that have the same cardinal number [‡] as M.

4.1.1   If it were not for the unfortunate fact that (as we show in 4.2.7) the *set of all sets* is a self-contradictory notion, it might add light to the meaning of this definition to observe that "have the same cardinal number" is an equivalence

† Given by G. Frege in 1879, and independently by B. Russell in 1901.
‡ Since we previously defined (1.5.1) "have the same cardinal number," the verbal vicious circle is not actual.

relation (II 8.1) in the set of all sets, and the cardinal numbers are the classes of the corresponding class decomposition (II 8.5). Some authors, although aware of the self-contradictory character of the set of all sets, use the statement just made as a definition of cardinal number, but it seems preferable to use it as an intuitive aid rather than as a definition. We can avoid mentioning a *set* of all sets by saying "Let us divide all possible sets into classes, putting two sets A and B into the same class if and only if they have the same cardinal number." (Cf. Sierpinski [S₁; 20].) Then these classes are the cardinal numbers. Whether the concept of "all sets" has the same self-contradictory character as "the set of all sets" is a question; even the appearance of "all sets" in Definition (4a) might create an uneasy feeling in anyone familiar with the set-theoretic antinomies—although in (4a) only those sets having the same cardinal number as a given fixed set M are included in the term.

4.1.2   According to Definition (4a), the number 2 as a cardinal number is simply the class of all pairs—and to say that a given set A has 2 elements is simply to say that it is a member of this class. Similarly 1 is the set of all classes having a single element. Since any set determines its class [the $\overline{\overline{M}}$ of (4a) can be *any* element of $\overline{\overline{M}}$], we can choose any set M of $\overline{\overline{M}}$ as a sort of yardstick or *norm;* thus the "set of all moons of the earth" is perhaps a good norm for 1. Just as the standard yard in Washington, D. C., is the final arbiter of measurement in yards, so the "set of all moons of the earth" can be used to determine whether a set has 1 element or not! This becomes less trivial if we consider $\aleph_0$. This symbol now becomes the symbol for the class of all denumerable sets. To determine that a given set is an element of $\aleph_0$, we usually use the set N as a norm.

4.1.3   It should be noted that, by using (1-1)-correspondence exclusively heretofore and avoiding use of the words "A and B have the same cardinal number," we might now introduce the latter terminology to mean that A and B are elements of the same class as defined in (4a). In the final analysis, however, we arrive at the same concepts by following either path.

Note, too, that the natural numbers are special cases of cardinal numbers. The cardinal number of the null set, $\emptyset$, is denoted by 0.

4.2   If A and B have the same cardinal number, we express the fact symbolically by writing $\overline{\overline{A}} = \overline{\overline{B}}$. What shall we mean by $\overline{\overline{A}} < \overline{\overline{B}}$, analogous to $2 < 5$? We define this relation as follows:

(4b)   Definition. If α and β are cardinal numbers, then $\alpha < \beta$ if, for arbitrary $A \, \varepsilon \, \alpha$, $B \, \varepsilon \, \beta$, A has the same cardinal number as a subset of B but the converse fails.

4.2.1   That $2 < 5$ by Definition (4b) is clear (take A as a set of two coins and B as a set of five books, for example). That is, (4b) corresponds exactly to the "$<$" indicated for the natural numbers when we speak of their "natural order" (sometimes called "order of magnitude"; see III 4.1f).

Consider $\aleph_0$ and c. Here we may use N and R as the representative sets A and B of (4b). As N is a subset of R, the identity correspondence of N with N as a subset of R shows that N has the same cardinal number as a subset of R. However, R cannot have the same cardinal number as a subset of N, since this would imply that R is denumerable (see Problem 1). Hence, by definition (4b), $\aleph_0 < c$.

4.2.2   The cardinal number f

Let E denote the set of all mappings (3.2.3.1) of R into $\{0, 1\}$. Then, if E_1 denotes the set of all subsets of R, $\overline{\overline{E}} = \overline{\overline{E_1}}$ (by 3.2.3.2). Let us denote $\overline{\overline{E}}$ by f. By Theorem 3.2.1.3, $c \neq f$. Also, $\aleph_0 \neq f$ since the contrary would imply $\aleph_0 = c$.† Hence f is a new cardinal number. Is $c < f$?

For each $r \, \varepsilon \, R$, let f_r be the mapping of R into $\{0, 1\}$ obtained by pairing (3.2.3.1) each $x \, \varepsilon \, R$ with 0 if $x \neq r$, and by pairing r with 1. For $r, r' \, \varepsilon \, R$, and $r \neq r'$, f_r and $f_{r'}$ are different mappings, and the collection $\{(r, f_r)\}$ constitutes a (1-1)-correspondence between the elements of R and the elements of a subset $E' = \{y \mid (y \, \varepsilon \, E) \, \& \, (y \text{ is an } f_r)\}$ of E. Thus R has the same cardinal number as a subset of E. To show that $c < f$, we have to show that R has no subset R' such that between the elements of R' and the elements of E there exists a (1-1)-correspondence. Now we shall prove a theorem which shows that, if the latter correspondence did exist, then we would have $c = f$. Since this is impossible, it follows that such a correspondence cannot exist, and hence $c < f$. The theorem that we need here, and, as a rule, in all similar situations is:

4.2.3   Bernstein equivalence theorem.‡ *If A and B are sets such that A has the same cardinal number as a subset B_1 of B, and B has the same cardinal number as a subset A_1' of A, then A and B have the same cardinal number.*

---

† As shown below, E has a subset E' which has the cardinal number c. Hence a (1-1)-correspondence between the elements of N and the elements of E would induce a (1-1)-correspondence between the elements of an infinite subset N' of N and the elements of E'; the latter would then have cardinal number $\aleph_0$ (cf. Problem 1).

‡ Sometimes called "Cantor-Bernstein theorem," since it was conjectured by Cantor (it was proved by F. Bernstein in Cantor's seminar); also called "Schröder-Bernstein theorem," since it was independently proved by E. Schröder (on the basis of a logical calculus). This theorem is a special case of a theorem of Banach; see Sierpinski [S₁; 90ff]. (An interesting and simple proof of Banach's theorem may be obtained if one is familiar with the theory of linear graphs; see König [Kö; 85ff].)

Proof of 4.2.3.   Let f denote a (1-1)-correspondence between A and B_1, and g a (1-1)-correspondence between B and A_1'. Then, since (1-1)-correspondences are transitive, the combination of f and g (the latter applied to B_1 alone) gives a (1-1)-correspondence T between A and a subset A_1 of A_1'. Now T is also a (1-1)-correspondence between the elements of A_1 (as a subset of A) and a subset A_2 (of A_1); and, for general $n \, \varepsilon \, N$, we have in T a (1-1)-correspondence between the elements of a set A_n (as a subset of A) and a subset A_{n+1} of A_n (definition by induction). If, then, we let $A = A_0$, and for each n let A_{n+1}' be the subset of A_n that corresponds to A_n' in T, we can define a (1-1)-correspondence T' between the elements of A and the elements of A_1' as follows:

(a) For each n, T' agrees with T for elements of $A_{n-1} - A_n'$; i.e., between the elements of $A_{n-1} - A_n'$ as a subset of A, and the elements of $A_n - A_{n+1}'$ as a subset of A_1', the (1-1)-correspondence T' is the same as T.

(b) T' is the identity correspondence for elements of $A_n' - A_n$ (all n), and for elements of $\bigcap_{n=1}^{\infty} A_n$.

Finally, the combination of T' and g gives a (1-1)-correspondence between the elements of A and the elements of B.

4.2.3.1   It should be noted that the (1-1)-correspondence established in the above proof between the elements of A and the elements of B is effectively defined (3.1.8) if the given correspondences f and g are effectively defined.

4.2.3.2   Note, too, that from 4.2.3 it follows that, if A has the same cardinal number as a subset of B, then either $\overline{\overline{A}} = \overline{\overline{B}}$ or $\overline{\overline{A}} < \overline{\overline{B}}$, inasmuch as the first half of the condition for $\overline{\overline{A}} < \overline{\overline{B}}$ (4b) is already fulfilled. We shall express this relation by $\overline{\overline{A}} \leqq \overline{\overline{B}}$.

4.2.4   We remarked in 3.2.3.1 that the set of all mappings of a set S into a set A is usually denoted by the symbol A^S. When A is the set $\{0, 1\}$, we usually use the symbol 2^S (3.2.3.4); and the cardinal number of 2^S is denoted by $2^{\overline{\overline{S}}}$. Thus the cardinal number of the set of all mappings of N into $\{0, 1\}$ is denoted by $2^{\aleph_0}$; this is also the cardinal number of the set of all subsets of N. Since we showed in 3.2.2.2 that this cardinal number is c, we have the classical relation

(4.2.4a) $2^{\aleph_0} = c.$

And, since we showed in 4.2.1 that $\aleph_0 < c$, we have

(4.2.4b) $\aleph_0 < 2^{\aleph_0}.$

Similarly, since $f = 2^c$, by 4.2.2, and $c < f$, we derive the relation

(4.2.4c) $c < 2^c$.

Relations (4.2.4a) and (4.2.4c) suggest that, perhaps for every cardinal number α, $\alpha < 2^\alpha$. This may be easily proved from the Bernstein equivalence theorem:

4.2.4.1   Theorem. *For every cardinal number α,*

$$\alpha < 2^\alpha.$$

Proof. Let $A \, \varepsilon \, \alpha$; then $2^A \, \varepsilon \, 2^\alpha$. Hence we need only show that (i) A has the same cardinal number as a subset of 2^A, and (ii) no subset of A has the same cardinal number as 2^A. The (1-1)-correspondence in which, for each fixed $a \, \varepsilon \, A$, a is paired with the element $\{a\}$ of 2^A shows that (i) holds. If (ii) held, then, by 4.2.3, $\alpha = 2^\alpha$, in contradiction to Theorem 3.2.1.3.

4.2.4.2   A special case of Theorem 4.2.4.1 is the well-known formula $n < 2^n$ of arithmetic (see 3.2.1.4).

4.2.5   Lemma. *The relation $<$ defined in (4b) is transitive; i.e., $\alpha < \beta$, $\beta < \gamma$ imply $\alpha < \gamma$. And, if $\alpha < \beta$, then $\alpha \neq \beta$.*
[We leave the proof to the reader.]

4.2.6   Existence of infinitely many transfinite cardinal numbers

Cardinal numbers of infinite sets, such as the numbers $\aleph_0$, c, and f, are called *transfinite* cardinal numbers. The *finite* cardinal numbers are 0 and the natural numbers 1, 2, $\cdots$, n, $\cdots$.

Theorem 4.2.4.1 gives a means of demonstrating the existence of infinitely many transfinite cardinal numbers. Starting with $\aleph_0$, we get $c = 2^{\aleph_0}$ and $f = 2^c$. And in addition we may now consider 2^f. By virtue of Lemma 4.2.5, this is not one of the numbers $\aleph_0$, c, f, since $f < 2^f$. And evidently by this process of "exponentiation" we exhibit an infinite collection of different transfinite cardinal numbers (which would not necessarily constitute *all* the transfinite cardinals, however).

It may be argued that we can go even further. For let $\alpha_1, \alpha_2, \cdots$, $\alpha_n, \cdots$ be cardinal numbers, such that $\alpha_n < \alpha_{n+1}$ for all n. Let $A_n \, \varepsilon \, \alpha_n$. Then the cardinal number α of the set $A = \bigcup_{n=1}^{\infty} A_n$ satisfies the relation $\alpha_n < \alpha$ for all n (Problem 18).

4.2.7   Self-contradictory character of "the set of all sets"

Let us suppose that there exists a *set* of all sets; that is, a set $\mathfrak{X}$ of which *every* set is an element. Denote the cardinal number of $\mathfrak{X}$ by τ. Then, by Theorem 4.2.4.1,

$$(4.2.7a) \qquad\qquad \tau < 2^\tau.$$

But a subset of $\mathfrak{X}$ is in particular a *set*, hence an element of $\mathfrak{X}$, so that $2^\mathfrak{X} \subset \mathfrak{X}$. But the identity correspondence then gives $2^\tau \leqq \tau$, which, by (4.2.7a) and Lemma 4.2.5, gives

$$2^\tau < 2^\tau.$$

And, as this contradicts the latter part of Lemma 4.2.5, the assumption of the existence of $\mathfrak{X}$ leads to contradiction.

4.2.7.1   We might expect the concept of "the set of all sets" to be untenable, since if it existed it should have the "Russell set" $\mathfrak{U}$ of III 2 as a subset, and we have already shown that set to be self-contradictory. However, we may object that there is no reason to suppose, a priori, that the existence of a set implies the existence of all its subsets, so that the self-contradictory character of $\mathfrak{U}$ would be no guarantee of the self-contradictory character of $\mathfrak{X}$. Of course the same objection would throw into question the existence of 2^A, for arbitrary given A, and hence in particular the argument of 4.2.6. These matters we leave to Part II, however.

4.2.8   By Lemma 4.2.5, the relation $<$ for cardinal numbers satisfies axioms (2) and (3) of *simple order* (II 7) for any collection C of cardinal numbers. We cannot conclude, however, that axiom (1) of simple order holds. For there is no guarantee, a priori, that, given two sets A and B, there will exist a (1-1)-correspondence between one of these sets and a subset of the other.† A priori, given two sets A and B, there are four possibilities. Let us use the arrow "$\rightarrow$" to denote the existence of a (1-1)-correspondence; i.e., $A \rightarrow B$ or $B \leftarrow A$ will denote that there exists a (1-1)-correspondence between A and a subset of B. *Non-existence* of such a correspondence will be denoted by $\nrightarrow$. Then the four possibilities are:

$$(4.2.8a) \qquad\qquad \begin{array}{c} A \rightarrow B \\[4pt] A \leftarrow B \end{array}$$

† Contrary to the assertion in Young [Y; 80].

(4.2.8b)
$$A \rightarrow B$$
$$A \nleftarrow B$$

(4.2.8c)
$$A \nrightarrow B$$
$$A \leftarrow B$$

(4.2.8d)
$$A \nrightarrow B$$
$$A \nleftarrow B$$

Case (4.2.8a) is that in which $\overline{\overline{A}} = \overline{\overline{B}}$, by the Bernstein equivalence theorem (4.2.3). Cases (4.2.8b) and (4.2.8c) correspond respectively to $\overline{\overline{A}} < \overline{\overline{B}}$ and $\overline{\overline{B}} < \overline{\overline{A}}$. Case (4.2.8d) allows neither of the relationships $=$, $<$ between $\overline{\overline{A}}$ and $\overline{\overline{B}}$.

If we could show that (4.2.8d) never occurs, no matter what the sets A and B, then the cardinal numbers would form a simply ordered collection relative to $<$ (although we would have to be wary about speaking of "the *set* of all cardinal numbers"; see Problem 20). As we shall see in the next chapter, non-occurrence of (4.2.8d) is *equivalent* to the acceptance of the Choice Axiom (III 6.3).

At present, the most we can assert is that, relative to $\leqq$, the cardinal numbers are partially ordered (see Problem 8 of Chapter II).

Since a study of the notion of *order* will throw additional light on the problem of eliminating (4.2.8d), and is basic in many mathematical concepts, we shall devote the next chapter to it.

4.2.9   In concluding this chapter we raise another question—one which, unfortunately, we shall not be able to answer: Consider the natural numbers. Between 1 and 2, in the natural order, there is no cardinal number; 2 is the "immediate successor" of 1. And, in general, for any $n \, \varepsilon \, N$, $n + 1$ is the immediate successor of n.

4.2.9.1   Question. Is there any cardinal number α such that $\aleph_0 < \alpha < c$? Or is c the immediate successor of $\aleph_0$?

4.2.9.2   In a way, this is not a good question to ask unless we rule out (4.2.8d). However, it is legitimate, even though we do not know that the cardinal numbers are simply ordered. If we grant the simple ordering, it will be noted that 4.2.9.1 is equivalent to asking: Does every infinite subset of R have either the cardinal number $\aleph_0$ or the cardinal number c? We shall return to this question in V 3.3.3.

5 Further enumerations of the rational numbers

Although the (1-1)-correspondence established in 1.2 between the elements of N and the elements of F is sufficient for proving the denumerability of F, it does not yield a correspondence enabling one to determine directly what element of F corresponds, say, to the natural number 1099; nor what element of N corresponds to some given fraction, as for instance to 33/49. For some purposes (cf. 3.1.1) it is desirable to have a (1-1)-correspondence that allows of such determinations. In the present section we shall cite two such correspondences.

5.1 Faber's enumeration

The first, due to Faber [a], gives a (1-1)-correspondence between the natural numbers and the rational numbers between 0 and 1. It is based on the fact that a rational number x between 0 and 1 may be represented uniquely in the form

$$x = a_1/2! + a_2/3! + \cdots + a_n/(n+1)!$$

where $0 \leqq a_k < k$ for $k = 2, 3, \cdots, n$ ($r!$ is the usual abbreviation for the product $1 \cdot 2 \cdot 3 \cdots r$); and on the fact that to such a number x corresponds uniquely the natural number

$$y = a_1 + a_2 \cdot 2! + \cdots + a_n \cdot n!$$

Either x or y may be given and the a's calculated to find the corresponding number (see Faber, loc. cit.).

5.2 Niven's enumeration

The second method, due to Niven [a], is based on the binary representation (3.2.2.1) of numbers:

"For any positive integer n, let r be the number of zeros occurring in the representation of n in the binary scale of notation. These r zeros divide the representation into $r + 1$ blocks of 1's, some blocks being perhaps empty: for $j = 2, 3, \cdots, r$, let a_j denote the number of 1's between the $(j - 1)$th and the jth zeros, counted from the right; define a_1 and a_{r+1} as the number of consecutive 1's on the right and left ends of the representation. E.g., if n is 110010 in the binary scale, then $r = 3$ and $(a_1, a_2, a_3, a_4) = (0, 1, 0, 2)$. If $n = 1$, then $r = 0$ and $a_1 = 1$. Note that n determines a unique set of values $a_1, a_2, \cdots, a_{r+1}$, with positive a_{r+1}, and conversely.

"Now define $b_j = -a_j/2$ for even a_j, and $b_j = (a_j + 1)/2$ otherwise: this is a one-to-one correspondence between the non-negative integers

a_j and all integers b_j. Finally, if p_1, p_2, p_3, $\cdots$ are the consecutive primes 2, 3, 5, $\cdots$, we define

(1)
$$f(n) = \prod_{j=1}^{r+1} p_j{}^{b_j}.$$

Thus to any positive integer n corresponds a unique positive rational number $f(n)$. Conversely, any positive rational number f, except 1, can be written uniquely in the form (1) with $b_{r+1} \neq 0$. The exponents b_j determine a unique set a_j, with $a_{r+1} \neq 0$, and these give a unique positive integer n. E.g., if $f = 33/49$, then $(b_1, b_2, b_3, b_4, b_5) = (0, 1, 0, -2, 1)$ and $(a_1, a_2, a_3, a_4, a_5) = (0, 1, 0, 4, 1)$ so that $n = 1011110010$ in the binary scale.

"We now obtain a one-to-one correspondence between the positive integers and all positive rational numbers, by letting $n + 1$ correspond to $f(n)$, written $n + 1 \leftrightarrow f(n)$, for all positive integers n, and in addition we let $1 \leftrightarrow 1$. On the other hand, if we want a one-to-one correspondence between the positive integers and all rational numbers, we can use the correspondences $1 \leftrightarrow 0$, $2 \leftrightarrow 1$, $3 \leftrightarrow -1$, $2n + 2 \leftrightarrow f(n)$, $2n + 3 \leftrightarrow -f(n)$, where n ranges over all positive integers." †

SUGGESTED READING

Cantor [C₁]

Grelling [Gr; 16–25]

Hobson [Ho; §§ 6, 58–62]

Kamke [Ka₁; I–II]

Richardson [R; XV]

Sierpinski [S₁; II–V]

Young [Y; VI, VIII]

PROBLEMS

1. Show that every infinite subset of N has the cardinal number $\aleph_0$ (cf. Problem 18 of Chapter III).

2. Show that F may also be defined as the set of all elements of R whose decimal parts ultimately begin to repeat (such as $\frac{1}{5} = .19999 \cdots$, $\frac{1}{7} = .142857142857\text{-}142857 \cdots$).

3. Show that, if in the proof of 2.4 we made each block a single digit, then there would not result a (1-1)-correspondence of the type desired.

4. Modify the proof of 2.4 to show that the subset $E^3 = \{(x, y, z) \mid (0 < x < 1)$ & $(0 < y < 1)$ & $(0 < z < 1)\}$ of coordinate 3-dimensional space has the cardinal number c. How about space of four dimensions, in which each point has *four* coordinates (x, y, z, w); five dimensions; etc.?

5. In a Hilbert space, each point is represented by an infinite sequence of coordinates $(x_1, x_2, \cdots, x_n, \cdots)$, where x_n is a real number. Show that the set $E^\omega = \{(x_1, x_2, \cdots, x_n, \cdots) \mid 0 < x_n < 1$ for all $n\}$ has the cardinal number c.

† Quoted by permission of I. Niven and *American Mathematical Monthly*.

6. Interpret the results of Problems 4 and 5 in terms of collections of sequences of real numbers, without reference to geometry.

7. Show that the set of positive real numbers has the cardinal number c. As a corollary, the set of non-negative real numbers has the cardinal number c.

8. Show that the set of all real numbers between 0 and 1 has the cardinal number c. As a corollary, the subset $\bar{R}^1 = \{x \mid 0 \leq x \leq 1\}$ of R has the cardinal number c.

9. That 2.5.3 is stated as a corollary of Theorem 2.5.2 implies that the set I must be Dedekind infinite. Why is this so? [Hint: Cf. 3.1.1–3.1.3.]

10. Show that, if a set S has a proper subset S_1, such that there exists a (1-1)-correspondence between the elements of S and the elements of S_1, then S_1 is Dedekind infinite.

11. Show that, if we did not stipulate a unique way of representing real numbers (i.e., as in the form given in 1.4), then the proof of 1.4 would run into a difficulty (specifically, in regard to the number r being a different real number from every number r_n).

12. In the set $\bar{R}^1 = \{x \mid (x \, \varepsilon \, R) \, \& \, (0 \leq x \leq 1)\}$, let $x \approx y$, where $x, y \, \varepsilon \, \bar{R}^1$, mean that $x - y \, \varepsilon \, F$. Show that $\approx$ is an equivalence relation in $\bar{R}^1$. How many elements are there in each class of the class decomposition of $\bar{R}^1$ corresponding to $\approx$? What would you guess is the cardinal number of the set of all classes in this class decomposition?

13. Contrast the decomposition of $\bar{R}^1$ defined in Problem 12 with the following (due to Sierpinski): We define a function $f(x)$, $x \, \varepsilon \, \bar{R}^1$, as follows: First express x as a "non-finite decimal" in the ternary scale, $x = (0.a_1 a_2 \cdots a_n \cdots)_3$, such that for no n are all $a_n, a_{n+1}, a_{n+2}, \cdots$ zeros unless $x = 0$. Then, if $x = 0$, or infinitely many of the digits a_n are 2's, let $f(x) = 0$. Otherwise, let n be the smallest (Problem 18 of Chapter III) natural number such that all digits $a_n, a_{n+1}, a_{n+2}, \cdots$, are all 0 or 1; then let $f(x) = (0.a_n a_{n+1} a_{n+2} \cdots)_2$. Finally, for every t such that $0 \leq t \leq 1$, let $R_t = \{x \mid f(x) = t\}$.

14. Prove that every real number is the limit of a sequence of rational numbers $x_1, x_2, \cdots, x_n, \cdots$ that can be effectively defined; do this in two essentially different ways.

15. If $S = \emptyset$, why does 3.2.1.3 hold?

16. Show that the set of all finite subsets of N is countable.

17. Show that, if E' is the set of all single-valued functions defined over $\bar{R}^1$ with values restricted to 0 and 1, then the cardinal number of E' is f.

18. Prove that, if $\alpha_1, \alpha_2, \cdots, \alpha_n, \cdots$ are cardinal numbers such that $\alpha_n < \alpha_{n+1}$ for all n, then the cardinal number α of the set $\bigcup_{n=1}^{\infty} A_n$, where $A_n \, \varepsilon \, \alpha_n$, satisfies the relation $\alpha_n < \alpha$ for all n.

19. Apply the Bernstein equivalence theorem to prove: If $A \subset B$, then $\bar{\bar{A}} \leq \bar{\bar{B}}$. Conversely, show that this theorem has the Bernstein equivalence theorem as a consequence.

20. Is *the set of all cardinal numbers* a self-contradictory notion?

21. Show that in the coordinate plane the set $K = \{(x, y) \mid (x \, \varepsilon \, F) \, \& \, (y \, \varepsilon \, F)\}$ is denumerable. Then use Theorem 3.1.6 to show that the set of all circles with radii elements of F and centers in K is denumerable. Work the analogous problem for three-dimensional space.

22. Use the results of Problem 21 to show that, if physical space is assumed to be euclidean, then the set of all physical objects (assuming some kind of a division of the material universe into things called "objects") is countable.

23. In order to carry out the proof implied for Corollary 2.5.5, it is necessary to know that the set of transcendental numbers is Dedekind infinite. Prove this.

24. Show that, if B is a Dedekind infinite set, and A a set such that $A \supset B$, then A is Dedekind infinite.

25. Compare the material in 3.1, especially 3.1.8.1, with the following ("Richard paradox"): If a specific English dictionary, D, is used to form sentences, some of them may designate natural numbers; e.g., "Let N be the number of moons of the earth" would designate the number 1. However, consider the sentence, "Let N be the smallest natural number not definable in twenty words or less from the dictionary D."

V

Well-Ordered Sets; Ordinal Numbers

1 Order types

Although there are *two* ways of ordering the elements of a set $\{a, b\}$ which has only two elements—$a < b$ or $b < a$—the result in either case is just an *ordered pair*. Similarly, although a set having three elements can be simply ordered in *six* ways, the result in any case is an *ordered triple*. And, in general, although a set having n elements, $n \in N$, can be simply ordered in $n!$ † ways, the result is always an *ordered n-ple*.

1.1 Let us make the above precise; we haven't even defined the italicized terms. In the terminology of II 4.4.4, all that we have said in the preceding paragraph is that *every two simply ordered sets of n elements are isomorphic with respect to the simple order axioms.* Another way of putting this is to say that, if we add to the simple order axioms (II 7) the axiom, *The set C has exactly n elements*, $n \in N$, then the resulting system of axioms is categorical (II 4.5.1).

1.1.1 The analogous statements do not hold for infinite sets. In particular, to add to the simple order axioms the axiom, *The set C has exactly $\aleph_0$ elements*, does not render the axiom system categorical. For consider the set N. It can be assigned its *natural order:* $n < n + 1$ for all n. Let us call this ordered set ON. Another simple ordering of N is obtained as follows: (i) if $a, b \in N$, and a is odd, b is even, then $a < b$; (ii) if a and b are both odd, then $a < b$ denotes the natural order $(1 < 3$, etc.); (iii) if a and b are both even, then $a < b$ means that $b < a$ in the natural order (i.e., $4 < 2$, $6 < 4$, etc.). Schematically, the order just defined is

$$1, 3, 5, \cdots, 2n + 1, \cdots; \cdots, 2n, \cdots, 6, 4, 2.$$

† Where $n!$ denotes n *factorial;* i.e., $1 \cdot 2 \cdot 3 \cdots \cdots \cdot n$.

Let us call this ordered set ON_1. The sets ON and ON_1 are not isomorphic with respect to the simple order axioms (Problem 1). Generally, we abbreviate this statement to: ON and ON_1 do not have the same order type.

(1a)   Definition. If A and B are two simply ordered † sets which are isomorphic relative to the simple order axioms, then we say that A and B *have the same order type.*

(1b)   Definition. The *order type* of a simply ordered set A is the collection of all simply ordered sets that have the same order type as A.

The reader will notice the analogy to the terms "have the same cardinal number" and "cardinal number" as defined in IV 1.5.1 and IV (4a). Remarks analogous to those of IV 4.1.1 may also be made here.

1.1.2   To say that a set is an *ordered pair* is to say that it is an element of the collection of all simply ordered sets having two elements; generally, to say that a set is an *ordered n-ple* is to say that it is an element of the collection of all simply ordered sets having n elements. We shall prefer the term *order type n* instead of ordered n-ple, and shall usually say that a set *is of order type n* to indicate that it is an ordered n-ple. (Because of their universality, however, we may still sometimes say *ordered pair* instead of order type 2, or *ordered triple* instead of order type 3.)

In conformance with ordinary usage, if τ is an order type, then, instead of saying of a set A that "A is an element of the order type τ," we shall say that "A has the order type τ," or "A is of order type τ."

1.1.3   We have observed above that a simply ordered set of n elements has only one order type, i.e., the order type n. But an infinite set, such as N, may have many order types. Not all of these are sufficiently important to have been assigned special symbols. However, the order type of the set ON of 1.1.1 is denoted by ω. The symbol $*\omega$ was used by Cantor to indicate the order type of the negative integers in their "natural order" $(-2 < -1$, etc.); this order type also contains the ordered set of natural numbers with "$<$" meaning the reverse of the natural order. The order type ON_1 may then be denoted by $\omega + *\omega$; the use of "$+$" here is in accord with the following:

---

† Obviously we could say "partially ordered" (Problem 8 of Chapter II) here instead of "simply ordered." The latter is more significant for our purposes, however.

1.1.4   Addition ($+$) of order types is defined as follows: If Ω_1 and Ω_2 are order types, $A_i \, \varepsilon \, \Omega_i$, $i = 1$, 2, then $\Omega_1 + \Omega_2$ is the order type determined by $A = \bigcup_{i=1}^{2} A_i$, ordered so that $<$ is the same as originally for each A_i, but, if $a_i \, \varepsilon \, A_i$, then $a_1 < a_2$. Note that $*\omega + \omega$ would not be the same as $\omega + *\omega$, so that this addition is not commutative. See Sierpinski [S_1; VIII].

We shall not go into the "arithmetic" of order types, but the addition of order types is an aid to the understanding of the ordinal number symbols to be introduced in the sequel (3.2). If n is used to denote the order type n, notice that $n + \omega$ is the same as ω; however, this is not the case with $\omega + n$.

2   The order type ω

The order type ω, because of its central importance, has been subjected to axiomatic treatment. (When we speak of "infinite sequence" in elementary algebra, we mean an ordered set having the order type ω.) If, on the basis of Peano's axioms (III 5.1), we define "$<$" suitably in terms of "successor," we can show that the axioms yield the order type ω (cf. Problem 22 of Chapter III). As a definition directly in terms of $<$, we may use the following:

2.1   An axiomatic definition of ω in terms of <

Let N be a non-empty set and $<$ a binary relation between elements of N. Then N is called of order type ω if

(a) N is simply ordered with respect to the binary relation $<$.†
(b) If $a \, \varepsilon \, N$, then the set $\{x \mid x < a\}$ is finite.
(c) N has no last ‡ element.

Any set of order type ω obviously satisfies these axioms. They can be shown to form a categorical system. (We leave this to the reader as an exercise.)

2.2   An axiomatic definition of ω in terms of cuts

The notion of "cut" is widely used for defining certain basic order types.

(2a)   Definition. If A and B are subsets of an ordered set S, then $A < B$ means that $A \neq \emptyset \neq B$, and that $a \, \varepsilon \, A$, $b \, \varepsilon \, B$ imply $a < b$.

† This means, of course, that the single axiom (a) implies all three axioms of simple order as given in II 7.

‡ In a simply ordered set, an element x is called the *last* element of a set A if $x \, \varepsilon \, A$ and if, for every other $y \, \varepsilon \, A$, $y < x$. "First" is defined analogously. Uniqueness of first and last elements (when such exist) follows from the simple order axioms.

If $S = A \cup B$ and $A < B$, then we say that A and B form a *cut* † of S; we shall denote such a cut by the symbol $[A, B]$ (always implying $A < B$).

We can then define a set N to be of order type ω if
(a) N is simply ordered with respect to the binary relation $<$.
(b) N has a first element.
(c) N has no last element.
(d) If $[A, B]$ is a cut of N, then A has a last element and B has a first element.‡

2.2.1   Incidentally, it is interesting to note that the sets which are of the same order type as the elements of F (IV 1.1) in their natural order (order of magnitude) may be characterized, as to their order relations, by the assumption of denumerability, axioms (a) and (c), and denials of (b) and (d) (the latter in the strict sense that it fails for *every* cut $[A, B]$).§

2.3   An axiomatic definition of ω in terms of spanning sets

A very useful notion, in dealing with ordered sets, is that of spanning set.

2.3.1   Definition.   If S is a simply ordered set, then a subset X of S will be said to *span* S if $s \, \varepsilon \, S$ implies the existence of an $x \, \varepsilon \, X$ such that $s \leq x$. We also call X a *spanning set* of S.

2.3.1.1   Evidently, if a simply ordered set S has a last element x, then the set $X = \{x\}$ is a spanning set of S. Also, S spans itself. In the case where S is N and $<$ is the natural order, the set X of all odd numbers is a spanning set. In the case where S is R with $<$ meaning the order of magnitude, the set N is a spanning set.

2.3.2   In terms of spanning sets, we can define a non-empty set N to be of order type ω if
(a) N is simply ordered with respect to the binary relation $<$.
(b) Every infinite subset of N is a spanning set of N.
(c) N has no last element.

2.4   Recognition of type ω among the well-ordered sets

Of fundamental importance in the sequel is the notion of a well-ordered set.

† Frequently called "Dedekind cut" because of its use by Dedekind in the study of irrational numbers. See Dedekind [D₁].
‡ See Sierpinski [S₁; 143ff].
§ See Sierpinski [S₁; 145ff]; Sierpinski denotes this order type by η.

(2b)   A simply ordered set is called *well-ordered* † if every non-empty subset of it has a first element.

Well-ordered sets are frequently called "sequences" or "well-ordered sequences."

An axiomatic definition of well-ordered set may be obtained by adding, to the axioms of II 7, the axiom (4): "Every non-empty subset of C has a first point."

2.4.1   A *well-ordering* of a set S is the result of an assignment of a binary relation $<$ between the elements of S in such a way that the set S becomes simply ordered with respect to $<$ and satisfies Definition (2b). A *well-ordering type* is an order type whose elements are well-ordered sets.

2.4.2   *Every finite simply ordered set is well-ordered* (with respect to the order relation $<$ defining the simple order).

2.4.3   The set N, ordered so as to be of order type ω (the natural order; ON of 1.1.1) is well-ordered. However, when ordered so as to be of order type $*\omega$, it is not well-ordered, since a well-ordered set has a first element (as a subset of itself). Thus an infinite set, when simply ordered, may or may not be well-ordered (with respect to the order defining the simple order). The set ON_1 of 1.1.1 is not well-ordered. The set F, ordered according to magnitude, is not well-ordered; the subset consisting of its positive elements has no first element. The null set, $\emptyset$, is well-ordered since it satisfies Definition (2b) vacuously.

2.4.4   Consider the following example: The order type $\omega + 1$, as defined in 1.1.4, is a well-ordering type. One of its elements is obtained by adding to ON a new element, p, such that, for all $x \, \varepsilon \, ON$, $x < p$ by definition. (It can of course be exemplified by redefining $<$ for N so that, for all $x \, \varepsilon \, N$ for which $x \neq 1$, $x < 1$; and, for $x,y \, \varepsilon \, N$ $- \{1\}$, $x < y$ is the natural order.) This example shows the necessity for axiom (c) in the set of axioms given below.

2.4.5   *If S is a well-ordered set, and $s \, \varepsilon \, S$, then the set $\{x \mid s < x\}$, if not empty, has a first element s'.* We call s' the *immediate successor* of s.

† It may sometimes be necessary to say "well-ordered with respect to $<$," where $<$ is the binary relation with respect to which the set is simply ordered. This will always be the case when more than one ordering of a set is under consideration. English writers frequently use the term "normally ordered." This has the advantage of allowing the noun "normal ordering," whereas the (universally used in the United States) term "well-ordered" leads to "well-ordering," which sounds suspiciously like a grammatical error.

2.4.6   We can now define a non-empty set N to be of order type ω if the following axioms hold:

(a) N is well-ordered.

(b) N has no last element.

(c) If N_1 is a subset of N such that the first element of N is in N_1, and such that, if $s \,\varepsilon\, N$ is in N_1 then the immediate successor s' of s is in N_1, then $N_1 = N$.

Axiom (c) is of course the mathematical induction principle used in Peano's system (III 5.1, axiom 4). As we shall see below, (c) is intimately related to well-ordering, through a weakened † type of induction principle called "transfinite induction."

3   The general well-ordered set

In Section 2 we studied some of the properties of sets of type ω, the most important, from the viewpoint of its wide variety of applications, of the types of well-ordered sets. In this section we turn to the general types of well-ordered sets. That they must constitute a wide class is probably already apparent from the above discussion; for example, each $\omega + n$ is a well-ordering type. So also is $\omega + \omega$. And in general, if W_1 and W_2 are well-ordering types, then $W_1 + W_2$ (see 1.1.4) is a well-ordering type. Thus we can generate new well-ordering types from old by the process of addition.

3.1   The transfinite induction principle

It follows from 2.4.6 that, among the well-ordered sets, the sets of type ω are characterized by the property of having no last element and satisfying the mathematical induction principle [axiom (c)]. In the present section we study a related principle and its relation to well-ordering.

3.1.1   Definition. If S is a simply ordered set and $s \,\varepsilon\, S$, then by S/s we denote the set $\{x \mid x < s\}$, and by s/S the set $S - S/s$; each of these being considered sets ordered relative to the same binary relation $<$ with respect to which S is simply ordered. We call S/s the *section of S determined by s.*

Axiom (b) of 2.1 stipulates that all sections of the set N are finite.

If the set S of 3.1.1 has a first element a, then evidently $S/a = \emptyset$ and $a/S = S$. And, if S is well-ordered, then both S/a and a/S are well-ordered sets. The latter statement is a particular case of

† In the sense that its hypothetical "if" requires more than the corresponding part of (c).

3.1.2   *If W is a well-ordered set with respect to some binary relation $<$, then every subset W' of W is well-ordered with respect to the same relation $<$.*

In the sequel, when we speak of a *well-ordered subset W' of a well-ordered set W*, we shall mean the set W' of 3.1.2, unless another ordering is specified.

(3a)   Transfinite induction principle. A simply ordered set W is said to *satisfy the transfinite induction principle* provided that: (1) W has a first element, and (2) if W_1 is a subset of W which contains the first element of W, and which is such that, if W_1 contains a section W/w then it contains w, then $W_1 = W$. The property (2) is called the *transfinite induction principle*.

3.1.3   Theorem. *In order that a non-empty simply ordered set W should be well-ordered, it is necessary and sufficient that W satisfy the transfinite induction principle.*

Proof of necessity. That W has a first element, w_1, follows from Definition (2b). Let W_1 be a subset of W satisfying the "if" part of (3a). Suppose $W - W_1 \neq \emptyset$. Then by Definition (2b), $W - W_1$ has a first element, w. As w is the first element not in W_1, $W/w \subset W_1$. But then, by (3a), $w \, \varepsilon \, W_1$, which contradicts the definition of w. We conclude, then, that $W = W_1$.

Proof of sufficiency. Let W be a non-empty simply ordered set satisfying the transfinite induction principle. To show W well-ordered, we have to show that, if W' is a non-empty subset of W, then W' has a first element. Suppose not. Then let us define a subset W_1 of W as follows: $W_1 = \{x \mid (x \, \varepsilon \, W) \, \& \, (x < W')\}$. Then W_1 contains w_1, the first element of W, else w_1 is the first element of W'. And, if $w \, \varepsilon \, W$ is such that $W/w \subset W_1$, then $w \, \varepsilon \, W_1$, since otherwise w would be the first element of W'. But then W_1 satisfies the hypothetical "if" portion of (3a), so that $W_1 = W$. But this implies $W' = \emptyset$, contradicting the non-empty character of W'. We conclude, then, that W' has a first element.

3.1.4   Proof by transfinite induction

Just as the mathematical induction principle is used to demonstrate that *all* elements of a type ω sequence have a certain property (see III 5.2.1 for instance), so is the transfinite induction principle used to show that all elements of a well-ordered set possess a given property. It should be noted, incidentally, that, in case W is of order type ω, then the transfinite induction principle becomes identical with the mathematical induction principle (III 5.1, axiom 4).†

If it is desired to prove that all elements of a given denumerable set S have a certain property P, then the proof may take the following form: As S is denumerable, its elements may be put in the form of a type ω sequence:

$$x_1, x_2, \cdots, x_n, \cdots.$$

We then prove that x_1 has property P, and that, if for any n an x_n has property P, so will x_{n+1} too. That all elements of S have property P then follows from the mathematical induction principle; for, if we form a set G consisting of all elements that have property P, then, as we have shown, $x_1 \varepsilon G$, and $x_n \varepsilon G$ implies $x_{n+1} \varepsilon G$, and hence by the mathematical induction principle $G = S$. This is called *proof by mathematical induction*, and we have already used it in the proof of Theorem 5.2.1 in Chapter III.

Now suppose that W is any set whatsoever, and we wish to prove that all its elements have a certain property P. Even though W may be uncountable, it may be that for certain reasons (which we do not go into at present) W can be assigned a well-ordering (2.4.1). And then, with W well-ordered, it may be that we can prove that: (1) the first element, w_1, of W has property P; (2) if for any element w of W, all elements of W/w in the well-ordering have property P, then w has property P. We may then conclude that *all* elements of W have property P. For, by Theorem 3.1.3, the well-ordering of W satisfies the transfinite induction principle, and hence, if we form a set W_1 by placing an element of W in W_1 if it has property P, it will follow from the transfinite induction principle that $W_1 = W$ (as in the case of G and S above). This type of proof is called *proof by transfinite induction*, and it evidently has proof by mathematical induction for type ω sequences as a special case.

3.1.5 Definition by transfinite induction

If for every $n \varepsilon N$ we wish to define a mathematical entity E_n, we frequently (1) define E_1, and (2) define E_{n+1} in terms of E_n; often E_{n+1} is defined in terms of several or all of the terms $E_1, E_2, \cdots, E_n$ [as for example in sequences $\{u_n\}$ where $u_{n+1} = (u_n + u_{n-1})/2$]. We used this type of definition in III 5.3, for instance; it is called *definition by induction*. Its justification by means of the mathematical induction principle is similar to the argument of 3.1.4.

---

† As a matter of fact, proofs concerning ω sequences frequently assume the property embodied in the transfinite induction principle.

And, as in 3.1.4, we can use the transfinite induction principle to justify *definition by transfinite induction*. Let W be a well-ordered collection, and suppose that we define some mathematical entity $E(w_1)$, w_1 being the first element of W; if we then give, for each $w \, \varepsilon \, W$, a definition $E(w)$ in terms of the section W/w or its elements, we may conclude from the transfinite induction principle that we have defined an $E(w)$ corresponding to *every* $w \, \varepsilon \, W$. This procedure is called definition by transfinite induction, and again definition by induction for sequences of type ω is a special case.

3.1.6   Application to existence of a "Hamel basis" for R

It may prove enlightening to exemplify the methods indicated above. They are to be classed among the most important mathematical procedures, and examples of their use in modern mathematics are numerous. Unfortunately most of these examples pertain to subjects that are highly technical and do not, therefore, lend themselves readily to purposes of exemplification. This is not the case, however, with the definition by transfinite induction of the existence of a Hamel basis for the collection, R, of all real numbers, which we shall exhibit below.

First, it is necessary to know that there exists a well-ordering for the collection R. For this, we appeal to the well-known theorem of Zermelo [a, b], the *complete* proof of which we shall defer for the present (see 5.1.4), but for which we *indicate* the general outline of a proof which may suffice for those readers who do not care to read the detailed proof to be given later.†

3.1.6.1   Well-ordering Theorem (Theorem of Zermelo). *If S is any set whatsoever, then there exists a well-ordering ‡ of S.*

Indication of proof. Let $\mathfrak{S} = 2^S - \{\emptyset\}$; then, as the elements S_ν of $\mathfrak{S}$ are non-empty sets, there exists by III 6.4 a set $\mathfrak{R}$ whose elements are pairs (S_ν, x_ν) in which $x_\nu \, \varepsilon \, S_\nu$, and such that each $S_\nu \, \varepsilon \, \mathfrak{S}$ occurs in one and only one pair. Denote each x_ν by $x(S_\nu)$; thus $x(S)$ is the representative element of S itself.

Now a non-empty well-ordered set W whose elements are also elements of S will be called a WS-sequence, if, for every element w of W,

---

† The proof indicated here is not that to be given later; see Zermelo [a], Kamke [Ka; 130ff], [Ka₁; 112f].

‡ Cf. 2.4.1. Notice that we do not say "one can well-order S," which might be taken to imply that there exists an effective procedure for the well-ordering; since the latter does not at present exist in the lterature, we use the "non-committal" "there exists . . ."

$x(S - W/w) = w$.[†]   In particular, $w_1 = x(S)$ is a WS-sequence and, moreover, the first element of every WS-sequence is w_1 [since, for the first element w of a WS-sequence, $W/w = \emptyset$ and hence $x(S - W/w) = x(S) = w_1$]. Furthermore, of two different WS-sequences, one is always a section of the other, so that, if $x, y \,\varepsilon\, S$ that lie in some WS-sequence W, we can define $x < y$ to mean that $x < y$ in W. Then it can be shown that the collection of all elements of S that lie in WS-sequences is well-ordered with respect to this binary relation $<$, and, finally, that *every* element of S lies in a WS-sequence, thus giving a well-ordering of S.

3.1.6.2   Definition. A collection B of real numbers is called a *basis* for R if (1) the elements of B are independent in the sense that there exists no relation of the form

(3.1.6.2a) $$\sum_{i=1}^{n} f_i b_i = 0$$

in which $b_i \,\varepsilon\, B$, $f_i \,\varepsilon\, F$ (the set of all rational numbers), and no f_i is zero; (2) if r is any real number not zero, then there exists a relation

(3.1.6.2b) $$r = \sum_{i=1}^{n} f_i b_i, \qquad 0 \neq f_i \,\varepsilon\, F, \; b_i \,\varepsilon\, B.$$

Condition (2) could be expressed alternatively: If r is any real number not zero, then the elements of $B \cup \{r\}$ are not independent in the sense of (1).

3.1.6.3   Theorem (Hamel).[‡]   *There exists a basis for R.*

Proof. By Theorem 3.1.6.1 there exists a well-ordering, W, of R. We then define a subset B of R as follows: Using the method of transfinite induction, we first define for each element w of W a set $B(w)$ as follows: (1) if the first element of W is the number zero, we delete it from W; then, for the first element, w_1, of (the new) W, we define $B(w_1) = \{w_1\}$; (2) having defined $B(w)$ for all elements of a section W/w_ν, let $B'(w_\nu) = \bigcup_{w < w_\nu} B(w)$; then we define $B(w_\nu) = \emptyset$ or $\{w_\nu\}$ according as there does or does not exist a relation of the type (3.1.6.2a) between elements b_i of the set $B'(w_\nu) \cup \{w_\nu\}$. This defines $B(w)$ for all elements of W. Finally, let $B = \bigcup_{w \,\varepsilon\, W} B(w)$. We assert that B is a basis for R. The proof of this will be left to the reader (Problem 11).

[†] Cf. 3.1.1. Although W/w is more than just a set—namely a set together with an order relation—we shall use it as though it were just a set in set operations such as $S - W/w$, rather than to introduce a new symbol to denote the collection of its elements.

[‡] This theorem was originally proved by G. Hamel [a].

3.1.6.4   Theorem 3.1.6.3 was introduced by Hamel in order to show the existence of discontinuous solutions $f(x)$ of the functional equation

(3.1.6.4a) $f(x + y) = f(x) + f(y)$

where $f(x)$ is a single-valued real function of a real variable (i.e., a mapping of R into R in the sense of IV 3.2.3.1). Cauchy had noted that the only *continuous* function satisfying (3.1.6.4a) is the function $f(x) = cx$, where c is a constant. However, without the continuity restriction, Hamel showed that the equation has infinitely many solutions. For example, we may define $f(x)$ quite arbitrarily for the elements of the basis B, and let $f(0) = 0$. Then, for an $r \, \varepsilon \, R$ not in B, there is a relation of type (3.1.6.2b), which is easily shown to be unique because of the properties of a basis (3.1.6.2). By placing $f(r) = \sum_{i=1}^{n} f_i f(b_i)$, the function $f(x)$ is defined for all $x \, \varepsilon \, R$ and is easily shown to satisfy the required condition (3.1.6.4a).†

3.1.7   Application to comparability of well-ordered sets

We shall next show, by transfinite induction, that, given two well-ordered sets, either there exists a (1-1)-correspondence between their elements that preserves order, or there exists an order-preserving (1-1)-correspondence between the elements of one and the elements of a *section* of the other; and, moreover, that this correspondence is unique.

3.1.7.1   Theorem. *Let W and W' be well-ordered sets. Then either W and W' are of the same order type, or one is of the same order type as a section of the other.*

If W is empty, the theorem holds trivially. Otherwise, let w_1 be the first element of W; then either all elements of W' are already in order-preserving (1-1)-correspondence with elements of W/w_1 (meaning $W' = \emptyset$) or not; if they are not, pair w_1 with the first element w_1' of W'. In general, if $w \, \varepsilon \, W$ and each element of W/w is already paired with some element of W', then either all elements of W' are already in order-preserving (1-1)-correspondence with elements of W/w or not; if they are not, we pair w with the first element of W' not already paired with elements of W. By the transfinite induction principle, either all elements of W' are paired in this manner with elements of W, or conversely. We leave the details of the proof to the reader.

3.1.7.2   Theorem. *If W/w_1 and W/w_2 are different sections of a well-ordered set W, then they are of different order types.*

Proof. Suppose $w_1 < w_2$. If w_1 is the first element of W, the theorem follows trivially. Otherwise, suppose that it holds for each element, w_1, of a section W/w', where w' is not the first element of W. Then it holds for w'. For suppose not, and hence that there exists a

---

† This result has interesting applications in topology, showing the existence of certain "pathological" configurations; see Jones [a], for instance.

(1-1)-correspondence T, preserving order, between the elements of W/w' and the elements of some section W/w_2 such that $w' < w_2$. Let the element of W/w' that is paired with w' (as an element of W/w_2) in T be denoted by v'. But then W/v' and W/w' are of the same order type (according to T), in contradiction of the supposition that the theorem holds for all elements of W/w'. The theorem now follows by the transfinite induction principle.

3.1.7.3   Corollary. *No well-ordered set W is of the same order type as one of its sections.*

Proof. Augment W by a new element e, and define $w < e$ for all $w \, \varepsilon \, W$; apply 3.1.7.2.

3.1.7.4   Theorem. *If W and W' are non-empty well-ordered sets, then the order-preserving (1-1)-correspondence implied by Theorem 3.1.7.1 is unique.*

3.2   Ordinal numbers

(3.2b)   Definition. The order types of well-ordered sets are called *ordinal numbers*. The ordinal number of a well-ordered set W is the order type of which W is an element, and may be denoted, following Cantor, by $\overline{W}$.

3.2.1   Symbols for ordinal numbers

Since a *finite* set, when simply ordered, is of a unique order type, and this is a well-ordering type, we may use the symbols for the cardinal numbers of the finite sets as ordinal numbers also. Thus, to say that the ordinal number of a set is n, $n \, \varepsilon \, N$, is to imply that it is of order type n (1.1.2) (hence the term *n-ple*). The ordinal number of the null set is denoted by 0.

However, in view of the fact that an infinite set may be so ordered as to belong to more than one well-ordering type (cf. 1.1.1 and 2.4.4 for example), the cardinal number symbols for infinite sets cannot be used to denote ordinal numbers. It would be meaningless, for instance, to speak of a set "having the ordinal number $\aleph_0$." It was in recognition of this fact that a special symbol, ω, was introduced above for the order type of the natural numbers in their natural order. Order types $\omega + n$, $n \, \varepsilon \, N$, have also been mentioned above (Section 3), as well as $\omega + \omega$. The latter may be denoted by $\omega \cdot 2$, however, since, if 2 is understood as the ordinal number 2, $\omega \cdot 2$ becomes $\omega + \omega$ in accordance with the following definition:

3.2.1.1   Definition. If ω_1 and ω_2 are ordinal numbers, then the *product* $\omega_1 \cdot \omega_2$ is the symbol for the order type of the well-ordered set obtained by replacing each element of a well-ordered set O_2 of ordinal number ω_2 by a well-ordered set O_1 of ordinal number ω_1; the order in the new set agreeing with the original order between elements of the replacement sets O_1, and with that of O_2 between elements of different replacement sets.†

Hence $2 \cdot \omega$ would be ω, since by the above definition it is the order type obtained by replacing each element n of N by an ordered pair (n_1, n_2). Likewise, $n \cdot \omega$ is the same as ω, but $\omega \cdot n$ is the order type obtained from n successive sequences of type ω. The symbols $\omega \cdot \omega$, $\omega \cdot \omega \cdot \omega$, . . . , are usually replaced respectively by ω^2, ω^3, ...‡

3.2.1.2   A simple example of order type ω^2 is obtained by ordering the natural numbers in the following manner: (1) Arrange the numbers that are *not* powers of primes in their natural order; thus, 6, 10, 12, $\cdots$. Call this sequence S_1. (2) Arrange the powers of 2 in their natural order; thus, 2, 4, 8, $\cdots$. Call this sequence S_2. $(n + 1)$ In general, arrange the powers of the nth prime, p_n, in their natural order,§ and call the resulting sequence S_{n+1}. Retaining the natural order in each S_n, if $n, n' \, \varepsilon \, N$ such that $n < n'$, we let $S_n < S_{n'}$; thus $12 < 4$, $4 < 3$, etc.

3.2.2   Ordering of the ordinal numbers

Suppose ω_1 and ω_2 are ordinal numbers, and let $O_1 \, \varepsilon \, \omega_1$, $O_2 \, \varepsilon \, \omega_2$. By $\omega_1 = \omega_2$ we mean "$=$" as for the *sets* ω_1, ω_2 (III 3.1.3). If $\omega_1 \neq \omega_2$, then O_1 and O_2 are not of the same order type, so that (Theorem 3.1.7.1) O_1, say, is of the same order type as a section of O_2. Then we write $\omega_1 < \omega_2$. That this definition of $<$ satisfies the simple order axioms (II 7) follows from the results stated in 3.1.7.

Furthermore, if Φ is any collection of ordinal numbers, then there exists a smallest element in Φ. For let $\overline{W} \, \varepsilon \, \Phi$, and suppose $\overline{W}$ not the smallest element of Φ. Then, with $W \, \varepsilon \, \overline{W}$, every element $\overline{W}'$ of Φ such that $\overline{W}' < \overline{W}$ is represented by a section W/w' of W. But, as W is well-ordered, the elements w' appearing in such sections W/w' have a first element w_1' in W and the corresponding W/w_1' is of an order type $\overline{W}_1'$ which is the smallest in Φ. And we can state

---

† Thus, if $x < y$ in O_2, then, for every element x_1 of the O_1 replacing x and every element y_1 of the O_1 replacing y, $x_1 < y_1$.

‡ We shall not go into the complete arithmetic of ordinal numbers, however; as in the case of cardinal numbers, the reader is referred to Sierpinski [S₁; VIII, X].

§ We assume the fundamental number-theoretic theorem that the number of primes is infinite; see Courant and Robbins [C-R; 22–23].

3.2.2.1   *Every collection of ordinal numbers is well-ordered by the above definition of $<$.*

We may glimpse the "march of the ordinal numbers" by considering them in the order defined above:

$$(3.2.2a)\quad 0, 1, 2, \cdots, n, \cdots; \omega, \omega + 1, \cdots, \omega + n, \cdots; \omega\cdot 2, \omega\cdot 2 + 1,$$

$$\cdots, \omega\cdot 2 + n, \cdots; \cdots; \omega\cdot n, \cdots; \omega^2, \omega^2 + 1, \cdots; \omega^2 + \omega,$$

$$\omega^2 + \omega + 1, \cdots; \cdots; \omega^n, \omega^n + 1, \cdots; \cdots$$

If the reader will refer to IV 3, he will now see the origin of the subscripts that were used to differentiate the various sequences of irrational numbers constructed there. Notice that *each ordinal number is the order type of the well-ordered set of ordinal numbers that precede it.*

3.2.2.2   *Every ordinal number α is the order type of the well-ordered set B of all ordinal numbers β such that $\beta < \alpha$.*

Proof. Let $W \varepsilon \alpha$. Consider any ordinal number $\beta < \alpha$, and let $B \varepsilon \beta$. Then, by definition, B is of the same order type as a section W/b of W. Conversely, an element b of W determines a section W/b having an ordinal number β such that $\beta \neq \alpha$ (by Corollary 3.1.7.3) and hence such that $\beta < \alpha$.

The pairs (β, b) constitute a (1-1)-correspondence between the elements of B and the elements of W. This correspondence is order-preserving. For example, if $\beta' < \beta < \alpha$, then, since W/b as defined above is of order type β, for any $B' \varepsilon \beta'$ there is a section of W/b determined by an element b' that is of order type β'; this section is also a section of W and $b' < b$. That conversely a relation $b' < b$ implies a correspondence relation $\beta' < \beta$ will follow from the fact that W/b' is a section of W/b.

It should also be noticed that the procedure followed in IV 3 virtually forced the generation of a well-ordered collection of numbers. As a matter of fact, this was the type of procedure which led Cantor to the study of well-orderings,† and it is a common form of application of the well-ordering idea and ordinal number symbols.

Notice, too, that all the symbols specifically stated in (3.2.2a) designate order types whose elements are *countable* sets (cf. Theorem IV 3.1.6). Indeed, one derives the feeling, as one studies the "march

---

† The procedure referred to here was the generation of successive *derived sets* or *derivatives* of point sets; an ω-type sequence of such derivatives generally does not exhaust the set of different derivatives, so that it is necessary to go on to "transfinite derivatives." The successive derivatives, in any case, form a well-ordered collection. See Hobson [Ho; §§ 52–54, 57, 68].

of the ordinal numbers," that they never seem to reach the "uncount-able stage." Yet we have shown that R is uncountable (IV 1.4) and that there exists a well-ordering of R (3.1.6.1—the Well-ordering Theo-rem). Hence the "march" must continue to ordinal numbers repre-senting uncountable sets! Furthermore, by 3.2.2.1 there must be a *first* such ordinal, which we may designate by ω_1. Does ω_1 correspond to a well-ordering of R? We return to this question below.

3.2.3   The Burali-Forti antinomy

In III 1.1 we mentioned the announcement by Burali-Forti in 1897 of the existence of contradiction in the "unrestricted" theory of sets.[†] As usually formulated, the Burali-Forti antinomy consists of the argu-ment that, if we allow a "set Γ of all ordinal numbers," then Γ must be well-ordered by 3.2.2.1 and hence itself have an order type; but this is impossible, since, if ω' is any order type, then there is an order type $\omega' + 1$ (obtained by adding a new element to any set of order type ω', as in 2.4.4 for instance). Thus if γ is the ordinal number of Γ, then, since $\gamma + 1 \; \varepsilon \; \Gamma$, we should have $\gamma + 1 < \gamma$!

3.3   The alephs; the continuum problem

Because of the Well-ordering Theorem (3.1.6.1), and because of the existence of uncountable infinite sets $(R, \; 2^R, \; \cdots)$ of various cardinal numbers, the ordinal numbers are divided into distinct categories ac-cording to the "cardinality" of the sets occurring as elements of the various order types. The cardinal numbers corresponding to these categories are called "alephs," aleph being the Hebrew "capital A" —$\aleph$. We have already used the symbol $\aleph_0$ to designate the cardinal number of denumerable sets; and, since all the transfinite (meaning $\geqq \omega$) ordinal numbers specifically designated in (3.2.2a) correspond to denumerable sets, the latter numbers must all be in the $\aleph_0$ category, or *class* (which is the term usually employed in this connection).

By convention, the so-called *finite* ordinals, $0, 1, 2, \cdots, n, \cdots$, are put into one class called the *first class* of ordinals; this is the only class containing ordinals corresponding to sets of different cardinality. The *second class* of ordinals consists of all those ordinals that correspond to sets containing $\aleph_0$ elements, namely $\omega, \; \omega + 1, \; \cdots; \; \omega \cdot 2, \; \cdots; \; \cdots;$ that is, if ω' is an ordinal in the second class, and $W \; \varepsilon \; \omega'$, then $\overline{\overline{W}} = \aleph_0$.

Now (cf. 3.2.2.1) let ω_1 denote the first (in the order defined in 3.2.2) ordinal such that, if $W \; \varepsilon \; \omega_1$, then W is uncountable. Let $\aleph_1$ denote the cardinal number of such a W. Then all ordinal numbers ω' such

---

† In [a], Bernstein stated that Cantor was already aware of this contradiction in 1895 and communicated it by letter to Hilbert in 1896.

that, for $W \varepsilon \omega'$, $\overline{\overline{W}} = \aleph_1$ constitute the *third* class of ordinals. We call $\aleph_1$ the cardinal number corresponding to the third class of ordinals (and $\aleph_0$ the cardinal number corresponding to the second class of ordinals). Continuing in this manner, we obtain a series of alephs, $\aleph_0, \aleph_1, \aleph_2, \cdots$ corresponding to distinct classes of ordinal numbers.

We shall not go into all the ramifications of this theory and its relation to the ordinal numbers,† but shall be content to point out some of its consequences that are of greatest significance for our purposes.

Not all mathematicians, as for instance the intuitionists (cf. Chapter X), admit the existence of ordinal numbers of arbitrarily large class; not even, indeed, the set of all ordinals of the second class. See Lusin [L; 27], and Borel's preface to Sierpinski [S_1], for example.

3.3.1   In the first place, because of the Well-ordering Theorem *every cardinal number is an aleph*. For, if S is any set, then by the Well-ordering Theorem there exists a well-ordered set W whose elements are the elements of S. Hence the cardinal number of W, which is an aleph, is the same as the cardinal number of S.

3.3.2   In the second place, the possibility (4.2.8d) of Chapter IV cannot occur, since, of two alephs, one must be $\leqq$ the other (this follows directly, of course, from the Well-ordering Theorem and Theorem 3.1.7.1, with the A and B of IV (4.2.8d) forming the W and W' of the latter theorem). We express this fact by saying that every two sets are *comparable*; and that the principle involved, namely that IV (4.2.8d) is impossible, is *comparability*. It should be noticed that, if we use $\Rightarrow$ for implication—$A \Rightarrow B$ meaning A implies B—then we have

(3.3.2a)   Choice Axiom $\Rightarrow$ Well-ordering Theorem $\Rightarrow$ Comparability.

The power of the choice axiom becomes more and more evident!

3.3.3   The continuum problem; continuum hypothesis

Thirdly (recalling the question raised in IV 4.2.9.1), where, in relation to the other cardinal numbers, does the cardinal number c stand, from the standpoint of $<$ (IV 4.2)? In particular, is $c = \aleph_1$? This is known as the continuum problem, and may also be formulated as the query: Has every infinite subset of R either the cardinal number $\aleph_0$ or the cardinal number c? Two proofs that the answer is affirmative have been published,‡ but these have not been generally accepted as definitive.§

† See, however, Sierpinski [S_1; XI].

‡ D. Hilbert [a] and F. Bernstein [b]. Hilbert's paper also appears as Anhang VIII (pp. 262–288) in the appendix of [H_2].

§ For example, Sierpinski [S_1; 210f] remarks, "à mon avis, la démonstration de M. Hilbert ne peut être regardée comme suffisante."

Cantor conjectured that $c = \aleph_1$, and it has been found that a large number of mathematical theorems, some of them very important, can be based on the hypothesis that the conjecture really holds. It has become customary to call this conjecture "the continuum hypothesis." Some theorems turn out to be *equivalent* to the continuum hypothesis; others which originally were proved on the basis of the hypothesis have subsequently been proved without its use. In no case has a theorem based upon it ever been shown to be false. In spite of this, it is felt by some mathematicians that the hypothesis is probably false.† Others feel that it is impossible to prove or disprove it on the basis of ordinary set theory; that it constitutes an independent axiom. However, Gödel has shown ‡ that, if its generalized form (see next paragraph) be added to a certain well-known axiom system for set theory, along with the choice axiom, then any contradiction that might be implied by these axioms could be transformed into a contradiction implied by the axioms for set theory alone!

Since $c = 2^{\aleph_0}$ (IV (4.2.4a)), the continuum hypothesis may be stated in the form $\aleph_1 = 2^{\aleph_0}$. One may, then, state a generalized continuum hypothesis in the form of the assumption that $\aleph_{\alpha+1} = 2^{\aleph_\alpha}$ for all cardinal numbers $\aleph_\alpha$. Without the Well-ordering Theorem, the hypothesis would of course take the form: If e is a cardinal number $\geq \aleph_0$, then there exists no cardinal number m such that $e < m < 2^e$.

For a discussion of these hypotheses and their relations to other mathematical principles and theorems, the reader is referred to Sierpinski [S₂]. For a hypothesis alternative to the continuum hypothesis, namely $2^{\aleph_0} = 2^{\aleph_1}$, see Lusin [a] and Sierpinski [a].

It has recently been shown by Sierpinski [b] that the generalized continuum hypothesis implies the Choice Axiom.§

4 The second class of ordinals

If the order type ω is the most important of the order types of well-ordered infinite sets, then it is probably true that the order type ω_1 is the second most important.‖ For instance, it is a fruitful source of examples, such as models for axiom systems (we see an instance of this

---

† See Gödel [a] for comment and references. On p. 524, loc. cit., Gödel remarks ". . . one may on good reason suspect that the role of the continuum problem in set theory will be this, that it will finally lead to the discovery of new axioms which will make it possible to disprove Cantor's conjecture."

‡ K. Gödel, [G].

§ Sierpinski remarks that this result was previously announced, without proof, by A. Lindenbaum and A. Tarski, in 1926.

‖ That is, important from the standpoint of frequency of application, number and importance of theorems dependent thereon, etc.

below in VI 1.2.6.2). And it may be expected that, in any method of proof which makes use of the continuum hypothesis, the collection of all ordinals of the first and second classes may be involved. For, inasmuch as the order type of this class is ω_1, the set R may (using the continuum hypothesis) be well-ordered so as to be of type ω_1.†

It is useful, therefore, to know some of its chief properties. One of these is expressed in the following:

4.1   Theorem. *No well-ordered set of type ω_1 is spanned* (2.3.1) *by a countable subset.*

Proof. Suppose that W is a well-ordered set of type ω_1 and that W_1 is a countable subset of W that spans the latter. As W_1 is countable, we may order its elements in a type ω sequence

(4.1a) $$x_1, x_2, \cdots, x_n, \cdots,$$

although this is of course *not* necessarily the order in which these elements occur in W.

Now, for each n, the set $W(x_n) = x_n \cup W/x_n$ (3.1.1) is countable. Also, as *sets* the W's satisfy the relation $W = \bigcup_{n=1}^{\infty} W(x_n)$. But this implies, by virtue of Theorem IV 3.1.6, that W is denumerable. As W is of type ω_1, however, it is uncountable.

4.2   An axiomatic characterization of type ω_1

The result of the preceding section can be used to give an axiomatic characterization of sets of type ω_1:

Let W_1 be any set and $<$ a binary relation between elements of W_1 such that

(a) W_1 is well-ordered with respect to the relation $<$.
(b) If $a \ \varepsilon \ W_1$, then the section W_1/a is countable.
(c) No countable subset of W_1 spans W_1.

(Compare this with the characterization of type ω in 2.1.) We leave to the reader (Problem 12) the proof that this is a categorical axiom system characterizing sets of type ω_1.

4.3   One can define limits for ordinal numbers as follows:

4.3.1   Definition. A (type ω) sequence of ordinal numbers,

(4.3.1a) $$\alpha_1, \alpha_2, \cdots, \alpha_n, \cdots$$

is called an *increasing sequence* if $\alpha_n < \alpha_{n+1}$ for all n.

---

† Just as, for example, when we wish a well-ordering of a denumerable set (such as F), we usually select a type ω sequence for it, rather than an $\omega + 1$, $\omega \cdot 2$, or ω^2 sequence.

4.3.2   Definition. An ordinal number α is called the *limit* of an increasing sequence (4.3.1a) if, for every ordinal number $\beta < \alpha$, all but a finite number of the α_n satisfy the relation $\beta < \alpha_n < \alpha$.†

And we can then state:

4.3.3   Theorem. *Every increasing sequence of ordinals of the first and second class has a limit of the second class.*

Proof. Consider any increasing sequence (4.3.1a). By Theorem 3.2.2.2, the ordinals of the first and second classes form a well-ordered set of type ω_1, and, by Theorem 4.1, there exist ordinals of the first or second class which are preceded by *all* elements of (4.3.1a). Of these there is a first in the order defined in 3.2.2; denote it by α. Evidently $\omega \leqq \alpha$ [cf. axiom (b) of 2.1], so that α is of the second class.

If β is an ordinal number such that $\beta < \alpha$, then there exists an α_n such that $\beta \leqq \alpha_n$; for otherwise α would not fulfill the condition stated in its definition. Then, for all $m > n$, $\beta < \alpha_m < \alpha$.

4.3.4   Definition. If an ordinal number has an immediate predecessor, we call it an ordinal number *of the first kind;* by convention we also term the number 0 of the first kind. All numbers not of the first kind we call *of the second kind.*

4.3.5   Theorem. *Every ordinal number α of the second class which is of the second kind is the limit of an increasing sequence of type* (4.3.1a).

Proof. The number α, being of the second class, designates the order type of a well-ordered set of cardinal number $\aleph_0$; in particular, the ordinals β such that $\beta < \alpha$ form a denumerable set, and may be rearranged in a sequence

$$(4.3.5a) \qquad \beta_1, \beta_2, \cdots, \beta_n, \cdots$$

of type ω (the order in this sequence being *not* necessarily that of the numbers in the sense of 3.2.2).

Form a sequence $\{\alpha_n\}$ as follows: Let α_1 be β_1. As α has no immediate predecessor, there is an ordinal α' such that $\alpha_1 < \alpha' < \alpha$; and, as α' is in the sequence (4.3.5a), we can define a number α_2 as the β_i, say $\beta_{n(1)}$, of *smallest* subscript $n(1)$, which satisfies the relation $\alpha_1 < \beta_{n(1)} < \alpha$.

In general, having defined α_k, we let α_{k+1} be the β_i, say $\beta_{n(k)}$, of smallest subscript $n(k)$, such that $\alpha_n < \beta_{n(k)} < \alpha$. This defines, by induction, a sequence $\{\alpha_n\}$ of type (4.3.1a).

† Cf. Problem 14.

We assert that α is the limit of this sequence. For suppose not. Then there is an ordinal number $\beta < \alpha$ such that, for all n, $\alpha_n < \beta$. Now β is an element of (4.3.5a), say β_m. Let $\alpha_{n'}$ be the last β_n that precedes β_m in the sequence (4.3.5a)—then $\alpha_{n'} = \beta_{n(n'-1)}$, and the number $\alpha_{n'+1} = \beta_{n(n')}$ comes *after* β_m in the sequence (4.3.5a). However, since $\alpha_{n'} < \beta_m < \alpha$, the choice of $\beta_{n(n')}$ for $\alpha_{n'+1}$ is contrary to the rule that it have the smallest subscript satisfying the required relation to $\alpha_{n'}$ and α. Hence the supposition that α is not the limit of the sequence $\{\alpha_n\}$ leads to contradiction.

5   Equivalence of Choice Axiom, Well-ordering Theorem, and Comparability

In 3.1.6.1 we gave an outline of a proof that the Choice Axiom implies the Well-ordering Theorem. And in 3.3.2 we saw that the latter implies comparability; i.e., of two arbitrary sets A and B, one at least has the same cardinal number as a subset of the other. In this section we shall show the actual equivalence of all three of these properties of sets.

5.1   Let us first notice the more obvious implications. Thus in 3.3.2 we observed that comparability is a direct result of the Well-ordering Theorem, since, if we take the two given sets A and B in well-ordered form and apply Theorem 3.1.7.1 (which states that one of these sets is then of the same order type as the other or as a section of the other), we obtain immediately a (1-1)-correspondence between the elements of one and the elements of a subset of the other.

5.1.1   Similarly, the implication

$$\text{Well-ordering Theorem} \Rightarrow \text{Choice Axiom}$$

is virtually immediate.† For (using the symbols of III 6.3), if $\mathfrak{S}$ is a collection of disjoint non-empty sets S_ν, let $S = \bigcup_\nu S_\nu$. By the Well-ordering Theorem there exists a well-ordered set W whose elements are the elements of S. Since W is well-ordered, every non-empty subset of W has a first element, so that now we can *define* the representative element of S_ν to be the *first* element of S_ν in the well-ordered set W.

† This was pointed out by É. Borel [a] upon the appearance of Zermelo's first paper [a]. And as a consequence Borel expressed the opinion that Zermelo's Well-ordering Theorem was therefore only to be considered as part of the proof of the *equivalence* of the two properties, not as a proof *establishing* the possibility of well-ordering every set; the latter would demand, in Borel's opinion, an effective procedure for well-ordering.

5.1.2   We already have, then, the implications

(5.1.2a)   Choice Axiom $\Leftarrow$ Well-ordering Theorem $\Rightarrow$ Comparability.

And in order to complete the proof of the equivalence of all three properties we have to show that the implication arrows in (5.1.2a) can be reversed.

5.1.3   Comparability $\Rightarrow$ Well-ordering Theorem.† We let the reader prove the following lemmas, which follow quickly from the definition of well-ordering.

5.1.3.1   Lemma. *If W is a simply ordered set such that for every $w \varepsilon W$ the set W/w is a well-ordered subset of W, then W is well-ordered.*

5.1.3.2   Lemma. *If W and W' are well-ordered sets such that there exists an order-preserving (1-1)-correspondence between the elements of W and the sections of W' (where $W'/w_1 < W'/w_2$ if $w_1 < w_2$), then W and W' are of the same order type.*

5.1.3.3   Let S be any non-empty set, and let us consider all the possible well-orderings of subsets W of S. These form a collection $\mathfrak{W}$, non-empty, since, if $s \varepsilon S$, then $\{s\}$ is a well-ordered subset of S. In $\mathfrak{W}$, order-preserving (1-1)-correspondence is an equivalence relation $\approx$ (II 8). Let K be the collection of classes which are elements of the class decomposition (II 8.5) of $\mathfrak{W}$ corresponding to this $\approx$.

The collection K forms a well-ordered set, which we shall continue to call K, if, for $\mathfrak{f}_1, \mathfrak{f}_2 \varepsilon$ K we let $\mathfrak{f}_1 < \mathfrak{f}_2$ if and only if, for $W_1 \varepsilon \mathfrak{f}_1$, $W_2 \varepsilon \mathfrak{f}_2$, there is a section W_2/x_2 such that $W_1 \approx W_2/x_2$—in brief, if, and only if, there is a $W_2/x_2 \varepsilon \mathfrak{f}_1$. For consider any $\mathfrak{f}_2 \varepsilon$ K. If $\mathfrak{f}_1 < \mathfrak{f}_2$, and $W_2 \varepsilon \mathfrak{f}_2$, the W_2/x_2 defined above is unique by virtue of Theorem 3.1.7.2. Conversely, a W_2/x_2 determines a unique class $\mathfrak{f}_1$ such that $W_2/x_2 \varepsilon \mathfrak{f}_1$. Hence the collection $\{\mathfrak{f}_1 \mid \mathfrak{f}_1 < \mathfrak{f}_2\}$ is of the same order type as W_2/x_2, hence well-ordered. Then since $\mathfrak{f}_2$ was arbitrary, the collection K is well-ordered by Lemma 5.1.3.1.

Each $W_2 \varepsilon \mathfrak{f}_2 \varepsilon$ K is of the same order type as the section K$/\mathfrak{f}_2$. For, as we have just shown, for any $\mathfrak{f}_1 < \mathfrak{f}_2$ there is a corresponding section $W_2/x_2 \varepsilon \mathfrak{f}_1$, etc., and that K$/\mathfrak{f}_2$ and W_2 are of the same order type follows from Lemma 5.1.3.2. It follows that K *cannot be of the same cardinal number as S or as any subset of S.* For, if K did have the same cardinal number as a subset S_1 of S, then S_1 would have a well-ordering which we denote by W_1, and hence there would exist a $\mathfrak{f}_1 \varepsilon$ K such that $W_1 \varepsilon \mathfrak{f}_1$. But W_1, as just shown, is of the same order

† The proof given in this section is due to Hartogs [a].

type as the section K/f_1. It would then follow, from the transitivity of the relation of having the same order type, that K and K/f_1 have the same order type, violating Corollary 3.1.7.3. In symbols, then

$$\overline{\overline{K}} \neq \overline{\overline{S}} \text{ and } \overline{\overline{K}} \nmid \overline{\overline{S}}.$$

5.1.3.4   However, if we now assume the comparability property of sets, it follows that

$$\overline{\overline{K}} > \overline{\overline{S}}.$$

This implies that, between the elements of S and the elements of a subset of K, there exists a (1-1)-correspondence; and this induces a well-ordering of S.

5.1.3.5   It is worthy of note that in 5.1.3.3, without any use of either the Choice Axiom or the comparability property, it was shown that:

Theorem. *If S is any set, then there exists a well-ordered set K such that neither of the relations* $\overline{\overline{K}} = \overline{\overline{S}}$, $\overline{\overline{K}} < \overline{\overline{S}}$ *holds.*

5.1.4   Choice Axiom $\Rightarrow$ Well-ordering Theorem.[†]   Continuing with the symbols used in 5.1.3, let us denote the order type of K by β, and suppose that, for every ordinal number $\alpha < \beta$, $\overline{\overline{S}} \neq \overline{\alpha}$, where $\overline{\alpha}$ is the cardinal number of a set of order type α.

Now, as we saw in III 6.4, the choice axiom implies that for every subset S' of S there may be assumed to exist a definite representative element which we denote by $x(S')$. Let $x_0 = x(S)$. Then, for any ordinal $\alpha < \beta$, if we have defined an x_γ for all $\gamma < \alpha$, we may define x_α to be $x(S - S_\alpha)$, where $S_\alpha = \bigcup_{\gamma < \alpha} x_\gamma$ (we may assume $S - S_\alpha \neq \emptyset$, since by our supposition $\overline{\overline{S_\alpha}} \neq \overline{\overline{S}}$ and $S_\alpha \subset S$). Then by the transfinite induction principle [which is applicable (3.1.3) to all ordinals of the well-ordered set of ordinals representing sections of K] we have defined for every $\alpha < \beta$ an element x_α of S, and, for $\alpha' < \alpha < \beta$, $x_{\alpha'} \neq x_\alpha$. But this implies that $\overline{\beta} = \overline{\overline{K}} \leq \overline{\overline{S}}$, which we showed above not to be the case. Hence the supposition that, for all $\alpha < \beta$, $\alpha \neq \overline{\overline{S}}$ leads to contradiction.

We conclude, then, that, for some $\alpha < \beta$, $\alpha = \overline{\overline{S}}$, and since α is an ordinal number this implies that there is a well-ordered set A whose elements are in (1-1)-correspondence T with the elements of S. The correspondence T induces a well-ordering of S.

[†] Cf. Sierpinski [S_1; 230ff].

5.2   Zorn's Lemma

A useful principle, usually called "Zorn's Lemma," is frequently employed in applications of set theory as an alternative to the method of transfinite induction.

5.2.1   Zorn's Lemma. *If every simply ordered subset of a partially ordered set S has an upper bound, then S has at least one maximal element.*

(The notion of partially ordered set S was defined in Problem 8 of Chapter II. An element u of S is called an upper bound of a simply ordered set T if, for all $x \varepsilon T$, $x \leqq u$. An element m of a partially ordered set S is called a maximal element of S if for no element y of S is $m < y$.)

5.2.2   The principle embodied in 5.2.1 is well known to be equivalent to the Choice Axiom (and hence to the Well-ordering Theorem and Comparability). For a discussion of this equivalence, as well as statements of other equivalent principles, the reader is referred to Birkhoff [Bi; 42–44]; therein will also be found citations relative to the origin of the principle. For direct proofs of the principle from the Choice Axiom, see the papers of Kneser [a] and Szele [a]; the latter embodies proofs of the equivalence of the Choice Axiom, Zorn's Lemma, and the Well-ordering Theorem (as well as of two related principles). Also see Rosenbloom [Ros; 146ff].

SUGGESTED READING

Birkhoff, G. [Bi; III]   Hobson [Ho; §§64–66]
Gödel [G]   Huntington [Hu; VII]
Grelling [Gr; 25–40]   Kamke [Ka₁; IV]
          Sierpinski [S₁; IX], [S₂; I]

PROBLEMS

1. Show that the sets ON, ON_1 of 1.1.1 are not isomorphic with respect to the simple order axioms.

2. Show that the set ON, and the set OF which consists of the elements of F ordered in their natural order of magnitude, are not isomorphic with respect to the simple order axioms.

3. Show that the set of all points in the coordinate plane can be so ordered as to be an element of the same order type as the set R (the latter ordered in its natural order of magnitude). Do this in at least two different ways.

4. Show that a set of order type $\omega_1 \cdot \omega_2$ as defined in Definition 3.2.1.1 is well-ordered.

5. Show that, if we assume the Choice Axiom, then a simply ordered set S is well-ordered if and only if it has no subset A of order type $*\omega$ (the order relations between elements of A being the same as in S).

6. Show that the finite well-ordered sets are characterized by the properties of having a last element and of satisfying the mathematical induction axiom (c) of 2.4.6.

7. Supply the proof for the assertion in the statement of 3.1.2.

8. Given a set N and binary relation $<$ between elements of N, show that N is of order type ω with respect to this $<$ if and only if

(a) N is simply ordered with respect to $<$.

(b) N has a first element.

(c) Between † any two elements of N there exist at most a finite number of elements of N.

(d) N is Dedekind infinite.

9. Given N, $<$, as in Problem 8, show that N is of order type ω if and only if

(a) N is well-ordered.

(b) Every element of N except the first has an immediate predecessor.

(c) N is infinite.

10. Prove directly from the axioms for a well-ordered set (2.4) the validity of the transfinite induction method of showing that all elements of a well-ordered set have a certain property.

11. Show that the set B defined in the proof of 3.1.6.3 is a basis for R.

12. Prove that the axiom system of 4.2 is a categorical system characterizing the sets of order type ω_1.

13. Show that a set W and binary relation $<$ between elements of W form a set of order type ω_1 if and only if

(a) W is well-ordered with respect to $<$.

(b) W is uncountable.

(c) Between any two elements of W there exist only a countable set of elements of W.

14. How would you, in analogy to 4.3.2, define *limit* for an increasing sequence of ordinal numbers in case the sequence is now to be of some ordinal type $\alpha > \omega$?

† In any simply ordered set, if $x < y$ and $y < z$, then y is said to be *between* x and z.

VI

The Linear Continuum
and the Real Number System

Our discussion of the axiomatic method in Chapters I and II led to a consideration of sets and the theory of the infinite. In the latter connection we generalized the number concept as it is represented by the natural numbers, finding two complementary types—the cardinal and the ordinal numbers.

In the present chapter we shall use the notions thus developed to study the concepts which form the foundation of modern mathematical analysis, viz., the linear continuum and the real number system. We defer to Part II our discussion of the philosophical and technical criticisms that have of late been directed at these concepts.

1 Analysis of the structure of R as an ordered system

We defined R in IV 1.4 as a collection of numbers each of which can be represented by an unending decimal, in the ordinary decimal system, of the form

(1a) $$\pm k_1 k_2 \cdots k_m . a_1 a_2 \cdots a_n \cdots$$

where each k and each a are one of the digits 0, 1, $\cdots$, 9; $k_1 k_2 \cdots k_m$ is the "integral part" of the number; $a_1 a_2 \cdots a_n \cdots$ is the "decimal part"; and no n exists such that all digits a_n, a_{n+1}, $\cdots$ are all zero (with the single exception that the number zero is represented by $0.a_1 a_2 \cdots a_n \cdots$ where all a_n are zero).

In several instances we have referred, in the past, to the "natural order" of the collection R, with the remark that we meant the order according to magnitude. Here we shall be more explicit about this, since the type of order with which we are dealing has some very surprising aspects which can be appreciated only by a more careful examination of the order relation itself.

134

1.1 Definition of $<$ for R

Given two positive real numbers r and r', then, just how can we give an explicit definition of what we mean by the relation $r < r'$? Suppose that we use the form (1a), with a $+$ sign, to represent r, with a similar form to represent r', but with primes on the k's, a's, and m in the latter case. Since the integral parts of these numbers are natural numbers, we can first specify that, if

(1b) $$k_1k_2 \cdots k_m < k_1'k_2' \cdots k_{m'}'$$

where the $<$ in (1b) is that of the natural order in N, then $r < r'$. If the converse of (1b) holds—$k_1'k_2' \cdots k_{m'}' < k_1k_2 \cdots k_m$—we define $r' < r$. But, in case these numbers are equal, we then consider the decimal parts of r. The first inequality (in the order of the subscripts), $a_n < a_n'$ (or $a_n' < a_n$), will now determine the order. Thus, if $a_1 < a_1'$, then $r < r'$. Or, if $a_1 = a_1'$, $a_2 = a_2'$, and $a_3 < a_3'$, then $r < r'$. If, however, $a_n = a_n'$ for every n, then the relation $r = r'$ holds.

For the case where not both r and r' are positive, we of course employ the above criterion when *both* r and r' are negative but *reverse* the order; thus $-22.6 \cdots < -3.14 \cdots$, $-5.238 \cdots < -5.237 \cdots$. If r is negative and r' not negative, $r < r'$.

1.2 Separability property of R

There is little difficulty in showing that the order relation defined in 1.1 satisfies the simple order axioms (II 7), and we leave this to the reader. What we should like to do next is to consider the relation of the set F to the set R in terms of this order. We shall restrict ourselves to positive numbers throughout this section, since the extension to the "mixed" case is obvious.

Since every element of F may be expressed in the form p/q, where p and q are integers, we may use the ordinary division algorithm to obtain the form (1a) for each element of F. Thus $F \subset R$. We shall prove:

1.2.1   Theorem.   *If r and r' are (positive) real numbers, and $r < r'$, then there exists $f \varepsilon F$ such that $r < f < r'$.*

Proof.   Let r and r' be represented as in 1.1, and suppose that $r < r'$. If $k_1k_2 \cdots k_m < k_1'k_2' \cdots k_{m'}'$, let a_k' be the first non-zero digit in the sequence a_1', a_2', $\cdots$, a_n', $\cdots$. Let f be the number $k_1'k_2' \cdots k_{m'}'.a_1'a_2' \cdots (a_k' - 1)99 \cdots$, which has integral part $k_1'k_2' \cdots k_{m'}'$ and digits $a_1'a_2' \cdots a_{k-1}'$, the same as in r', but with

a_k' replaced by $a_k' - 1$ and all a_n' for $n > k$ replaced by the digit 9. Then $f \, \varepsilon \, F$ and $r < f < r'$ by the rule given in 1.1.

If the integral parts of r and r' are the same, let i be the first value of n such that $a_n < a_n'$. Then let k be the first subscript greater than i such that a_k' is not zero. Let $f = k_1' k_2' \cdots k_m'.a_1' \cdots a_i' \cdots (a_k' - 1)999 \cdots$, a number which agrees with r' in its integral part and in the first $k - 1$ digits of its decimal part, but replaces a_k' by $a_k' - 1$ and all successive digits by 9. Then $f \, \varepsilon \, F$ and $r < f < r'$.

If in a simply ordered set we say that an element y *separates* elements x and z if y is between x and z, then we can state:

1.2.2   Corollary. *Every two elements of R are separated by an element of R.*

1.2.2.1   The property of R stated in 1.2.2 is frequently called the *density* property of R. A simply ordered set satisfying 1.2.2 is called *dense*.

1.2.3   If a real number can be represented in the decimal system in the form $k_1 k_2 \cdots k_m.a_1 a_2 \cdots a_n \cdots$, where *all* a_n from some subscript n on are all zero, then we call it a *finite decimal*. (Thus, $2.499 \cdots 9 \cdots$ is a finite decimal since it can be represented in the form 2.5. On the other hand, $\frac{1}{3}$ is not a finite decimal, nor is any irrational real number.)

Now the numbers f defined in the proof of 1.2.1 are finite decimals; hence we can state:

1.2.4   Theorem. *If r and r' are real numbers, $r < r'$, then there exists a finite decimal d such that $r < d < r'$.*

1.2.5   We showed in IV 1.2 that F has the cardinal number $\aleph_0$; in IV 1.4 that the cardinal number of R is a number c different from $\aleph_0$; and in IV 4.2.1 that $\aleph_0 < c$. Thus, although the number of elements in R is greater than the number of elements in F, it turns out that between every two elements of R there is an element of F. For finite sets there is nothing surprising about such a property, but in the present case we might erroneously reason that, since each *two* elements of R are separated by *one* element of F, the number of elements in R is at most *twice* as great as that in F, i.e., $\aleph_0 + \aleph_0$, which we showed in IV 2.5.1, is $\aleph_0$.† The "paradox" is explained if we notice that the *same* element of F separates many different pairs of elements of R.

---

† We did not define addition or multiplication in Chapter IV for cardinal numbers; but, as the reader would probably surmise, $2 \cdot \aleph_0 = \aleph_0 + \aleph_0$, and to obtain the latter we would select disjoint sets A, $B \, \varepsilon \, \aleph_0$ and find the cardinal number of $A \cup B$.

1.2.6   The set F is called a *countable separating set* for R, and the *existence* of such a set is designated the *separability* property of R. Although the separability property implies density, not all simply ordered sets having the density property have the separability property; not even if, in addition, they have cardinal number c. For consider the following examples:

1.2.6.1   Example (Huntington [Hu; 45]). In the coordinate plane, let S denote the set $\{(x, y) \mid (0 \leq x \leq 1) \,\&\, (0 \leq y \leq 1)\}$. Define $<$ for S as follows: If $p = (x, y)$, $q = (x', y')$, let $p < q$ mean that either (1) $x < x'$, or (2) $x = x'$ and $y < y'$. That $p = q$ means $x = x'$ and $y = y'$. Then S is simply ordered with respect to this $<$. Also, S has the density property (1.2.2.1). We proved in IV 2.4 that the cardinal number of S is c. But S does not have the separability property.

For consider any real number r such that $0 \leq r \leq 1$. Let $I_r = \{(r, y) \mid 0 \leq y \leq 1\}$. Also let $p_r = (r, 0)$, $q_r = (r, 1)$. Then $p_r < q_r$, and a point x_r between p_r and q_r would have to be an element of I_r. Since the cardinal number of the collection of sets I_r is c, any set M having the property that $M \cap I_r \neq 0$ *for all* r would have to have cardinal number equal to c. Hence any set M having the property that, for every p, $q \,\varepsilon\, S$ there exists $x \,\varepsilon\, M$ such that x is between p and q must have the cardinal number c!

1.2.6.2   Example. Let Ω denote the collection of all ordinal numbers of the first and second classes (V 3.3). For each successive pair α, $\alpha + 1 \,\varepsilon\, \Omega$, introduce a set R_α of the same order type as the set of real numbers $\{r \mid 0 < r < 1\}$, defining $\alpha < x_\alpha < \alpha + 1$ for all $x_\alpha \,\varepsilon\, R_\alpha$. And, if $\alpha < \beta$, where $\alpha, \beta \,\varepsilon\, \Omega$, let $x_\alpha < x_\beta$, for all $x_\alpha \,\varepsilon\, R_\alpha$, $x_\beta \,\varepsilon\, R_\beta$. And finally, if $\alpha < \beta < \gamma$, where $\alpha, \beta, \gamma \,\varepsilon\, \Omega$, let $\alpha < x_\beta < \gamma$ for all $x_\beta \,\varepsilon\, R_\beta$. The set $\Gamma = \Omega \cup \bigcup_{\alpha \,\varepsilon\, \Omega} R_\alpha$ is then a simply ordered set having the density property.

The set Γ does not have the separability property. For, if Γ' were a countable separating set for Γ, then for every $\alpha \,\varepsilon\, \Omega$ there would exist a $\gamma \,\varepsilon\, \Gamma'$ such that $\alpha < \gamma$. Then Γ' would be a countable spanning set (V 2.3.1) of Γ. However, this would imply the existence of a countable spanning set of Ω, which is impossible by Theorem V 4.1 (cf. Problem 5).

Since $\overline{\overline{\Omega}} = \aleph_1$ and $\aleph_1 \leq c$, and evidently $c \leq \overline{\overline{\Gamma}}$, it can be shown that $\overline{\overline{\Gamma}} = c$. For the proof the reader is referred to the material in Sierpinski [S_1; 33ff, 96ff].

It should be noted that the ordered sets S (1.2.6.1) and Γ are not of the same order type (Problem 6).

1.3   The possible types of cuts of R

Our investigation of the order type of R would not be complete without a study of the cuts of R. The notion of a cut of a simply ordered system was introduced in V 2.2, Definition (2a), and used there to characterize sets of order type ω. In a set of order type ω, every cut $[A, B]$ is of a single type, viz., the type in which A has a last element and B has a first element.

Cuts of R are of *two* types: that in which A has a last element and B no first element, and that in which A has no last element and B has a first element. The former is exemplified in the case where $A = \{x \mid (x \leq 0)\}$, $B = \{x \mid 0 < x\}$; the latter by $A = \{x \mid x < 0\}$, $B = \{x \mid 0 \leq x\}$. The type of cut found in sets of order type ω is *never* found in R, in view of Corollary 1.2.2.

1.3.1   Theorem. *If $[A, B]$ is a cut of the collection R, ordered as in 1.1, then either A has a last element or † B has a first element.*

Proof. It will be sufficient to prove the theorem for the set $E^1 = \{r \mid (r \, \varepsilon \, R) \, \& \, (0 < r < 1)\}$ instead of R, since R and E^1 are of the same order type (Chapter IV, Problem 8). Hence we assume that $[A, B]$ is a cut of E^1.

Suppose that A has no last element and that B has no first element. By Theorem 1.2.4, the set, F', of all positive finite decimals, with integral part zero, is a countable separating set (1.2.6) for E^1. The set F' is denumerable, and its elements can therefore be represented by symbols

$$(1.3.1a) \qquad\qquad d_1, d_2, \cdots, d_n, \cdots, \qquad n \, \varepsilon \, N,$$

where the order in (1.3.1a) is, of course, not that in R. Since the d's do occur in two orders, let us agree that "$<$" denotes the order relation in R, and that "$<'$" denotes the order in (1.3.1a)—thus $d_n <'$ d_{n+1} for all n, although, for some values of n, $d_{n+1} < d_n$ may hold.

Let $d_{n(1)}$ denote the first ‡ (in terms of $<'$) element of (1.3.1a) that is an element of A. Having defined $d_{n(k)}$ for a $k \, \varepsilon \, N$, let $d_{n(k+1)}$ be the first (in terms of $<'$) element of (1.3.1a) such that $d_{n(k+1)} \, \varepsilon \, A$ and $d_{n(k)} < d_{n(k+1)}$. That such an element exists for all k follows from the supposition that A has no last element. We have defined, then, by induction a sequence

† As stated before [II 7f], we always use "or" in the sense of "and/or," not as a complete disjunction. The complete disjunction actually holds here, however, as stated in the preliminary remarks above. Incidentally, "or" is another of our logical "universals" which we constantly find ourselves explaining. Cf. I 3.4.

‡ V 2.1, second footnote.

(1.3.1b) $\qquad d_{n(1)}, d_{n(2)}, \cdots, d_{n(k)}, \cdots$

of distinct elements of A such that (1) $d_{n(k)} < d_{n(k+1)}$ for all $k \, \varepsilon \, N$ and (2) if $a \, \varepsilon \, A$, then there exists k such that $a < d_{n(k)}$.

That (2) holds may be shown as follows: Suppose that there exists an $a \, \varepsilon \, A$ such that for no k is $a < d_{n(k)}$. Let $b \, \varepsilon \, A$ such that $a < b$. Then there exists a d_n of the sequence (1.3.1a) such that $a < d_n < b$; let n' be the smallest value of n satisfying these inequalities. Now $d_{n(1)} <' d_{n'}$, since otherwise $d_{n'}$ would have been the first element of (1.3.1a) in A. Let $n(i)$ be the largest subscript in (1.3.1b) such that $d_{n(i)} <' d_{n'}$. Then $d_{n'} <' d_{n(i+1)}$. But this is impossible, since $d_{n(i)} < d_{n'}$ and $d_{n(i+1)}$ was supposed, by the induction definition, to be the first element of (1.3.1a) to lie in A and satisfy the relation $d_{n(i)} < d_{n(i+1)}$! We must conclude, then, that (2) holds.

Since each $d_{n(k)}$ is a finite decimal, we may denote it by the symbol $0.a_1{}^k a_2{}^k \cdots a_{m(k)}{}^k$. And, since $d_{n(k)} < d_{n(k+1)}$, the digit $a_1{}^k$ is always less than or equal to the digit $a_1{}^{k+1}$. But the $d_{n(k)}$'s are infinite in number, so there must exist an $n(k)$, say $n(k) = i_1$, such that for all natural numbers $k > i_1$, $a_1{}^k = a_1{}^{k+1}$. For the sake of definiteness, we let i_1 be the smallest such natural number, and let a_1 be the common digit $a_1{}^k$, $k > i_1$. Similarly, there is a smallest $i_2 > i_1$ such that, for all $k > i_2$, $a_2{}^k = a_2{}^{k+1}$. Let a_2 be the digit $a_2{}^k$, $k > i_2$. Having defined i_j for a natural number j, let i_{j+1} be the smallest natural number greater than i_j such that, for all $k > i_{j+1}$, the digits $a_{j+1}{}^k$ and $a_{j+1}{}^{k+1}$ are the same, and let a_{j+1} denote this digit. Finally, let $d = 0.a_1 a_2 \cdots a_j \cdots$. Then $d \, \varepsilon \, R$, and hence $d \, \varepsilon \, A$ or $d \, \varepsilon \, B$.

For every k, $d_{n(k)} < d$; this follows from the definition of d in terms of the digits of the $d_{n(k)}$'s.† Hence, if $a \, \varepsilon \, A$, then $a < d$. For by (2) above there exists k such that $a < d_{n(k)}$. Thus $d \notin A$, and consequently $d \, \varepsilon \, B$. But, as B has no first element, there exists $b \, \varepsilon \, B$ such that $b < d$. The number b can be represented in the infinite decimal form $0.b_1 b_2 \cdots b_n \cdots$. And, since $b < d$, there is a smallest n, say $n = h$, such that $b_h < a_h$. But, for all large enough k, the numbers $d_{n(k)} = 0.a_1{}^k a_2{}^k \cdots a_{m(k)}{}^k$ are such that $a_n{}^k = a_n$, $n = 1, 2, \cdots$, $h + 1$. It follows that, for such k's, $b \leqq d_{n(k)}$, which is impossible since $b \, \varepsilon \, B$, $d_{n(k)} \, \varepsilon \, A$, and $A < B$.

Thus the supposition that A has no last element and B has no first element leads to contradiction.

† It should be recalled that, for the definition of $<$ in 1.1, elements of R were expressed in their "infinite decimal" form (1a). However, in this form $d_{n(k)}$ becomes $0.a_1{}^k a_2{}^k \cdots (a_{m(k)}{}^k - 1)999 \cdots$, so that $d_{n(k)} < d$ follows from a consideration of the digits $a_1{}^k, a_2{}^k, \cdots, a_{m(k)}{}^k - 1$.

1.3.2   Remarks. We pointed out in IV 2.1 that, on the basis of an axiom system for ordinary euclidean geometry, such as that of Hilbert, it can be shown that the "Cantor axiom" holds. In the terminology that we have since introduced, this "axiom" states that, if L is the set of all points on any euclidean straight line, and $<$ is introduced in the usual manner for points of L, then L and R are of the same order type.

It follows that the theorems proved above concerning order in R can also be stated for L. So far as Theorem 1.2.1 is concerned, this results independently from the fact that on L every finite interval has a midpoint and it is not difficult to set up a process of "bisecting" intervals on L so as to define, by induction, a set of points on L analogous to the countable separating set F (see Problem 7). However, to obtain the analogue of Theorem 1.3.1 requires a continuity axiom of some kind, which may well take the form of 1.3.1 itself. Indeed, as we shall see directly, these properties (separability, and the "cut property" stated in 1.3.1) virtually characterize the structure of the euclidean line.

1.3.2.1   An interesting by-product of the proof of Theorem 1.3.1 is a constructive procedure by which, given any real number d, and the sequence (1.3.1a), we may set up a sequence (1.3.1b) of finite decimals "approximating" d in a sense easily defined. (See Problem 14 of Chapter IV.) However, as the reader may prove for himself, if $0.a_1a_2 \cdots a_n \cdots$ is any infinite decimal, the finite decimals $0.a_1$, $0.a_1a_2$, $\cdots$, $0.a_1a_2 \cdots a_n$, $\cdots$ are the most obvious candidates for such a sequence. Of course, in the proof of 1.3.1 the number d had to be constructed from the sequence, rather than the reverse!

1.4   Axiomatic definition of the order type of R

We can use the properties of R which we have found above to give a categorical system of axioms which characterize the order type of R.†

1.4.1   Let C be a set of undefined elements and $<$ an undefined binary relation between elements of C such that

(1) C is simply ordered with respect to $<$.
(2) If $[A, B]$ is a cut of C, then either A has a last element or B has a first element.
(3) There exists a non-empty, countable subset S of C such that, if $x, y \in C$ such that $x < y$, then there exists $z \in S$ such that $x < z < y$.

† Compare Huntington [Hu; V], Sierpinski [S₁; 151].

(4) C has no first element and no last element.

These axioms can be briefly designated as, respectively,

(1) Simple order axiom.
(2) Dedekind cut axiom.
(3) Separability axiom.
(4) Unboundedness axiom.

1.4.1.1   Definition. Any set C with relation $<$ satisfying the axioms (1) to (4) of 1.4.1 will be called a *linear continuum* with respect to this $<$.
We shall designate the above axiom system by Λ.

1.4.2   Consistency of the axiom system Λ

Is it possible to show the axiom system Λ consistent? Here is a case where we cannot, for a model, exhibit any finite collection of physical objects, such as we did for the system Γ of I 2.2. As a matter of fact, for our consistency proof we resort to the concept which underlies the axioms (see I 5, II 6)! The collection R and $<$ defined as in 1.1 form a model of the system Λ. (Cf. Problem 8.)

1.4.3   Independence of the axioms of Λ

The following interpretations, together with the system $(R, <)$, show the independence of the axioms of Λ (cf. II 3, Definition 3.1.1).

1.4.3.1   Interpretation of $[\Lambda - (1)] + {\sim}(1)$. Let M_1 be an ordered set defined as follows: The elements of M_1 are the points in the coordinate plane of the sets $S_1 = \{(x, y) \mid (x \leqq 0)\ \&\ (y = 0)\}$, $S_2 = \{(x, y) \mid (x > 0)\ \&\ (x = y)\}$, $S_3 = \{(x, y) \mid (x > 0)\ \&\ (x = -y)\}$. Definition of $<$: For p, $q\, \varepsilon\, S_i$, $i = 1, 2, 3$, where $p = (x_1, y_1)$, $q = (x_2, y_2)$, $p < q$ means $x_1 < x_2$. For all $p\, \varepsilon\, S_1$, $q\, \varepsilon\, S_i$, $i = 2, 3$, $p < q$. For $p\, \varepsilon\, S_2$, $q\, \varepsilon\, S_3$, there is no $<$ relation. For M_1, axiom (1) fails, axioms (2) to (4) are satisfied.

1.4.3.2   Interpretation of $[\Lambda - (2)] + {\sim}(2)$. Let M_2 consist of the elements of F with $<$ defined as in 1.1.

1.4.3.3   Interpretation of $[\Lambda - (3)] + {\sim}(3)$. Let M_3 be the set S and relation $<$ of 1.2.6.1, with the points $(0, 0)$ and $(1, 1)$ deleted. Or let M_3 be the set Γ and relation $<$ of 1.2.6.2, with the first element of Γ deleted. (Cf. Problems 9 and 10.)

These interpretations also show, incidentally, that the assumption of density (1.2.2.1) alone in axiom (3) would not have been sufficient to characterize the order type of R. (The integers in their usual order suffice as a model of $[\Lambda - (3)] + \sim(3)$, but they do not have the density property.) For both S and Γ have the density property, yet neither is of the same order type as R, nor is either of the same order type as the other (cf. Problem 6).† The "lines" S and Γ are "too long" to put in euclidean spaces (to "straighten out" S, imagine that the position of S in the plane is the result of a folding process, accordion fashion, and perform the unfolding process on it).

1.4.3.4   Interpretation of $[\Lambda - (4)] + \sim(4)$. Let M_4 be any one of the following ordered subsets of R: $\{x \mid 0 \leqq x \leqq 1\}$, $\{x \mid 0 \leqq x < 1\}$, $\{x \mid 0 < x \leqq 1\}$.

1.4.3.5   Remark. It is of some interest to observe that the system $\Lambda - (4)$ has only four possible types of interpretations. That is, with isomorphism with respect to $\Lambda - (4)$ as an equivalence relation $\approx$ in the set K of all interpretations of $\Lambda - (4)$, there are exactly four classes in the class decomposition of K corresponding to $\approx$ (II 8.4, 8.5).

1.4.4   Categoricalness of the system Λ

To show that Λ is a categorical system, we first show that, if M is any model of Λ, then M and R are isomorphic with respect to Λ. Then, if M_1 and M_2 are any two models of Λ, the transitivity of isomorphism renders M_1 and M_2 isomorphic with respect to Λ, and consequently Λ is a categorical system.

Let M, then, be any model of Λ. Denote elements of M by the letter x with or without suitable indices, and the order relation in M by $<'$. Denote elements of R by the letter r with or without suitable indices, and the order relation in R by $<$ (as defined in 1.1).

Let us denote the subset of M whose existence is asserted in axiom (3) by S', and the elements of S' by $x_1, x_2, \cdots, x_n, \cdots$. And let us denote the elements of F by $r_1, r_2, \cdots, r_n, \cdots$. It will aid our exposition if we let the latter sequence be the sequence (F) of IV 1.2; then $r_1 = 0, r_2 = -1, r_3 = 1$, etc.

The set S' is non-empty, hence contains at least the element x_1. We shall set up an order-preserving (1-1)-correspondence T between the elements of R and the elements of M in which we have the pair (r_1, x_1). Let $T_1 = \{(r_1, x_1)\}$. Now $r_2 \, (= -1)$ satisfies the relation $r_2 < r_1$ (since $r_1 = 0$). We shall pair with r_2, then, the element $x_{n(2)}$ of S', whose subscript $n(2)$ is the smallest natural number n such that $x_n <' x_1$. That such an element $x_{n(2)}$ exists follows from the reason-

† The example S was also used by Young [Y; 84ff] for the same purpose.

ing: By axiom (4), M has no first element, hence there exists x such that $x <' x_1$. By axiom (3) there is an element x_n of S' such that $x <' x_n <' x_1$; and, since N in its natural order is a well-ordered (type ω) set, there exists a smallest such natural number $n(2)$ as desired above. Let $T_2 = \{(r_1, x_1), (r_2, x_2)\}$.

Having defined a collection T_k of pairs (r_1, x_1), $(r_2, x_{n(2)})$, $\cdots$, $(r_k, x_{n(k)})$, such that the resulting (1-1)-correspondence T_k is order-preserving, we consider r_{k+1}. We determine the element $x_{n(k+1)}$ of S' whose subscript $n(k+1)$ is the smallest natural number n such that, if we augment T_k by the pair $(r_{k+1}, x_{n(k+1)})$, then the new (1-1)-correspondence T_{k+1} is order-preserving. That such an $x_{n(k+1)}$ exists follows from reasoning similar to that used in showing the existence of $x_{n(2)}$. In this manner, we arrive at a denumerable collection T_ω of pairs such that the correspondence T_ω is an order-preserving (1-1)-correspondence between the elements of F and the elements of a subset S'' of S' consisting of $x_1, x_{n(2)}, \cdots, x_{n(k)}, \cdots$.

We assert $S'' = S'$. For suppose not. Then there exists x_h with smallest subscript h such that $x_h \, \varepsilon \, S' - S''$. Evidently $x_1 \neq x_h$, so that there exists a k, say k', such that $n(k') < h$, and $x_{n(k')}$ is the last (in the process of selecting elements of S') one of the elements $x_1, x_2, \cdots, x_{n-1}$ to be selected for the sequence S''. (That is, $x_1, x_{n(2)}, \cdots,$ $x_{n(k')}$ is the "*shortest*" section of the sequence S'' to contain *all* the elements $x_1, x_2, \cdots, x_{h-1}$.) And, as soon as $x_{n(k')}$ is selected, x_h becomes the *first* candidate, in all selections thereafter, for any of the elements $x_{n(k'+1)}, x_{n(k'+2)}, \cdots$. And ultimately it will certainly be chosen; for suppose, for instance, that $x_{n(2)} <' x_h <' x_1$, and that none of the elements $x_{n(3)}, \cdots, x_{n(k')}$ is between $x_{n(2)}$ and x_1 in M. Then, as soon as we come, in F, to the first r_n such that $r_2 < r_n < r_1$, x_h will be selected for S''. Other possibilities as to the relative order between x_h and the elements $x_1, x_{n(2)}, \cdots, x_{n(k')}$ yield the same conclusion.

Then T_ω constitutes an order-preserving (1-1)-correspondence between the elements of F and the elements of S'. To extend this to an order-preserving (1-1)-correspondence T between the elements of R and the elements of M, consider any $r^1 \, \varepsilon \, R - F$. Define a cut $[A_1, B_1]$ of F as follows: Let $A_1 = \{r_n \mid r_n < r^1\}$, $B_1 = \{r_n \mid r^1 < r_n\}$. Neither A_1 nor B_1 is empty. Then let A_1' be the set of all elements of S' paired with elements of A_1 in T_ω, and $B_1' = S' - A_1'$. And let $A' = \{x \mid x <' B_1'\}$, $B' = M - A'$. Then $[A', B']$ is a cut of M in which A' has a last element x^1, and we place the pair (r^1, x^1) in T.

That this defines T as an order-preserving (1-1)-correspondence between R and M we shall leave to the reader to show.

1.4.4.1   The proof of Theorem 1.4.4 was carried through in such detail partly to show the manner in which the irrational numbers, that is, the elements of $R - F$, may be determined by cuts of F (as in the case of r^1 and $[A_1, B_1]$ above). The reader may notice for himself that these correspond precisely to those cuts $[A_1, B_1]$ of F in which A_1 has no last element and B_1 has no first element. It should be noted also that, by virtue of Theorem 1.2.4, cuts of the set, D, of all *finite* decimals could have been used above; although a cut $[A_1, B_1]$ for which A_1 has no last and B_1 no first element may then determine a rational number.

1.4.5   A notable unsolved problem

Regarding the axiomatization of the order type of R, there is a well-known unsolved problem. Because of its seeming simplicity, and the failure of all attempts at solving it, it has received widespread attention. In order to state the problem, we need the notion of *interval:*

1.4.5.1   Definition. If $(C, <)$ is a simply ordered system (II 7.1) and $a,b \, \varepsilon \, C$, then the subset $\{x \mid a \leq x \leq b\}$ of C is called a *closed interval*, or simply *interval*, of C. If we wish to designate the determining points a and b, we say "the interval ab." The subset $\{x \mid a < x < b\}$ of C is called an *open interval;* to designate the determining points, we say "the open interval ab."

1.4.5.2   Theorem. *Every set of disjoint open intervals of a linear continuum $(C, <)$ is countable.*

Proof. If $\{I_\nu\}$ is a collection of disjoint open intervals, then by axiom (3) of 1.4.1 there exists, for each ν, an $x_\nu \, \varepsilon \, S$ (where S is the countable set S specified in this axiom) such that $x_\nu \, \varepsilon \, I_\nu$. As no two open intervals I_ν have a common element, and $\overline{\overline{S}} = \aleph_0$, it follows that the collection $\{I_\nu\}$ is countable.

1.4.5.3   Problem of Souslin. Because Theorem 1.4.5.2 is virtually a direct corollary of axiom (3), it is natural to ask whether it is not equivalent to axiom (3) in the presence of the other axioms. Specifically, if we temporarily designate by axiom (3′) the statement "Every collection of disjoint open intervals is countable," then *are the system of 1.4.1, and the system of 1.4.1 with C assumed non-empty, dense, and (3) replaced by (3′), equivalent?* (Cf. Problems 11–14 of Chapter II.)

This question was propounded in 1920 † by the Russian mathematician Souslin, and, although many attempts have been made to an-

† See *Fund. Math.*, vol. 1 (1920), p. 223, Problem 3; also see Sierpinski [S₁; 152–153].

swer it and numerous papers have been published relating to it,[†] it remains unanswered to this day.

2   Operations in R

Throughout Section 1 we have not once considered the possibility of adding or multiplying elements of R. Our attention was focused entirely on the order type of R. However, as a *real number system*, R is something more than an *order type*. Its elements are added, subtracted, etc.

2.1   Definitions of operations

It will be assumed that the reader is familiar with the arithmetic commonly taught in the elementary schools, at least to the extent of knowing how to add, subtract, multiply, and divide *finite* decimals,[‡] and of familiarity with the Laws of Signs ("the product of two negative numbers is positive," etc.; cf. VII 2.2.5, VII 2.7.2).

2.1.1   To add two positive real numbers $r_1 = k_1 k_2 \cdots k_m . a_1 a_2 \cdots a_n \cdots$ and $r_2 = t_1 t_2 \cdots t_s . b_1 b_2 \cdots b_n \cdots$, we let $r_1^0 = k_1 k_2 \cdots k_m$ and (for every $n \, \varepsilon \, N$) $r_1^n = k_1 k_2 \cdots k_m . a_1 a_2 \cdots a_n$; and $r_2^0 = t_1 t_2 \cdots t_s$ and $r_2^n = t_1 t_2 \cdots t_s . b_1 b_2 \cdots b_n$; and finally let $r_1^n + r_2^n = s_n$. Then, since $r_1^n \leqq r_1^{n+1}$, $r_2^n \leqq r_2^{n+1}$, we have $s_n \leqq s_{n+1}$.

Now r_1^n never exceeds $r_1^0 + 1$ and r_2^n never exceeds $r_2^0 + 1$; hence s_n never exceeds $r_1^0 + r_2^0 + 2$. Ultimately, then, the integral part of s_n stays fixed; i.e., there exists an integer N such that, for $n > N$, $n' > N$, s_n and $s_{n'}$ have the same integral parts. There will also exist an integer $i_1 > N$ such that, for $n > i_1$, $n' > i_1$, s_n and $s_{n'}$ have the same digit in the first place after the decimal point. Pursuing the same type of reasoning as was used in the proof of Theorem 1.3.1 to show the existence of the number d, we show here the existence of an $s \, \varepsilon \, R$ such that for any $k \, \varepsilon \, N$ there exists an i_k such that, for $n > i_k$, s_n and s have the same integral parts and the same digits in their first k decimal places.

We now *define* $r_1 + r_2$ to be s and write $r_1 + r_2 = s = r_2 + r_1$.

2.1.2   Obviously all the above operation amounts to is the usual "approximating" process used by everyone who computes. If we wish to find the digits representing the sum $\sqrt{2} + \pi$, we use $1.4 + 3.1 = 4.5$; or $1.41 + 3.14 = 4.55$; or $1.414 + 3.141 = 4.555$; or $\cdots$, depending upon how good an approximation we wish to the actual

[†] See, for instance, Miller [a], Dushnik and Miller [a], Sierpinski [c].

[‡] For a general discussion of arithmetic, Klein [Kl; Part I] is strongly recommended.

decimal representation of $\sqrt{2} + \pi$ (which is actually an infinite decimal, of course).[†]
The above description of the process, however, shows that there actually *exists* an
$s \, \varepsilon \, R$ which is being "approximated," so that we can give a definition of what we
mean by the "sum" $r_1 + r_2$.

When r_1 and r_2 are both negative, then $r_1 + r_2$ is of course $-s$. If
one is negative and the other positive, we find the difference d of their
numerical values and attach the sign of the numerically greater of
the numbers r_1, r_2, to d. For this purpose, however, we have to define, for positive r_1, r_2, and $r_1 > r_2$, what we mean by $r_1 - r_2$.

2.1.3   For the latter operation we do the obvious thing: For each
$n \, \varepsilon \, N$, let $d_n = r_1{}^n - r_2{}^n$, where $r_1{}^n$ and $r_2{}^n$ are as defined above.
We leave to the reader (Problem 11) to show that there exists a $d \, \varepsilon \, R$
such that for any $k \, \varepsilon \, N$ there exists an integer i_k such that, for $n > i_k$,
d_n and d have the same integral parts and the same digits in their
first k decimal places. We define $r_1 - r_2$ to be d and write $r_1 - r_2$
$= d$.

If $r_1 < r_2$, and r_1 and r_2 are both positive, then $r_1 - r_2$ is of course
$-(r_2 - r_1)$. The usual elementary rules governing signs for subtraction of integers will carry over to the cases where not both r_1 and r_2
are positive. (Thus $\sqrt{2} - \pi = -(\pi - \sqrt{2})$; $\sqrt{2} - (-\pi) = \sqrt{2}$
$+ \pi$; etc.)

2.1.4   Multiplication and division are handled along similar lines,
by performing the operations with the "approximations" $r_1{}^n$, $r_2{}^n$, ob-
serving the usual Laws of Signs in F. *Existence* of the corresponding
elements of R is proved by the same type of argument as used in the
case of addition. For our purposes we are more interested, however,
in finding what general characteristics of these operations may serve
as axioms for an axiomatization of the real number system.

2.2 Arithmetical "laws"

Certain "laws" commonly used in computation with integers and
finite decimals, and usually taken for granted, should be noted here.

2.2.1 Commutative laws

In defining addition for elements of R, we remarked that $r_1 + r_2 =$
$r_2 + r_1$. Similarly we would have for multiplication that $r_1 \times r_2 =$
$r_2 \times r_1$. These are respectively called the *commutative laws* of addi-
tion and multiplication. The corresponding laws do not hold for sub-

[†] However, in practice one usually "smooths off" these figures, as in the case of
the third sum, where 3.142 would probably be used instead of 3.141.

traction and division, of course. Later we shall see examples of "number systems" in which the commutative law of multiplication does not hold; these laws are not trivial, then, and they have to be specifically stated or implied in any axiomatic characterization of the real number system.

2.2.2 Associative laws

Everyone is familiar with the common device of adding a column of integers "down" and then "up" in order to check the sum. Involved here is not only the commutative law but also (assuming at least three integers are being added) the *associative law* of addition:

$$(2.2.2a) \qquad (r_1 + r_2) + r_3 = r_1 + (r_2 + r_3).$$

For any three finite decimals r_1, r_2, and r_3, it makes no difference in what order we carry out the addition. We can show from this fact that, if r_1, r_2, $r_3 \, \varepsilon \, R$, then in order to find a "sum," $r_1 + r_2 + r_3$, we may first find $r_1 + r_2 = r'$ and then $r' + r_3 = r$; and then we can prove that, if instead we first find $r_2 + r_3 = r''$, it will follow that $r = r_1 + r''$. The associative law (2.2.2a) holds for any elements of R, then.

2.2.2.1 It should be noticed, incidentally, that the definition of addition in 2.1.1 above does *not* tell us how to find a sum of *three* real numbers. Now that we have defined such a sum, and have the associative law (2.2.2a), we can in an obvious manner define by induction the sum of any finite number of real numbers and show that the *order* of adding is immaterial. Thus $r_1 + \cdots + r_n + r_{n+1} = (r_1 + r_2 + \cdots + r_n) + r_{n+1}$, etc.

For multiplication analogous statements may be made; in particular, the associative law of multiplication of real numbers is $(r_1 \times r_2) \times r_3 = r_1 \times (r_2 \times r_3)$.

2.2.3 The distributive law

In elementary algebra the reader probably first encountered the rule:

$$(2.2.3a) \qquad a \times (b + c) = (a \times b) + (a \times c),$$

and subsequently spent hours of labor in exercises illustrating "removal of parentheses." Relation (2.2.3a) is called the *distributive law*, and from its validity for integers and finite decimals may be proved its validity for any elements a, b, c (positive or not) of R (using $+$ and $\times$ as they have been defined above).

The distributive law, stated here chiefly for its theoretical importance, is not just an abstract principle useful for tormenting unwilling students of elementary algebra. Unfortunately the latter are all too frequently left with no understanding of its importance in ordinary calculations. No experienced computer, for example, would calculate the cost of 3 articles costing 98 cents apiece by multiplying 3 by .98; he would automatically use the distributive law:

$$3 \times (1.00 - .02) = 3.00 - .06 = 2.94$$

2.2.4 The monotonic law

Probably least manifest of all the rules of common arithmetic is the *monotonic law:*

(2.2.4a) $(x < y) \Rightarrow [(x + a) < (y + a)]$.

Interpreted, this means that, if x, y, and a are any three integers or finite decimals, and $x < y$, then $(x + a) < (y + a)$. Its validity for all real numbers easily follows from its validity for finite decimals.

2.2.5   The Laws of Signs we have already mentioned above (2.1, 2.1.4) and extended *by definition* to elements of R.

2.2.6   This completes our discussion of the order type of R and operations with elements of R. Further light will be thrown on these matters in the sequel, not only by the frequently used alternative approach to the real number system which is described below, but also by the axiomatic characterization which will be given. From the latter we shall see how fundamental properties of R may be proved as theorems.

It will be noted that we have not considered *infinite sums* ("series") or *infinite products* of elements of R. To do so would take us into the proper domain of *mathematical analysis,* and from this we have to abstain, although it is a natural continuation of what we have started above.

3 The real number system as based on the Peano axioms

Because it is one of the most commonly used methods of introducing the real number system, we shall sketch (leaving out many details) in this section the definition of real numbers, and operations with them, on the basis of the Peano axioms (III 5.1). An interesting feature of this approach is that it simulates, in many respects, the historical development. The parallel is not exact, to be sure, since the evolution of the real number system was by no means of an axiomatic or of a logical nature; numbers of a new type appeared as they were needed to satisfy the mathematical demands of the time (as, for example, in the introduction of fractions before negative numbers).

3.1   The positive integers and operations with them

Let us recall (III 5.1) that the Peano axioms deal with a set N of undefined elements called *numbers* (or "natural numbers") and an undefined binary relation, s, between numbers: $x \, s \, y$ is read "x is a successor of y." The axioms postulate (1) the existence of a number, designated by 1, such that $1 \, s \, x$ holds for *no* $x \, \varepsilon \, N$; (2) $x \, \varepsilon \, N \Rightarrow$ unique $y \, \varepsilon \, N$ such that $y \, s \, x$; and we call y the *successor* of x; (3) if $y \, s \, x$ and $y' \, s \, x'$, and $y = y'$,† then $x = x'$; and (4) the mathematical induction principle.

Since the successor of a given number is unique, we can define a symbol $S(x)$ to denote the successor of x; $S(x)$ is a single-valued function over N with values in N, or a mapping of N into N [not *onto* N because of axiom (1)] in the sense of IV 3.2.3.1.

3.1.1   Definition of addition

To define addition, we first define, for all x, $x + 1$ to be $S(x)$:

(3.1.1a) $\qquad\qquad x + 1 = S(x), \qquad x \, \varepsilon \, N.$

Then, for all y, we define:

(3.1.1b) $\qquad\qquad x + S(y) = S(x + y).$

Definitions (3.1.1a) and (3.1.1b) induce a definition, by the mathematical induction principle, of $x + y$ for all $x, y \, \varepsilon \, N$. ‡

Regarding the commutativity of addition, see Problem 12.

3.1.2   Definition of multiplication

With addition defined, multiplication may now be defined in terms of addition: We first define $1 \times y = y$ for all $y \, \varepsilon \, N$, and then for all $x \, \varepsilon \, N$ we define $S(x) \times y$ to be $(x \times y) + y$. This defines $x \times y$ for all $x, y \, \varepsilon \, N$ by the mathematical induction principle.

3.1.3   If we set up a (1-1)-correspondence between the elements of the set N of Peano's axioms and the natural numbers, in which the "1" of axiom (1) is paired with the natural number 1; and, having paired a number x of the set N of Peano's axioms with a natural number n, we then pair $S(x)$ with the natural number $n + 1$; it will then

† We shall use = to designate identity of the numbers symbolized; $x = y$ may be read "x is the same number as y."

‡ However, see Landau [La₁; ixff].

be seen that we have an isomorphism between N and the set N of natural numbers not only with respect to the axioms, but with respect to $+$ and $\times$, where for the natural numbers these operations have their usual meanings. This was obviously the motivation of the definitions in 3.1.1 and 3.1.2.

3.2   Definition of the integers and the operations with them

We now introduce methods which, if not encountered before, may seem strange, and perhaps puzzling. They depend strongly on the theory of sets, and embody a use of this theory reminiscent of the material in IV 3.2.

3.2.1   The integers and their ordering

Throughout the present section, we shall mean by "number" an element of the set N of Peano's axioms. And, since it is our intention to develop from the latter a system isomorphic to R, we must provide for the simple order found in R.

We have already suggested in V 2 how to define a suitable simple ordering for numbers. For every number x we define $x < S(x)$; stipulating transitivity for this relation, we extend it to all pairs of numbers in such a way as to satisfy the simple order axioms. The set N of Peano's axioms then becomes of order type ω, and we could use the usual symbols 1, 2, 3, $\cdots$, to denote the elements of N. This is the order which is induced by the correspondence indicated in 3.1.3 between the numbers and the natural numbers, and corresponds to what we call the "natural order" of the natural numbers.

Now, how are we to define a set that is isomorphic (with respect to order and operations) to the totality of all integers, positive, negative, and zero, as we commonly know them? Recalling that the principal function served by zero and the negative integers is to make *subtraction* possible ($3 - 3 = 0$, $3 - 4 = -1$, etc.), we may approach the answer to our question by agreeing that an *integer* is to be, in some sense, an *ordered pair* (a, b), like $(1, 2)$ or $(4, 3)$, and that mentally we perform the operation $a - b$ to get the integer designated. However, there are two difficulties here: (1) We have not defined subtraction, and cannot do so until we have defined all the integers (which we are now trying to do); and (2) we should like an integer to be a *unique* thing, whereas the device suggested above would make *any* of the ordered pairs $(1, 2)$, $(2, 3)$, $(3, 4)$, $\cdots$, correspond to -1.

The best way to surmount these difficulties is to use the notion of equivalence classes (II 8)—letting $(3, 4)$, $(4, 5)$, $(5, 6)$, $\cdots$, all fall into one class, and to avoid using subtraction by phrasing the definition, as we can, in terms of the addition already defined in 3.1.1. Recalling that in elementary arithmetic the relations $a - b = c - d$ and $a + d = b + c$ are equivalent, we may accomplish this in the following manner:

Let M be the set of all ordered pairs (a, b) where a and b are numbers. In M we define an equivalence relation $\approx$, such that (a, b) $\approx (c, d)$ if $a + d = b + c$, where $+$ is as defined in 3.1.1. The elements of the corresponding class decomposition (II 8.5) will be called *integers*. Then, for example, the class whose elements are $(1, 2)$, $(2, 3)$, $(3, 4)$, $\cdots$, where $2 = S(1)$, $3 = S(2)$, etc., will correspond to the negative integer -1. In case the class is such that, for all its elements (a, b), $a < b$, then the class is called a *negative integer;* if $a = b$, it is called *zero;* and, if $a > b$, a *positive integer*. We shall denote the collection of all these classes by $\mathfrak{M}$.

Now, the integers as we know them in arithmetic form a simply ordered system. The set $\mathfrak{M}$ may be simply ordered as follows: Let M_1, $M_2 \, \varepsilon \, \mathfrak{M}$, and let $(a, b) \, \varepsilon \, M_1$, $(c, d) \, \varepsilon \, M_2$. Then $M_1 < M_2$ if and only if $a + d < b + c$. By $M_1 = M_2$ is meant the identity of the *sets* M_1, M_2—which corresponds, of course, to $a + d = b + c$ according to the definition of $\approx$ above. That the relation $a + d < b + c$ is satisfied for *all* $(a, b) \, \varepsilon \, M_1$, $(c, d) \, \varepsilon \, M_2$, if it is satisfied for any such pair of elements, has to be proved, of course, but we omit this detail since we are only sketching the process.

3.2.1.1   A (1-1)-correspondence between the elements of $\mathfrak{M}$ and the set of all integers (as commonly understood) can now be set up as already indicated. This will be order-preserving, and will serve to suggest definitions of $+$ and $\times$ in $\mathfrak{M}$ such that an isomorphism not only with respect to $<$ but also with respect to $+$ and $\times$ results (between the elements of $\mathfrak{M}$ and the ordinary integers). These definitions are given below.

3.2.2   Operations with integers

If M_1, $M_2 \, \varepsilon \, \mathfrak{M}$, then $M_1 + M_2$ is defined as follows: Let $(a, b) \, \varepsilon \, M_1$, $(c, d) \, \varepsilon \, M_2$; then the element of $\mathfrak{M}$ determined by the pair $(a + c, b + d)$ is $M_1 + M_2$.

Subtraction may also be defined in $\mathfrak{M}$. Using symbols as in the preceding paragraph, by $M_1 - M_2$ is meant the class $M_3 \, \varepsilon \, \mathfrak{M}$ such that $M_3 + M_2 = M_1$. Its *existence* has to be proved, of course.

To define multiplication we let $M_1 \times M_2$ be the element of $\mathfrak{M}$ determined by the pair $(ac + bd, ad + bc)$, where ac means $a \times c$, etc., with $\times$ as defined in 3.1.2. Details regarding questions of uniqueness, etc., are omitted.

3.2.2.1   If we set up the isomorphism suggested in 3.2.1.1, we find that, while preserving symbolically the set $\mathfrak{M}$ and operations with its elements as defined above, it is convenient to replace these elements mentally by the concept which motivates our definitions, namely the ordinary integers and operations with them as commonly employed. This will be particularly useful when we commence to "pile class upon class," as we now do!

3.3   Rational numbers and operations with them

In IV 1 we defined the set F of all "real fractions," alternatively called rational numbers, as the set of all numbers (as we were then using the term "number") that can be put in the form p/q, where p is any integer and q is a natural number. Operations with elements of F are understood to be governed by the usual rules of arithmetic concerning addition, multiplication, etc., of fractions, and form the motivation of what follows:

3.3.1   Rational numbers

Denoting the element zero of $\mathfrak{M}$ corresponding to zero [i.e., the class whose elements are the pairs $(1, 1)$, $(2, 2)$, $(3, 3)$, $\cdots$] by M_0, we consider the collection $\mathfrak{F}$ of all pairs (M_1, M_2) of elements of $\mathfrak{M}$ such that $M_0 < M_2$ ($<$ defined as in 3.2.1). In $\mathfrak{F}$ we set up an equivalence relation $\approx$ such that $(M_1, M_2) \approx (M_3, M_4)$, if and only if $M_1 \times M_4 = M_2 \times M_3$ (with $\times$ as defined in 3.2.2). [Motivation: In ordinary arithmetic, $\frac{2}{3} = \frac{6}{9}$ is equivalent to $2 \times 9 = 3 \times 6$ ("clearing of fractions").] The elements of the collection Φ of all classes in the class decomposition of $\mathfrak{F}$ corresponding to this $\approx$ we call *rational numbers*.

If $\alpha, \beta \, \varepsilon \, \Phi$, then $\alpha < \beta$ will mean that, if $(M_1, M_2) \, \varepsilon \, \alpha$, $(M_3, M_4) \, \varepsilon \, \beta$, then $M_1 \times M_4 < M_2 \times M_3$. By $\alpha \times \beta$ is meant the element of Φ determined by the element $(M_1 \times M_3, M_2 \times M_4)$ of $\mathfrak{F}$, and by $\alpha + \beta$ is meant the element determined by $(M_1 \times M_4 + M_2 \times M_3, M_2 \times M_4)$. In fashion analogous to the definition of subtraction of integers, we let $\alpha - \beta$ be the class γ, element of Φ, determined by the relation $\alpha = \beta + \gamma$. And in addition we can now define division: For β different from the class determined by (M_0, M), where $M \neq M_0$, we let $\alpha \div \beta$ be the class δ determined by the relation $\alpha = \beta \times \delta$. Justification of these definitions, by exhibition of an isomorphism with the elements of the set F of IV 1, is omitted.

3.4   The real number system

In 3.2 we defined *integers* and their operations in terms of pairs of numbers and an equivalence relation; in 3.3 we have just defined *rational numbers* and their operations in terms of pairs of integers and an equivalence relation. We now show how to define *real numbers* in terms of *cuts* of Φ and an equivalence relation, bearing in mind the real number system R and cuts therein set forth in Section 1 as motivation.

3.4.1   Let Γ be the class of all cuts $[\Phi_1, \Phi_2]$ of Φ. If $[\Phi_1, \Phi_2]$, $[\Phi_1', \Phi_2'] \ \varepsilon \ \Gamma$ such that some fixed rational number α is the last element in Φ_1 and also the first element in Φ_2', then we define $[\Phi_1, \Phi_2] \approx [\Phi_1', \Phi_2']$; also, $[\Phi_1, \Phi_2] \approx [\Phi_1, \Phi_2]$ in every case. The elements of the class decomposition of Γ corresponding to $\approx$ are called *real numbers*.

3.4.2   Denoting by $\Re$ the collection of all real numbers so defined, we let $r_1 < r_2$, for $r_1, r_2 \ \varepsilon \ \Re$, provided that, if $[\Phi_1, \Phi_2] \ \varepsilon \ r_1$, $[\Phi_1', \Phi_2'] \ \varepsilon \ r_2$, there is a rational number α such that $\alpha \ \varepsilon \ \Phi_2 \ \cap \ \Phi_1'$. In terms of the same symbols, $r_1 + r_2$ is the element of $\Re$ determined by the cut $[\Phi_1'', \Phi_2'']$ in which $\Phi_1'' = \{\alpha_1 + \alpha_1' \ | \ (\alpha_1 \ \varepsilon \ \Phi_1) \ \& \ (\alpha_1' \ \varepsilon \ \Phi_1')\}$; and $r_1 \times r_2$ is the element of $\Re$ determined by the cut $[\Phi_1^*, \Phi_2^*]$ in which $\Phi_1^* = \{\alpha_1 \times \alpha_1' \ | \ (\alpha_1 \ \varepsilon \ \Phi_1) \ \& \ (\alpha_1' \ \varepsilon \ \Phi_1')\}$. Subtraction and division may be defined analogously to the same operations in Φ.

Again details, especially the justification of these definitions, is omitted. It is important, for our purposes, only that the reader get a general idea of the process by which we arrive at $\Re$ and its operations. Starting with the simple countable set N of Peano's axioms, and "pyramiding" classes, we finally arrive at $\Re$ in what must seem a highly abstract form. The latter is to be contrasted with the axiomatic formulation to be given in the next chapter. Before the present methods for "building up" $\Re$ are left, however, certain alternatives, etc., should be stated in regard to them.

3.5   Alternative methods

The above procedure may be schematically represented as follows:

(3.5a)   Natural numbers $\rightarrow$ integers $\rightarrow$ rational numbers $\rightarrow$

real numbers,

or, in the symbols used above,

(3.5a) $N \rightarrow \mathfrak{M} \rightarrow \Phi \rightarrow \Re.$

This sequence has certain advantages in that it is probably more natural, from some points of view, to "extend" to all the integers before considering fractions and the optional real numbers. Also, for the student familiar with modern algebra, $\mathfrak{M}$ will be familiar as an *integral domain* (see VII 2.4), and the step $\mathfrak{M} \rightarrow \Phi$ will be recognized as the formation of the *quotient field* of $\mathfrak{M}$.†

Were all details regarding the operations (Laws of Signs, etc.) to be carried through, there would be certain advantages in deviating from the above sequence (3.5.a). Consider the sequence

(3.5b)   Natural numbers $\rightarrow$ positive rational numbers $\rightarrow$

positive real numbers $\rightarrow$ real numbers.

Sequences (3.5a) and (3.5b) differ only in the intermediate terms; if we denote the positive rationals by Φ_+ and the positive reals by $\mathfrak{R}_+$, then (3.5b) becomes in symbols:

(3.5b) $N \rightarrow \Phi_+ \rightarrow \mathfrak{R}_+ \rightarrow \mathfrak{R}.$

3.5.1   The step $N \rightarrow \Phi_+$ consists in repeating the method for the step $N \rightarrow \mathfrak{M}$, except that the role of the operations $+$ and $\times$ is reversed. Thus, we again let M be the collection of all ordered pairs (a, b), $a, b \in N$, but this time $(a, b) \approx (c, d)$ is to mean $a \times d = b \times c$. [Motivation: $a/b = c/d$ is equivalent to $ad = bc$.] For $(a, b) \in M_1 \in \Phi_+$, $(c, d) \in M_2 \in \Phi_+$, where Φ_+ is the collection of all elements of the class decomposition of M corresponding to $\approx$, we let the element of Φ_+ determined by $(a \times c, b \times d)$ be $M_1 \times M_2$. For $M_1 + M_2$ we take the element of Φ_+ containing $[(a \times d) + (b \times c), (b \times d)]$. The collection Φ_+ with the operations $+$ and $\times$ so defined may be called the collection of *positive rational numbers*. It is simply ordered by defining $M_1 < M_2$ to mean, using symbols as before, that $a \times d < b \times c$. Its elements of the form $\{(a \times x, x), a$ fixed$\}$ form a collection isomorphic with N under the pairing of $\{(a \times x, x)\}$ with $a \in N$.

3.5.1.1   If desired, we could now make a step $\Phi_+ \rightarrow \Phi$ by using pairs (M_1, M_2), $M_1, M_2 \in \Phi_+$, and $(M_1, M_2) \approx (M_3, M_4)$, meaning $M_1 + M_4 = M_2 + M_3$. Then $\{(M_1, M_2)\} + \{(M_3, M_4)\} = \{(M_1 + M_3, M_2 + M_4)\}$, and $\{(M_1, M_2)\} \times \{(M_3, M_4)\}$ would be defined as $\{(M_1 \times M_3 + M_2 \times M_4, M_1 \times M_4 + M_2 \times M_3)\}$.

3.5.2   The step $\Phi_+ \rightarrow \mathfrak{R}_+$ can be made conveniently by using "half-cuts": A *half-cut* of Φ_+ is a non-empty subcollection Φ_1 of Φ_+ such that (1) Φ_1 has no last element, (2) if $M_1 \in \Phi_1$ then $\{M \mid M < M_1\}$ $\subset \Phi_1$, (3) $\Phi_+ - \Phi_1 \neq \emptyset$. The use of half-cuts simplifies matters: We call each half-cut a positive real number, and denote the collection of all half-cuts by $\mathfrak{R}_+$; to get $\Phi_1 + \Phi_1'$ we simply take

† See, for instance, van der Waerden [Wa; v. I, 219].

$$\{M_1 + M_1' \mid (M_1 \, \varepsilon \, \Phi_1) \, \& \, (M_1' \, \varepsilon \, \Phi_1')\},$$

and similarly $\Phi_1 \times \Phi_1' = \{M_1 \times M_1' \mid (M_1 \, \varepsilon \, \Phi_1) \, \& \, (M_1' \, \varepsilon \, \Phi_1')\}$. We let $\Phi_1 < \Phi_1'$ if Φ_1 is a *proper* subset of Φ_1'. By pairing with each element M_1 of Φ_+ the half-cut $\{M \mid M < M_1\}$, we obtain a subset of $\mathfrak{R}_+$ isomorphic with Φ_+.

3.5.3   The final step of (3.5b)—$\mathfrak{R}_+ \to \mathfrak{R}$—is made by the "pairing and equivalence" method already used above in the step $N \to \mathfrak{M}$.

3.5.4   Cauchy sequences

The step $\Phi \to \mathfrak{R}$ of (3.5a)—and similarly the step $\Phi_+ \to \mathfrak{R}_+$ of (3.5b)—is frequently made by using so-called "Cauchy sequences." In order to explain this briefly, we shall assume that all required notions regarding Φ, such as "absolute value" $\mid \alpha \mid$ of $\alpha \, \varepsilon \, \Phi$, have been supplied. (The reader may *think* of the elements of F (IV 1.1), of course.) By definition, a *Cauchy sequence* of rational numbers is a type ω sequence $\alpha_1, \alpha_2, \cdots, \alpha_n, \cdots, \alpha_n \, \varepsilon \, \Phi$, such that, if ϵ is any fixed positive element of Φ, then there is an n such that, for all $n' > n$, $n'' > n$, $\mid \alpha_{n'} - \alpha_{n''} \mid < \epsilon$. Two Cauchy sequences $\{\alpha_n\}$, $\{\alpha_n'\}$ are called *equivalent* provided that, if ϵ is any fixed positive element of Φ, there is an n such that, for all $k > n$, $\mid \alpha_k - \alpha_k' \mid < \epsilon$. Let Γ be the collection of all Cauchy sequences of rational numbers. The elements of the class decomposition of Γ corresponding to this equivalence relation are then called "real numbers." Operations, etc., are defined in a manner to be expected; for example, if r_1 and r_2 are real numbers, and $\{\alpha_n\} \, \varepsilon \, r_1$, $\{\beta_n\} \, \varepsilon \, r_2$, then $r_1 + r_2$ is the real number (= equivalence class of Cauchy sequences) determined by the sequence $\{\alpha_n + \beta_n\}$.

3.6   Remarks

This is as far as we shall go with the foundation of the real number system on the basis of the Peano postulates. The subject and the literature concerning it are large, and we have by no means exhausted the variety of methods that can be used. The methods that we have chosen to discuss are a fair sample, however, and probably the ones most commonly employed in teaching and in books on function theory. For supplementary material, as well as details that space limitations have forced us to omit, the reader is referred to such function theory classics as Hobson [Ho] and Pierpont [Pi]. The more elementary accounts in Klein [Kl] and Young [Y; X] are also recommended.

3.6.1   For one who reads German, an excellent summary of methods and bibliography will be found in F. Bachmann's article in *Encyklopädie der Mathematischen*

Wissenschaften [Encyk]. In particular, the several uses of the "pairing and equivalence" method above are set in their proper perspective as special cases of a group-theoretic extension theorem (loc. cit., pp. 12ff). Citations to the original source of the method of cuts (Dedekind), half-cuts (Pasch, Russell, et al.), etc., will also be found therein.

For an extended and detailed derivation of the arithmetic and ordering of the real number system (as well as of the arithmetic of the complex number system) from the Peano axioms, see the classical work of Landau [La2], now fortunately available in English [La1].

4   The complex number system

We close this chapter with a few remarks about the complex number system. As is well known, complex numbers were first introduced to satisfy the demand for solutions to such equations as $x^2 + 1 = 0$, which cannot be satisfied by real numbers; with them, all algebraic equations attain solutions. The "informal" manner of introducing such new numbers is to set up a new "unit," i, and to call any "number" of the form $a + bi$, where $a, b \in R$, a "complex number." It is stipulated that the new numbers satisfy the same laws (commutative, distributive, etc.) as the real numbers (excepting the monotonic law, which has no meaning in the new, non-ordered system), and that $i^2 = -1$.

4.1   The complex number system as an "extension" of the real number system

One can, however, build on the system $\mathfrak{R}$ of Section 3 in the following manner: Define a complex number as an ordered pair (a, b), a,b ε $\mathfrak{R}$. Define addition by the rule

(4.1a)   (a, b) + (c, d) = (a + c, b + d)

and multiplication by the rule

(4.1b)   (a, b) × (c, d) = [(a × c) − (b × d), (a × d) + (b × c)].

The commutative law, etc., follow from the same law for $\mathfrak{R}$. And evidently the complex numbers contain a subcollection, namely {(a, b) | b = 0}, isomorphic with $\mathfrak{R}$.

4.2   It will be noticed that if, in the above formulation, we denote (0, 1) by i (where 1 is the element of $\mathfrak{R}$ such that r × 1 = r for all r ε $\mathfrak{R}$), then, by the multiplication rule (4.1b), $i^2 = i \times i = (-1, 0)$, which corresponds in the above indicated isomorphism with the real number −1. Furthermore, with i so defined, the transition to the usual representation of complex numbers is made by the relations (a, b) = (a, 0) + (0, b) = (a, 0) + [(b, 0) × (0, 1)], where + and ×

are as defined in (4.1a) and (4.1b); the form $(a, 0) + [(b, 0) \times (0, 1)]$ corresponds to $a + bi$.†

SUGGESTED READING

Hobson [Ho; I]   Pierpont [Pi; I–II]
Huntington [Hu]   Young [Y; X–XII]

PROBLEMS

1. Show that the relation $<$ defined for R in 1.1 satisfies the simple order axioms.

2. In the last two sentences of the second paragraph of 1.2.6.1, we made assertions that certain sets M would have cardinal number c. It would have been sufficient to say "$\geqq c$." Why could we assert the former?

3. Show that, if we extended Definition V 3.2.1.1 in suitable manner to a definition of the product of two *simple order* types, then the example of 1.2.6.1 is such a product.

4. Can the example of 1.2.6.2 be represented as a product of two order types according to the definition suggested in Problem 3?

5. Prove the assertions in the last two sentences of the second paragraph of 1.2.6.2.

6. Show that the ordered set S of 1.2.6.1 with $(1, 1)$ deleted and the ordered set Γ of 1.2.6.2 are not of the same order type.

7. If L is a euclidean straight line ("infinitely long"), then, given any interval ab of L, there is a midpoint p of ab. Use this property, and the fact that L is the union of a denumerable set of such intervals ab, to prove that L has a countable separating set.

8. Would anything be gained, logically or otherwise, by using L as an interpretation of Λ rather than R, in order to prove the consistency of the system Λ?

9. Show that the set S and relation $<$ of 1.2.6.1 satisfy the Dedekind cut axiom.

10. Show that the set Γ and relation $<$ of 1.2.6.2. satisfy the Dedekind cut axiom.

11. Establish the existence of the number d of 2.1.3.

12. Prove the commutative law of addition as defined in 3.1.1 for the integers.

13. Prove the existence of rational numbers γ and δ satisfying the equations defining subtraction and division in 3.3.1.

14. Substantiate the assertion in 3.1.3 concerning the isomorphism between the N postulated in Peano's axioms and the arithmetic of positive integers (cf. Problem 22 of Chapter III).

† Complete references, etc., may be found in [Encyk., I 1, Heft 2; 23ff]. See also Young [Y; XII] and Klein [Kl; 55ff], in which will also be found elementary expositions of quaternions.

VII

Groups and
Their Significance
for the Foundations

Up to this point we have done very little of an algebraic nature. Of course, as a branch of mathematics, algebra is affected by such basic matters as logical laws, number, the infinite, etc., which have been discussed in the earlier chapters. And we have found minor uses for algebra, such as in the definition and enumeration of algebraic numbers (IV 1.3).

In the present chapter we shall take a new road, so to speak, and show how notions that have been developed in modern algebra have influenced and clarified the foundations of mathematics. In particular, the theory of the real number system can not only be placed on a more satisfactory foundation than is afforded by the methods of Chapter VI, but we shall also see many generalizations that the new approach makes possible and which lead to considerable enrichment of mathematics itself as well as of the particular field of algebra. Furthermore, we shall see geometry in a new perspective, not heretofore possible from the narrower, classical point of view.

1 Groups

The entering wedge, historically, was the notion of a group, which had for a long time been in use in various special forms in algebra and geometry. The ultimate formulation of the properties of an abstract group was an achievement of the axiomatic method, and furnishes an excellent example of the "economic" advantage of the method discussed in II 4.12 and II 6.2. In different branches of mathematics, *operations* such as those of addition and multiplication in elementary arithmetic, and such as those exemplified by the combining of transformations in geometry, had come to be studied from an abstract point of view, and it became apparent that there was an underlying common idea. This led inevitably to the axiomatic definition of group, and thence to a large body of theorems constituting *group theory,* available for application wherever groups could be recognized as playing a role in any field of mathematics. Later demands of modern mathematics led even to generalizations of groups, but we shall mention these more fully later.

1.1 Operations

In Chapter VI we called addition, multiplication, etc., "operations of arithmetic," but thus far we have not discussed the notion of operation for its own sake. As most commonly used, an operation in a set S is nothing but a single-valued function $f(x, y)$, $x,y \, \varepsilon \, S$. It can be most easily brought within the frame of IV 3.2.3.1 by use of the notion of product set:

1.1.1 Definition. If $S_1, S_2, \cdots, S_n$ are sets, then the *product set* $S_1 \times S_2 \times \cdots \times S_n$ is the collection of all ordered n-ples $(x_1, x_2, \cdots, x_n)$ in which $x_i \, \varepsilon \, S_i$, $i = 1, 2, \cdots, n$. In case $S_1 = S_2 = \cdots = S_n = S$, then the product set is the collection of all ordered n-ples $(x_1, x_2, \cdots, x_n)$, in which every $x_i \, \varepsilon \, S$; in this case the product set may be denoted by the symbol S^n.

1.1.2 Examples. The coordinate plane is the product set R^2, and, in general, coordinate n-space is the product set R^n, with, however, certain additional conditions which give it special "spatial" attributes [notably, the distance formula; thus, in the plane, the distance between (x_1, y_1) and (x_2, y_2) is $\sqrt{(x_1 - x_2)^2 + (y_1 - y_2{}^2)}$].

1.1.2.1 From the point of view of product set, a binary relation between elements of a set S is simply a subset of S^2; a mapping (IV 3.2.3.1) of a set S into a set S' (or single-valued function of S with values in S') is a special kind of subset of $S \times S'$. It should not be forgotten, however, that the notion of order relation (see II 7 and VIII 8.2.7.1) is basic to that of product set.

1.1.3 Definition. If S is any set, then an *operation* (more specifically, a *binary operation*) in S is a single-valued function $\mathbf{o}$ defined over S^2. For any element (x, y) of S^2, the value of this function may be denoted by $x \mathbf{o} y$. And that $x \mathbf{o} y$ is z may be denoted by the "equation" $x \mathbf{o} y = z$.

In the case of groups the value of the function is again in S, so that the function becomes a mapping (as defined in IV 3.2.3.1) of S^2 into S.

If, for all $x,y \, \varepsilon \, S$, $x \mathbf{o} y = y \mathbf{o} x$, then the operation is called *commutative*.

1.1.4   Examples. The addition function defined for N in VI 3.1.1 is an operation in N mapping N^2 onto the set $N - \{1\}$, since always $x + y$ is an $S(z)$ for some z, while 1 is not an $S(z)$.

1.1.4.1   If N is the set of natural numbers and $x \div y = x/y$—i.e., the real fraction $x/y \; \varepsilon \; F$—then the so-defined division is an operation mapping N^2 into F.

1.2   Definition of an abstract group †

By a *group* is meant any collection G and operation o in G such that:

1. (Closure.)   For all $x,y \; \varepsilon \; G$, x o y is an element of G. (In other words, the given operation is a mapping of G^2 into G.)

2. (Associative law.)   For all $x,y,z \; \varepsilon \; G$,

$$(x \text{ o } y) \text{ o } z = x \text{ o } (y \text{ o } z).$$

3. (Existence of an identity.)   There exists an element i of G such that, for all $x \; \varepsilon \; G$, x o $i = x$. The element i is called an *identity*, or *identical element*, of the group.

4. (Existence of inverse elements.)   If $x \; \varepsilon \; G$, then there exists an element x^{-1} of G such that x o $x^{-1} = i$. The element x^{-1} is called an *inverse*, or *inverse element* of x.

If G has n elements, $n \; \varepsilon \; N$, then we call G a group of *order* n with respect to the operation, or simply a *finite group* if the specific number of elements is not of importance. If G has infinitely many elements, then we call G of *infinite order*, or simply an *infinite group*. If, for all $x,y \; \varepsilon \; G$, x o $y = y$ o x, then we call G *commutative*, or *abelian*.

1.2.1   Examples. The ordinary integers of arithmetic with $+$ as operation form a group in which 0 is the identity, the inverse of any integer being the negative of that integer.

1.2.1.1   ˙ The rational numbers, without zero, and $\times$ as an operation form a group in which 1 is the identity, the inverse of p/q being q/p.

1.2.1.2   The integers 1, -1 with $\times$ as operation form a group of order 2. As a subset of the ordinary complex number system, 1, i,

† A great deal of work has been done on axiomatic definitions of *group*. The axioms given here form one of the most commonly used systems (except that frequently the commutativity of the identity with all elements and that of an element with its inverse element are assumed—which we prefer to prove by way of exemplification of the derivation of group-theoretic theorems). As they are given here, the axioms are capable of considerable weakening, incidentally. See, for example, Huntington [c].

-1, $-i$ with $\times$ as operation form a group of order 4. And in general, if r_1, r_2, $\cdots$, r_n are the nth roots of 1, then with $\times$ as operation they form a group of order n. Since the integer 1 with $\times$ as operation is a group of order 1, it follows that a group of order n exists for every natural number n.

1.2.1.3   Let $\{R_r\}$ be the set of all rotations of a circle in the plane about its center, where the index r has all values such that $0 \leqq r < 1$ and R_r denotes the rotation through the angle $r \cdot 360°$. Introduce an operation $\circ$ such that $R_r \circ R_{r'} = R_{r+r'}$, where $r + r'$ is to be addition "mod 1" (meaning that, if $r + r' \geqq 1$, then we are to substitute $r + r' - 1$ for the value of $r + r'$; thus, if $r = 0.7$ and $r' = 0.8$, then $R_{r+r'}$ is $R_{0.5}$). Geometrically, $R_r \circ R_{r'}$ means a rotation through $r \cdot 360°$ followed by a rotation through $r' \cdot 360°$ (or vice versa), the end result being the same as if one rotation R_k were made, with k the number "$r + r'$ mod 1." The collection $\{R_r\}$ with the operation so defined forms a group, called the *group of rotations of a circle*.

1.2.1.4   Let G denote the set of all transformations

(1.2.1.4a)
$$x' = ax + by + e$$
$$y' = cx + dy + f$$
$$(a,b,c,d,e,f \, \varepsilon \, R)$$

of the coordinate plane, each of which transforms a point (x, y) into a point (x', y') whose coordinates are related to those of (x, y) by (1.2.1.4a). We restrict (1.2.1.4a), however, by requiring $ad \neq bc$. If T_1 and T_2 are two such transformations, then by $T_1 \circ T_2$ we may denote the transformation obtained by first effecting T_2 and then effecting T_1; simple algebraic considerations show that the transformations so combined are equivalent to a single transformation whose coefficients a, b, c, d are determinate. The set G and this operation form a group called the *affine group* of the plane.

1.2.1.5   Thus far the groups exemplified, excepting 1.2.1.4, have all been abelian. A simple example of a non-abelian group is the set of all non-singular square matrices with elements in F, say, of order n ($\geqq 2$), with the usual multiplication of matrices as the operation. The non-abelian character is shown by the case $n = 2$ and the matrices

$$M = \begin{pmatrix} a & b \\ c & d \end{pmatrix} \quad N = \begin{pmatrix} 1 & 1 \\ 0 & 1 \end{pmatrix},$$

where $M \times N = \begin{pmatrix} a & a + b \\ c & c + d \end{pmatrix}$, $N \times M = \begin{pmatrix} a + c & b + d \\ c & d \end{pmatrix}$.

1.2.1.6   Another non-abelian example, important in its applications, is furnished by the so-called *substitution groups*, alternatively
called *permutation groups*. Consider, for example, the ordered pair
(a, b), and imagine an algebraic expression (e.g., a polynomial) in
which a and b occur in various powers. The substitution of b for a,
and a for b, in this expression, would presumably change its form unless the form is "symmetric" in a and b; the substitution would itself
give a test for such symmetry. Now this substitution may be represented by the matrix

(1.2.1.6a)
$$\begin{pmatrix} a & b \\ b & a \end{pmatrix},$$

in which (a, b) occurs in the first row and (b, a) in the second. There
being only *two* letters in the pair (a, b), there are only two possible
types of substitutions, barring repetitions, namely (1.2.1.6a) and the
so-called identity substitution,

(1.2.1.6b)
$$\begin{pmatrix} a & b \\ a & b \end{pmatrix}.$$

If we use an ordered triple (a, b, c), then *six* substitutions are possible:

$$S_1 = \begin{pmatrix} a & b & c \\ a & b & c \end{pmatrix}, \quad S_2 = \begin{pmatrix} a & b & c \\ b & a & c \end{pmatrix}, \quad S_3 = \begin{pmatrix} a & b & c \\ c & b & a \end{pmatrix},$$

(1.2.1.6c)

$$S_4 = \begin{pmatrix} a & b & c \\ a & c & b \end{pmatrix}, \quad S_5 = \begin{pmatrix} a & b & c \\ c & a & b \end{pmatrix}, \quad S_6 = \begin{pmatrix} a & b & c \\ b & c & a \end{pmatrix}.$$

And of course with n letters, $n!$ substitutions are possible, since in the
second row of the matrix $n!$ permutations of the n letters are possible.
An operation can be set up by the rule that, if S_1 and S_2 are substitutions, then $S_1 \circ S_2$ is the result of the substitution S_1 followed by the
substitution S_2. For example,

(1.2.1.6d)
$$\begin{pmatrix} a & b & c \\ b & a & c \end{pmatrix} \circ \begin{pmatrix} a & b & c \\ a & c & b \end{pmatrix} = \begin{pmatrix} a & b & c \\ c & a & b \end{pmatrix}.$$

With such a definition of the operation, the collection of $n!$ substitutions using n letters becomes a group, the so-called *symmetric group of
degree n*. That this group is generally non-abelian is exemplified by
reversing the order of the substitutions in the left-hand member of
equation (1.2.1.6d).

1.2.2   If G is a group, then any subset of G which, using the same operation, is again a group, is called a *subgroup* of G. Thus the pair S_1, S_2 of (1.2.1.6c) form a subgroup of the symmetric group of degree 3; so also do the pairs S_1, S_3 and S_1, S_4. The three substitutions S_1, S_5, S_6 of (1.2.1.6c) form a subgroup, of order 3, of the symmetric group of degree 3.

1.3   Some fundamental properties of groups

For our purposes, we need only a few elementary properties of groups. These we shall state as theorems to be proved on the basis of the axioms of 1.2. Some of the proofs will be left as exercises, in order that the reader may "get a feeling" for the methods used in abstract group theory. The latter make an excellent example, incicentally, of the methods used in modern algebra, as well as of the rigorous proof of theorems from axioms.

1.3.1   Lemma. *If $a,b,c \; \varepsilon \; G$ and $a = b$, then $a \circ c = b \circ c$ and $c \circ a = c \circ b$; and $a \circ c$, $c \circ a$, etc., are all elements of G.*
    Proof. By definition, $a = b$ means that a and b denote the same element e of G. By the definition (1.1.3) of operation and axiom 1, $e \circ c$ is a unique element of G and hence $a \circ c = b \circ c$. The other relation follows similarly.

1.3.2   Lemma (Right-hand cancellation law). *If $a,b,c \; \varepsilon \; G$ and $a \circ c = b \circ c$, then $a = b$.*
    Proof. From $a \circ c = b \circ c$ follows, by axiom 4 and Lemma 1.3.1, that $(a \circ c) \circ c^{-1} = (b \circ c) \circ c^{-1}$. Axiom 2 allows us to write $a \circ (c \circ c^{-1}) = b \circ (c \circ c^{-1})$, or, using axiom 4, $a \circ i = b \circ i$. This, by axiom 3, becomes $a = b$.

1.3.3   Theorem (Commutativity of i). *For all $a \; \varepsilon \; G$, $a \circ i = i \circ a$.*
    Proof. With a^{-1} as defined in axiom 4, the following relations hold by virtue of the axioms cited:

$(i \circ a) \circ a^{-1} = i \circ (a \circ a^{-1})$	Axiom 2
$= i \circ i$	Axiom 4
$= i$	Axiom 3
$= a \circ a^{-1}.$	Axiom 4

By Lemma 1.3.2, we then have $i \circ a = a$. But also $a \circ i = a$ by axiom 3, and, since logical identity is a transitive relation, $a \circ i = i \circ a$.

1.3.3.1   Corollary. *The group G has only one identity.*
Proof. For let i and j be identities. Then $i \circ j = i$ by axiom 3.
Also, $i \circ j = j \circ i$ by Theorem 1.3.3, and $j \circ i = j$ by axiom 3, thus
giving $i \circ j = j$. That $i = j$ now follows.

1.3.4   Theorem (Commutativity of inverses). *For each $a, a^{-1} \varepsilon G$,*
$a \circ a^{-1} = a^{-1} \circ a$.
Proof. The theorem follows from the relations

$$(a^{-1} \circ a) \circ a^{-1} = a^{-1} \circ (a \circ a^{-1}) \quad \text{Axiom 2}$$

$$= a^{-1} \circ i \quad \text{Axiom 4}$$

$$= i \circ a^{-1} \quad \text{Theorem 1.3.3}$$

and Lemma 1.3.2.

1.3.4.1   Corollary (Left-hand cancellation law). *If $a, b, c \varepsilon G$ and*
$c \circ a = c \circ b$, then $a = b$.

1.3.4.2   Corollary (Uniqueness of inverse). *For each $a \varepsilon G$, the in-*
verse a^{-1} is unique.

1.3.4.3   Corollary. *For each $a \varepsilon G$, $(a^{-1})^{-1} = a$.*

1.3.5   Theorem. *For arbitrary $a, b \varepsilon G$, the relations $a \circ x = b$,*
$y \circ a = b$ are satisfied by unique elements x, y, respectively, of G.

1.4 Isomorphic groups

If G and H are groups which are isomorphic (II 4.4.4) with respect
to the group axioms (1.2), then G and H are called *isomorphic* groups.
Two groups G and H are isomorphic, then, if there exists a (1-1)-corre-
spondence between their elements which preserves the group operation.

1.4.1   Operation table for a finite group. In the case of finite
groups, isomorphism between groups may be shown by examination of
their *operation tables*. Suppose that G is a finite group of order n with
elements $x_1, x_2, \cdots, x_n$, where x_1 is the identity. We may then make
a table of n rows and n columns in which the element in the ith column
and jth row is $x_i \circ x_j$. The first row and the first column will contain
the elements $x_1, x_2, \cdots, x_n$ in this order (cf. Theorem 1.3.3). Also, in
each row, and in each column, no element of G is repeated (as can be
shown by use of the cancellation laws), and hence each row and each
column contains all elements of the group.

For example, the operation table for a group of order 2 will look like the following, if we drop the "x's" and use only the subscripts:

	1	2
1	1	2
2	2	1

The element in the lower right-hand corner is perforce 1, since each row must contain all elements of the group. It follows that all groups of order 2 are isomorphic. Thus, as abstract groups, the groups of order 2 of 1.2.1.2 and 1.2.2 are the same. A like statement holds for groups of order 3—only one such abstract group is possible—but this is not the case for groups of order 4 (see Problem 10). The lowest order of non-abelian groups is 6, viz., the order of the group isomorphic with the symmetric group of degree 3.

1.4.2   Relation to substitution groups. The importance of substitution groups is due partially to the following theorem:

1.4.2.1   Theorem. *Every finite group is isomorphic with some substitution group.*

Proof.   Let M denote the operation table for a finite group G of order n, drawn up as indicated above. For $j = 1, 2, \cdots, n$, let S_j denote the substitution whose matrix has in its first row the numbers of the columns of M—i.e., $1, \cdots, i, \cdots, n$, and in its second row the elements of the jth row of M taken in order. Schematically, then,

$$S_j = \begin{pmatrix} 1 & \cdots & i & \cdots & n \\ j & \cdots & i \circ j & \cdots & n \circ j \end{pmatrix},$$

where $i \circ j$ indicates the subscript of the symbol for $x_i \circ x_j$.

Now, if S_j and S_k are two such substitutions,

$$S_j \circ S_k = \begin{pmatrix} 1 & \cdots & i & \cdots & n \\ j & \cdots & i \circ j & \cdots & n \circ j \end{pmatrix} \circ \begin{pmatrix} 1 & \cdots & i \circ j & \cdots & n \\ k & \cdots & (i \circ j) \circ k & \cdots & n \circ k \end{pmatrix}$$

$$= \begin{pmatrix} 1 & \cdots & i & \cdots & n \\ j \circ k & \cdots & (i \circ j) \circ k & \cdots & (n \circ j) \circ k \end{pmatrix}.$$

By the associative law, $(i \circ j) \circ k = i \circ (j \circ k)$, and hence $S_j \circ S_k = S_{j \circ k}$. It follows that, if N is the operation table for the substitutions $S_1, \cdots, S_j, \cdots, S_n$, then M and N are identical. These substitutions therefore form a subgroup of the symmetric group of degree n that is isomorphic with G.

1.4.2.2   It follows from Theorem 1.4.2.1 that, as abstract groups, one will find all the properties of finite groups exemplified in the substitution groups.†

1.5 Semigroups

The demands of modern mathematics frequently necessitate the study of sets with operations that do not have all the properties of a group. For example, if a set S and operation in S satisfy axioms 1 and 2 of 1.2, and in addition the right- and left-hand cancellation laws (1.3.2, 1.3.4.1), then they form a so-called *semigroup*. If such a semigroup has only a finite number of elements, it is also a group (see Problem 8), but for infinite groups this is no longer the case (as for instance in the case where S is the set of natural numbers and the operation is addition).

Other types of systems satisfying only part of the axioms of a group are found of use (as for example in number theory), but will not be discussed here.

2 Applications in algebra and to number systems

In number systems, such as the real and complex number systems, we deal with collections in which *two* operations are given. These operations are not independent, since they are related by the distributive law which we saw exemplified in the real number system (see VI 2.2.3). It is not strange, therefore, that in modern algebra we find great importance attached to the study of sets in which two operations, which we may denote by $+$ and $\times$, are given, satisfying distributive laws.

2.1   If we consider one of the simplest number systems, viz., that of the integers, we notice that with respect to addition, $+$, we have a group, but that with respect to multiplication, $\times$, the collection does not form a group because inverses do not exist. Let us study, then, some of the properties of an abstract system of this sort. Specifically, let X be a collection in which are given two operations denoted by $+$ and $\times$, respectively, and satisfying the following axioms:

† For an elementary exposition of substitution groups, see the series of articles by Miller [a]. For finite groups in general, see Matthewson [Ma] and Miller, Blichfeldt, and Dickson [M-B-D]. The student who reads German will find the little book of Baumgartner [Ba] easy to understand and very instructive.

1. X is a group with respect to $+$, its identity being denoted by 0 and the inverse of an element x by $-x$.†

2. With respect to the operation $\times$, X satisfies the closure axiom (axiom 1) and the associative law (axiom 2) for a group.

3. For all $x,y,z \in X$,

(3a) $x \times (y + z) = (x \times y) + (x \times z)$

(3b) $(x + y) \times z = (x \times z) + (y \times z)$.

A set X and operations $+$, $\times$ in X satisfying these axioms will be denoted by $(X, +, \times)$. It may also be called *a system* $(X, +, \times)$.

2.2   On the basis of these axioms we can prove certain basic theorems of arithmetic.

2.2.1   Theorem.   *If $a \in X$, then $a \times 0 = 0 \times a = 0$.*
Proof.   Since 0 is the identity for the operation $+$,

$$0 + 0 = 0.$$

And, since X satisfies the closure axiom for a group, Lemma 1.3.1 holds and we can write

(2.2a) $a \times (0 + 0) = a \times 0,$

where both $a \times (0 + 0)$ and $a \times 0$ are elements of X. By (3a) of axiom 3, (2.2a) becomes

(2.2b) $(a \times 0) + (a \times 0) = a \times 0,$

which can be written

$$(a \times 0) + (a \times 0) = (a \times 0) + 0.$$

And, since the left-hand cancellation law (1.3.4.1) holds in every group, we get

$$a \times 0 = 0.$$

The proof that $0 \times a = 0$ may be given analogously, except that (2.2a) becomes $(0 + 0) \times a = 0 \times a$, and the other half (3b) of the distributive law (axiom 3) is used to obtain, analogously to (2.2b), the relation $(0 \times a) + (0 \times a) = 0 \times a$.

† We must be careful not to think here of "$-$" as an operation; it is only part of the symbol "$-x$" for an inverse with respect to $+$. We are reserving, in accordance with custom, the symbol x^{-1} for the inverse with respect to $\times$, which will be introduced later.

2.2.2   Theorem. *For all $x,y \, \varepsilon \, X$, $(-x) \times y = -(x \times y)$.*

Proof. By Theorem 2.2.1, $0 \times y = 0$. In this relation, 0 can be replaced by $x + (-x)$, giving

$$(2.2c) \qquad\qquad [x + (-x)] \times y = 0.$$

Applying part (3b) of axiom 3 to relation (2.2c) gives

$$(2.2d) \qquad\qquad (x \times y) + [(-x) \times y] = 0.$$

Applying Corollary 1.3.4.2, relation (2.2d) shows that $(-x) \times y$ must be the inverse, with respect to $+$, of $x \times y$; i.e., $-(x \times y) = (-x) \times y$.

By a similar argument one can prove:

2.2.3   Theorem. *For all $x,y \, \varepsilon \, X$, $x \times (-y) = -(x \times y)$.*

2.2.4   Theorem. *For all $x,y \, \varepsilon \, X$, $(-x) \times (-y) = x \times y$.*

Proof. By Theorem 2.2.2, $(-x) \times y = -(x \times y)$ for all $x,y \, \varepsilon \, X$. Hence, replacing y by $-y$, we get $(-x) \times (-y) = -[x \times (-y)]$. By Theorem 2.2.3, this gives $(-x) \times (-y) = -[-(x \times y)]$. By Corollary 1.3.4.3, $-[-(x \times y)] = x \times y$.

2.2.5   Remark. Theorems 2.2.2 to 2.2.4 will be recognized as constituting the "Laws of Signs" for any system $(X, +, \times)$ satisfying the above axioms. As these "laws" are understood in elementary arithmetic, however, they are stated in 2.7.2 below.

2.3   Rings

One of the most important basic notions of modern algebra is that of a ring:

2.3.1   Definition. A system $(X, +, \times)$ satisfying axioms 1 to 3 of 2.1 is called a *ring* if $+$ is commutative (1.1.3).

An important case is that of a ring in which there exists a right-hand identity with respect to the operation $\times$; i.e., an element "1" such that $x \times 1 = x$ for all $x \, \varepsilon \, X$.

2.3.2   Theorem. *If the system $(X, +, \times)$ has a right-hand identity with respect to $\times$, then $+$ is commutative.*

Proof. Denote the identity with respect to $\times$ by 1. Let $x,y \, \varepsilon \, X$. Then by axiom 3 of 2.1 we have:

$$(x + y) \times (1 + 1) = [(x + y) \times 1] + [(x + y) \times 1] = x + y + x + y$$

$$(x + y) \times (1 + 1) = [x \times (1 + 1)] + [y \times (1 + 1)] = x + x + y + y.$$

By virtue of these relations and the associative law for $+$, we get

$$x + (y + x) + y = x + (x + y) + y,$$

which by 1.3.2 and 1.3.4.1 gives $x + y = y + x$.

2.3.3   Corollary. *If the system* $(X, +, \times)$ *of 2.1 has a right-hand identity with respect to* $\times$, *then it is a ring and is called a ring with a unit.*

2.3.4   Remark. We may prove similarly that both 2.3.2 and 2.3.3 hold if "right-hand" is replaced by "left-hand," a "left-hand" identity being an element 1 such that $1 \times x = x$ for all $x \, \varepsilon \, X$.

2.3.5   Examples. Examples of rings occur almost everywhere in mathematics.

2.3.5.1   The most common example is afforded by the integers and their elementary arithmetic; here we have a ring with a unit. The like holds also for the arithmetic of the set F, the set R, and the set of complex numbers. The even numbers $0, \pm 2, \cdots, \pm 2n, \cdots$ with $+$ and $\times$ in the arithmetic sense form a ring without a unit.

2.3.5.2   Various sets of functions, with $+$ and $\times$ suitably defined, also form rings. For example, the set of all real single-valued functions forms a ring with a unit. And, since sums and products of continuous functions are continuous, the set of all continuous single-valued real functions forms a ring—a "subring" of the set of all real single-valued functions. Another such subring is the set of all polynomials in a single real variable x with real coefficients.

2.3.5.3   For fixed natural number n, the set of all square matrices of order n with elements integers and $+$, $\times$ in the ordinary sense forms a ring with unit in which $\times$ is not commutative (compare 1.2.1.5).
A ring in which $\times$ is commutative is called a *commutative ring.*

2.3.5.4   Integers mod m. In a group G we may define, for any $g \, \varepsilon \, G$ and $H \subset G$, sets $g \circ H = \{x \mid x = g \circ h, \ h \, \varepsilon \, H\}$ and $H \circ g = \{x \mid x = h \circ g, \ h \, \varepsilon \, H\}$. If H is a subgroup of G such that $g \circ H = H \circ g$ for all $g \, \varepsilon \, G$,† then the subsets $H \circ g$ form the elements of a group denoted by G/H. The group operation in G/H is defined by the relation $(H \circ g) \circ (H \circ g') = H \circ (g \circ g')$. The group G/H is called the *factor group of G mod H*; its elements are called *cosets*,‡ or *cosets of G mod H.*

† Such a subgroup is called a *normal subgroup* or *normal divisor* of G. If G is abelian, every subgroup is of course normal. Note that $g \circ H = H \circ g$ does not necessarily imply that $g \circ h = h \circ g$ for every $h \, \varepsilon \, H$, however.

‡ When H is not normal, the sets $H \circ g$ are called *right cosets* of G mod H, and the sets $g \circ H$ are called *left cosets* of G mod H. "Mod" is an abbreviation for "modulo."

Consider, for example, the case where G is the set of all integers with the operation $+$, and H is the set of all even integers. Then G/H has exactly *two* elements, viz., H and the set H_1 of all odd integers. Note that H is the identity of G/H (this is always the case). In practice, H and H_1 are denoted by their elements 0 and 1, respectively. Notice that $1 + 1 = 0$. Out of this factor group we can make a ring with a unit if we define $1 \times 1 = 1$. We then get what is called *the ring of integers mod* 2. It is the smallest possible non-degenerate ring with a unit, in that it contains only the identities for $+$ and $\times$.

In a similar way we obtain the ring of integers mod m, $m > 2$, and the elements of G/H are denoted by 0, 1, 2, $\cdots$, $m - 1$, integers which are elements of the respective cosets. To make a ring out of G/H we form the product $i \times j$ $(i, j = 0, 1, \cdots, m - 1)$ as in the ring of integers and reduce by multiples of m to bring within the range $0 \le i \times j < m$. For example, the ring of integers mod 4 has elements 0, 1, 2, 3; and $2 \times 2 = 0$, $2 + 2 = 0$, $2 \times 3 = 2$, $2 + 3 = 1$, etc.

2.3.6 **Ideals.** In the examples just given, H is not only a subgroup of the *group* G *relative to the operation* $+$, but is an *ideal* in the *ring* $(G, +, \times)$. In general, any non-empty subset A of a commutative ring $(X, +, \times)$ such that (1) A is a subgroup of the group X relative to $+$, and (2) $a \, \varepsilon \, A$, $x \, \varepsilon \, X$ imply $(a \times x) \, \varepsilon \, A$, is called an *ideal* of the ring X. Ideals occupy a position in the theory of rings analogous to that of normal subgroups in the theory of groups; for just as a normal subgroup H of a group G yields the factor groups G/H, so does an ideal A in a ring X yield a *subring*. To get the elements of the latter, we simply form the factor group X/A of the group X relative to $+$; addition of cosets is as before (for the factor group), and $(A + x) \times (A + y)$ is defined to be $A + (x \times y)$. (Cf. Problem 22.) For a discussion of ideals the reader is referred to Albert [Al; 252ff] and van der Waerden [Wa; v. I, § 16].

2.4 Integral domains

A striking difference between the ring of integers and the ring of integers mod 4 is that in the latter case we may have—as in $2 \times 2 = 0$ —a product of factors equal to zero although neither of the factors is zero! This happens nowhere in the arithmetic of integers, rational numbers, real numbers, etc. Indeed, in elementary algebra we *assume* that such can never be the case, as for example in the solution of equations when we assert that, if $(x - 1)(x - 2) = 0$, then the only possible solutions are obtained from $x - 1 = 0$ or $x - 2 = 0$ since the product cannot otherwise be zero.

Another way of looking at this is to notice that the cancellation law of multiplication breaks down in the case of the ring of integers mod 4. Thus, $0 \times 2 = 2 \times 2$, but it does *not* follow that the "2" on the right of each member can be cancelled.

Evidently, then, we obtain a more restricted system and more nearly approximate the operations of ordinary algebra by ruling out these possibilities. Actually, it is sufficient to rule out one of them (see Problem 16). The result is what is variously called an *integral domain, domain of integrity,* or *ring of integrity:*

2.4.1   Definition.   A ring with a unit in which $\times$ is commutative and satisfies the cancellation law † is called an *integral domain.*

Thus the ring of integers mod 3 is an integral domain, but the ring of integers mod 4 is not. The ring of continuous real functions mentioned in 2.3.5.2 is not an integral domain (see Problem 21).

2.5   Fields

In the notion of integral domain we have not yet achieved the systems, such as the rational number system, which are used in ordinary algebra. Thus, the ring of integers is an integral domain, but it does not allow for *division.* The latter is attained in the notion of "field."

2.5.1   Definition.   An integral domain in which every element $x \neq 0$ has an inverse x^{-1} with respect to $\times$ is called a *field.* If a system $(X, +, \times)$ has all the properties of a field except that $\times$ is not commutative, then it is called a *non-commutative field.*

The case $X = F$, and $+$, $\times$ with their ordinary meanings of addition and multiplication, exemplifies a *field.* The set of all non-singular square matrices of fixed order $n \geq 2$, elements in F, is a non-commutative field if $+$ and $\times$ indicate respectively the addition and multiplication of matrices; the unit element is the matrix whose main diagonal elements are all 1 and in which all other elements are 0.

2.5.2   Some properties of fields.   In a field, division (defined below), except by 0, is possible.

2.5.2.1   Lemma.   *If $(X, +, \times)$ is a non-degenerate ring with a unit 1, then $0 \neq 1$.*

† When $\times$ is commutative, the right-hand and left-hand cancellation laws, being equivalent, are called "the cancellation law." The term "integral domain" is frequently used for systems satisfying Definition 2.4.1 without the requirement of a unit.

Proof. As X is non-degenerate, there exists $x \varepsilon X$ such that $x \neq 0$. Then $x \times 1 = x \neq 0$, whereas, if 1 and 0 were the same element, we would have $x \times 1 = 0$ (by Theorem 2.2.1).

2.5.2.2   Lemma. *If $(X, +, \times)$ is a non-degenerate ring with unit 1, then 0 has no inverse with respect to $\times$.*

Proof. For an inverse of 0, say 0^{-1}, would imply $0 \times 0^{-1} = 1$, whereas $0 \times 0^{-1} = 0$ by Theorem 2.2.1; and thus a contradiction of Lemma 2.5.2.1 would result.

2.5.2.3   Lemma. *In a field, the elements different from 0 form a group with respect to $\times$.*

2.5.2.4   Definition. If $(X, +, \times)$ is a field, and $y \varepsilon X$, then by $x \div y$, or x/y, is meant a unique element z of X such that $x = y \times z$.†

2.5.2.5   Theorem. *If $(X, +, \times)$ is a field, and $y \varepsilon X$, $y \neq 0$, then for all $x \varepsilon X$ the element $x \div y$ exists, being identical with the element $x \times y^{-1}$, where y^{-1} is the inverse of y with respect to $\times$.*

The proof is immediate, following from Lemma 2.5.2.3 and Theorem 1.3.5 if $x \neq 0$, and from the fact that there are no zero divisors (see Problem 16).

2.5.2.6   Theorem. *If $(X, +, \times)$ is a non-degenerate field, then $x \div 0$ does not exist.*

Proof. For $x \neq 0$, the theorem follows immediately from 2.2.1. For $x = 0$, both $z = 0$ and $z = 1$ satisfy the equation $0 = 0 \times z$, so that no *unique* z exists.

2.5.2.7   Although 2.5.2.4 is the usual definition of $x \div y$, an alternative definition would be that $x \div y$ is $x \times y^{-1}$, where y^{-1} is the inverse of y with respect to $\times$. Then Theorem 2.5.2.5 follows directly from Corollary 1.3.4.2, and Theorem 2.5.2.6 is an immediate corollary of Lemma 2.5.2.2.

2.5.2.8   Just as one goes about seeking the possible types of abstract groups of a given finite order by drawing up the operation table (cf. 1.4.1), so may one investigate the possible fields of a given finite number of elements by constructing addition and multiplication tables. It is easy, using the properties of rings and fields established above, to show that for the case of a field of only two elements only one type is

---

† If the field were non-commutative, we could of course define "right-hand" and "left-hand" division. This would necessitate special symbols for the two types of division, however.

possible, the latter being exemplified by the ring of integers mod 2 (cf. 2.3.5.4).

2.6 Vector spaces

The reader who has had some elementary physics or mechanics is familiar with vectors and their use. For example, he may recall that, in the plane, a vector V represents both a direction and a magnitude, and that, if $r \, \varepsilon \, R$, then rV is a vector of magnitude r times as great as that of V (the direction of rV being the reverse of that of V if r is negative). The number r is called a "scalar," and rV a scalar product. And, if he recalls the "parallelogram of forces," he knows that vectors are added.

In modern algebra these ideas find their generalization in the notion of a vector space over a field $\mathfrak{F}$: †

2.6.1 Definition. A *vector space* $\mathfrak{V}$ *over a field* $\mathfrak{F}$ is a collection of elements called *vectors*, such that (1) $\mathfrak{V}$ is an abelian group relative to an operation $+$, called addition, (2) for $\alpha \, \varepsilon \, \mathfrak{F}$, $V \, \varepsilon \, \mathfrak{V}$, there exists a unique element of $\mathfrak{V}$ denoted by αV; (3) for $\alpha, \beta \, \varepsilon \, \mathfrak{F}$, $V \, \varepsilon \, \mathfrak{V}$, $\alpha(\beta V) = (\alpha \times \beta) V$, and $(\alpha + \beta) V = \alpha V + \beta V$; ‡ (4) for $\alpha \, \varepsilon \, \mathfrak{F}$, $V_1, V_2 \, \varepsilon \, \mathfrak{V}$, $\alpha(V_1 + V_2) = \alpha V_1 + \alpha V_2$; (5) if 1 is the unit of $\mathfrak{F}$, then $1V = V$ for all $V \, \varepsilon \, \mathfrak{V}$.

2.6.2 In addition to the example of plane vectors, in which $\mathfrak{F}$ is R, an example very useful in algebra, and its application in modern mathematics is that in which the vectors are the mappings (IV 3.2.3.1) of some set S into a field $\mathfrak{F}$. In this case, $+$ is defined by the relation $(f + g)(x) = f(x) + g(x)$, $x \, \varepsilon \, S$, for each pair of mappings f and g; and $(\alpha f)(x) = \alpha \times f(x)$ for $\alpha \, \varepsilon \, \mathfrak{F}$, $x \, \varepsilon \, S$.

2.6.3 Some properties of vector spaces. (Throughout Section 2.6.3 we use $\mathfrak{V}$ and $\mathfrak{F}$ as defined in 2.6.1.) The proofs of the following two theorems are left to the reader:

2.6.3.1 Theorem. *If* $\alpha_1, \alpha_2, \cdots, \alpha_k \, \varepsilon \, \mathfrak{F}$ *and* $V_1, V_2, \cdots, V_k \, \varepsilon \, \mathfrak{V}$, *then* $\alpha_1 V_1 + \alpha_2 V_2 + \cdots + \alpha_k V_k$ *is a unique element of* $\mathfrak{V}$.

2.6.3.2 Theorem. *There exists a unique element of* $\mathfrak{V}$ *called the zero element, which may be denoted by* $0'$, *such that* $0V = 0'$ *for all* $V \, \varepsilon \, \mathfrak{V}$ (the "0" in "$0V$" being the zero element of $\mathfrak{F}$).

---

† As a matter of fact, vector spaces over rings are also studied in modern algebra; see van der Waerden [Wa; 46]. Sometimes the term "linear space" is used to mean vector space.

‡ If V_1 and V_2 are vectors, then $V_1 = V_2$ means that V_1 and V_2 are identical.

2.6.3.3   Definition. The elements V_ν of a set $\{V_\nu\}$ of vectors are called *linearly independent* if there exists no relation of the form

$$(2.6a) \qquad \alpha_1 V_1 + \alpha_2 V_2 + \cdots + \alpha_k V_k = 0',$$

where $\alpha_1, \alpha_2, \cdots, \alpha_k \; \varepsilon \; \mathfrak{F}$, $V_1, V_2, \cdots, V_k \; \varepsilon \; \mathfrak{B}$, and $\alpha_i \neq 0$, $i = 1, 2, \cdots, k$. When vectors V_1, V_2, $\cdots$, V_k satisfy a relation of the form (2.6a) in which not all $\alpha_i = 0$, then V_1, V_2, $\cdots$, V_k are called *linearly dependent*.

2.6.3.4   Definition. A set $\{V_\nu\}$ is called a *base* for $\mathfrak{B}$ if (1) its elements V_ν are linearly independent, and (2) if $V \; \varepsilon \; \mathfrak{B}$, then there exists a relation $V = \alpha_1 V_1 + \alpha_2 V_2 + \cdots + \alpha_k V_k$ in which $\alpha_i \; \varepsilon \; \mathfrak{F}$ and $V_i \; \varepsilon \; \{V_\nu\}$, $i = 1, 2, \cdots, k$.

2.6.3.5   Definition. The cardinal number of elements in a base for $\mathfrak{B}$ is called the *dimension* of $\mathfrak{B}$.

As stated, 2.6.3.5 implies that the dimension of a vector space is a unique cardinal number. Inasmuch as in general there are many bases for a given vector space, this implication is by no means obvious. For, although it is not difficult to prove if there exists some base that is finite, the proof that all bases of a given vector space have the same cardinal number is not elementary in the case where the dimension turns out to be infinite.†

A simple example of a vector space of infinite dimension is the collection of all finite linear forms in variables x_n, $n = 1, 2, 3, \cdots$, with rational coefficients; for example, $2x_3 + \frac{1}{2}x_7 - x_{16}$ would be an element of this vector space. The dimension in this case is $\aleph_0$. If linear forms in only three variables x_1, x_2, x_3 are used, then the dimension is 3 since x_1, x_2, x_3 themselves form a base. The latter vector space is a "subspace" of the former.

2.7   The real number system

Let us next consider the application of the above notions to the definition of the real number system. In Chapter VI we showed how the real number system may be considered either as a "ready-made" collection of infinite decimals, or as a construction based on the natural numbers. In the present section we return to the "ready-made" point of view.

By way of making connection with the algebraic ideas above, we notice that the real number system is a field; moreover it is an *ordered*

---

† For the case of finite dimension, see Birkhoff and MacLane [B-M; 178ff]; for the infinite dimensional case a proof will be found in S. Lefschetz, *Algebraic Topology*, Amer. Math. Soc. Coll. Pub., vol. 27, New York, 1942, pp. 73–74.

field, in that its structure is that of a linear continuum (VI 1.4.1, Definition 1.4.1.1). We make these two properties part of a new definition of the real number system:

2.7.1   Definition. A *real number system* is a field R in which there is a binary order relation $<$ with respect to which R forms a linear continuum,† satisfying the monotonic law (VI 2.2.4) and the requirement that $0 < x$, $0 < y$ imply $0 < x \times y$.

2.7.2   All the properties of the real number system are derivable from this definition. As an example, let us consider the derivation of the Laws of Signs. As these were derived in 2.2 for a system $(X, +, \times)$, they are not quite in the specialized form in which they are understood in arithmetic. The latter form is already partially stated in the above definition in the requirement that

(2.7.2a) $0 < x, 0 < y \Rightarrow 0 < x \times y.$

We should be able to *prove* that $x < 0$, $y < 0 \Rightarrow 0 < x \times y$ also. We may arrange the proof as follows (R denotes a real number system as defined in 2.7.1 and x, y, z denote elements of R):

2.7.2.1   Lemma. If $0 < x$, then $-x < 0$; and, if $x < 0$, then $0 < -x$.

[Here, as in a system $(X, +, \times)$, $-x$ denotes the inverse of x with respect to $+$.]

Proof.   If $0 < x$, then by the monotonic law $-x + 0 < -x + x$, or $-x < 0$. (The other half of the lemma is proved in similar fashion.)

2.7.2.2   Theorem. *If* $0 < x$ *and* $y < 0$, *then* $x \times y < 0$.

Proof.   By Lemma 2.7.2.1, $0 < -y$. Hence, by (2.7.2a), $0 < x \times (-y)$. By Theorem 2.2.3, $x \times (-y) = -(x \times y)$. Hence $0 < -(x \times y)$, which by Lemma 2.7.2.1 and Corollary 1.3.4.3 implies $x \times y < 0$.

2.7.2.3   Theorem. *If* $x < 0$ *and* $y < 0$, *then* $0 < x \times y$.
The proof is left to the reader.

2.7.3   The above theorems give a good example of how one would go about studying the real number system from an axiomatic point of view. Definition 2.7.1 can of course be stated in the form of axioms, and the lemmas, theorems, etc., embodying desired properties of R derived as in the case of 2.7.2.1 to 2.7.2.3 above. Such properties as

† If we were to write out each axiom for a field, each axiom for a linear continuum, etc., we would find that the separability axiom [VI 1.4.1, Axiom (3)] is not independent. See, for example, Albert [A1; 110ff].

the Laws of Signs then assume a status like that of the theorems of plane geometry, when the latter is properly axiomatized.†

2.8   This completes our discussion of the role which the group notion plays in modern algebra. We have also exhibited, to some extent, the important role which the axiomatic method plays in algebra. Indeed, no branch of modern mathematics makes greater or more effective use of the method. For extensions of the above ideas the reader is referred to Birkhoff and MacLane [B-M]; A. A. Albert [Al]; van der Waerden [Wa].

3   The group notion in geometry

We have already noted the existence of groups in geometry, such as the group of rotations of the circle (1.2.1.3) and the affine group of plane transformations (1.2.1.4). The former may of course be extended to the group of rotations, about a fixed point, of the entire plane. Such a group is another example of a group of transformations. Let us define, in general fashion, what is meant by a group of transformations:

3.1   Definition. Let S be any set. Then a *transformation* of S is a mapping of S onto S (IV 3.2.3.1) which is (1-1); i.e., if $y = f(x)$ denotes the mapping, then every element of S is a y for some x, and for only *one* x.

It follows from the definition that a transformation always has an inverse; in the above symbols, the inverse may be denoted by $x = f^{-1}(y)$. This is of importance in the attainment of a *group* of transformations:

3.2   Definition. If $f = f(x)$ and $g = g(x)$ are transformations of a set S, then by fg is meant the transformation $f(g(x))$; ‡ fg is called the *product* of f and g.

3.3   Definition. If $\mathfrak{X}$ is a set of transformations of a collection S, such that, in terms of the operation fg defined in 3.2 the set $\mathfrak{X}$ forms a

† See also the comment by Young [Y; 111]. Also see the geometric "proof" of the Laws of Signs cited by the same author [Y; 112ff].

There has been reported at least one case, in one of the teachers' "service journals," of a high school principal complaining that none of his mathematics teachers could "prove" the Laws of Signs; it being obvious that his idea of "proof" was impossible of realization.

‡ Since we are discussing a special type of group here, we drop the ∘ in $f \circ g$ in favor of the "multiplicative" form fg customarily used for transformations.

group, then $\mathfrak{T}$ is called *a group of transformations*, or *transformation group*.

In particular, we have:

3.4   Theorem. *If $\mathfrak{T}$ is a set of transformations of a collection S such that* (1) *the product of every two elements of $\mathfrak{T}$ is an element of $\mathfrak{T}$*, (2) *the identity transformation, $x = f_0(x)$, is an element of $\mathfrak{T}$, and* (3) *the inverses of elements of $\mathfrak{T}$ are elements of $\mathfrak{T}$, then $\mathfrak{T}$ is a transformation group.*

[Since axioms 1, 3 and 4 of 1.2 are provided for in the statement of the theorem, it is only necessary to notice that the associative law holds.]

3.5 Geometry according to Klein

In the applications to geometry, the set S in the above definitions is some kind of *space*. In modern mathematics, the term "space" has extremely broad connotations, the difference between "set" and "space" often being very slight, a "space" being simply a set to which certain special properties have been added. The most common property is that of having a *metric*, or *distance, function*.

3.5.1   The space of analytic geometry

Consider, for instance, the plane of analytic geometry. As a *set*, it is the collection S of all ordered pairs (x, y) of real numbers x, y. As a *space*, it is the set S together with the Pythagorean distance function $d(p, q)$ which expresses the distance between p and q; if p is (x_1, y_1) and q is (x_2, y_2), then we have the usual expression:

(3.5a) $d(p, q) = \sqrt{(x_1 - x_2)^2 + (y_1 - y_2)^2}.$

[In analytic geometry, when we draw the customary right triangle relative to rectangular axes and state that $d(x, y)$ is the length of the hypotenuse of this triangle, we really assume (3.5a) and thereby define our space.] All the other properties of the analytic plane follow from this definition.

Similarly, to get the space of three-dimensional analytic geometry we start with the *set* of all ordered triples (x, y, z) of real numbers x, y, z; to define the *space* we add a distance function similar to (3.5a). Analogous remarks hold for the spaces of four-dimensional, five-dimensional, and generally n-dimensional analytic geometry.

3.5.2   The most general types of space

The most general type of space is the *topological space*. If we analyze the intrinsic effect of the addition of the distance function (3.5a) to the collection of pairs (x, y) of real numbers, we see that it amounts to the assignment of *position* to the pairs (x, y) relative to one another. Thus, if p, q, and r are points and $d(p, q) = 2$, $d(p, r) = 3$, then we consider q "nearer" to p than r. And, as the distance between points decreases, in terms of the usual ordering by magnitude of the real numbers $d(p, q)$, we consider that they come more nearly to occupy the same position in the plane of analytic geometry.

If we consider *position* of elements of a set as basic, then we arrive at the notion of a *topological space* (one of the earliest alternative names for topology was *Analysis Situs*—"position analysis"—due to Gauss). There are other ways of defining relative position than by the method of distance functions, however. One way is to assign a *neighborhood* to each element of the set, S, which we want to make into a space. Thus, in the ordered set R of real numbers, if $r \varepsilon R$, then for any two real numbers a and b such that $a < r < b$ we may call the set

(3.5b) $\{x \mid a < x < b\}$

a neighborhood of r in R. Such notions as that of *limit* of a sequence, for example, are directly definable in terms of such neighborhoods as (3.5b). However, the most fundamental notion in a topological space T is that of *limit point*, a point p being a limit point of a set M of points in T if, for *every* neighborhood U of p in T, the set $M \cap (U - p)$ is not empty. Thus the number 0 is a limit point of the set of real numbers $\{x \mid 0 < x < 1\}$; also of $\{x \mid x = 1/n,\ n \varepsilon N\}$.

We notice, incidentally, that every simply ordered set can be considered a space, inasmuch as relative position of elements is given by the definition of $<$; it may not always be possible to express this by defining a distance function like (3.5a), but we can define neighborhoods by (3.5b). Notice, in the simply ordered set of ordinal numbers of the first and second classes, that ω, $\omega \cdot 2$, ω^2, etc., are all *limit points* of sets of ordinal numbers; this is the reason for calling them "limit numbers."

3.5.3   Usually there is some motive for the manner in which we turn a set into a space. For example, the motive underlying (3.5a) is to obtain a *euclidean* geometry; and the motive underlying (3.5b) is to express the intuitive notion of "limit" in the collection (thus ω is the limit of 1, 2, $\cdots$, n, $\cdots$ in a natural way). Any collection M can be turned into a topological space by defining each element to be a neighborhood of itself; but then the resulting space has no limit points and, unless there is a natural motive for this (such as, for example, where M is a finite collection, in which case we usually do not desire limit points), the resulting space is without significance.

3.5.4 Geometric properties and configurations

To sum up the foregoing remarks, to get a space from a set we add certain properties which in some way or other embody intuitive ideas of *position* in the set; the added properties or relations, and properties or relations definable from them, we may call *geometric*.

Thus, distance between points as defined by (3.5a) is a geometric property; it may also be considered a relation between p and q. Similarly, parallel, perpendicular, etc., are geometric relations between lines.

The elements of the space we usually call *points*, and special sets definable in terms of the geometric properties are called *geometric figures* or *configurations*. For example, the pairs (x, y) of the analytic geometry plane are called points, and the sets

$$\{(x, y) \mid (x - x_1)^2 + (y - y_1)^2 = r, \; r \, \varepsilon \, R\}$$

are called *circles* with *center* (x_1, y_1) and *radius* r. Properties definable in terms of sets alone, such as cardinal number, are not usually considered geometric (unless related particularly to a geometric property; see 3.5.5); and arbitrary collections of points, not defined in terms of geometric properties, are simply called *sets* of points, or *point sets*.

3.5.5 Geometric invariants

Now suppose that S is a space, P is a geometric property or relation of S, and T is a transformation of S. For example, S might be the space of plane analytic geometry defined in 3.5.1, P the distance function (3.5a), and T a rotation of S about the point $(0, 0)$. Then $d(p, q) = d(T(p), T(q))$; i.e., distance between a pair of points is the same as the distance between their images under T. We express the latter fact by saying that P is an invariant under the transformation T. On the other hand, with the same space S, but with P denoting the relation of perpendicularity between lines and T an affine transformation (1.2.1.4), generally it is not true that if lines L_1 and L_2 are perpendicular then $T(L_1)$ and $T(L_2)$ are perpendicular, so that perpendicularity will generally fail to be invariant under an affine transformation.

Now, if a property P is invariant under *all* transformations of a group $\mathfrak{X}$ of transformations of a space S, then we call P an *invariant* of S under $\mathfrak{X}$, or simply a $\mathfrak{X}$-*invariant* of S. For example, if $\mathfrak{X}$ is the group of affine transformations of the plane, S, of analytic geometry, then it is easy to show that parallelism of lines is a $\mathfrak{T}$-invariant of S. And, according to the point of view proposed by Klein in 1872,[†] one may speak of the $\mathfrak{T}$-*geometry of the space* S as the study of the properties of the space and its configurations that are invariant under $\mathfrak{T}$. That is, the $\mathfrak{T}$-*geometry of the space* S *is the study of the* $\mathfrak{T}$-*invariants of* S.

The importance of these ideas when they were first propounded cannot be fully appreciated without an understanding of the state of mathematics, particularly of geometry, at that time. Projective geometry had blossomed after the publication of the researches of such mathematicians as Poncelet in 1822 and von Staudt in 1847. Even some rudimentary but important beginnings had been recently made in topology by Riemann. But, with regard to the relations between the various geometries, their position in mathematics, and even the proper location of specific theorems, little had been done. Take for example the Euler polyhedral formula,[‡] still to be found in high school textbooks on geometry; it is now recognized as a theorem of topology, but at the time of which we are speaking it turned up in all sorts of places.

Of more significance, however, than special theorems was the application of Klein's idea to the classification of geometries themselves. To take an example, let us consider the geometry taught in high schools. What properties of figures do we study? They are such properties as length, area, congruence, parallelism, perpendicularity, similarity. All these are invariants under the *group of rigid motions;* this is the group whose elements are translations, rotations, and reflections through lines, as well as combinations of them of the sort defined in 3.2. The first part of high school geometry is devoted to the "rigid motion geometry of the plane and space." Later, attention is given to *similarity* or *equiform* geometry. Here the group is the group of *similarity transformations* which has the group of rigid motions as a subgroup, but contains also those transformations which preserve angles and reduce or increase distances between points in a certain ratio. Under

---

† See Klein [a]; this is a translation, with additional notes, of Klein's "Program on entering the philosophical faculty and the senate of the University of Erlangen in 1872," commonly called "Klein's Erlanger Program." It was customary, on appointment to a professorship in a German university, to deliver before the general faculty an "inaugural" lecture of this type.

‡ This is the theorem which states that, if the numbers of faces, edges, and vertices of a simple polyhedron are denoted by r, e, and v, respectively, then $r - e + v = 2$. The number 2 is here an invariant, although a cardinal number, since it is related to the geometric configuration (polyhedron) involved.

this enlarged group such properties as area, volume, and congruence are no longer the subject of study, being no longer invariants. However, "similar" figures such as similar triangles and polygons are investigated.

3.5.6 Affine geometry

If one enlarges the group $\mathfrak{T}$ of transformations, then not only is a different geometry obtained, but also the objects, i.e., invariants, of interest change. In the first place, there are fewer of them since, if new transformations are added, one may expect that properties which were invariant before are no longer so. And, secondly, the decrease in the number of invariants leads naturally to the search for invariants not noticed before. For example, if one takes for $\mathfrak{T}$ the set of all affine transformations of the plane (1.2.1.4), then no longer are angles invariant; however, parallelism of lines is an invariant property, and hence a subject for study in "affine geometry" of the plane.

When a transformation group $\mathfrak{T}_1$ is a subgroup of a transformation group $\mathfrak{T}$, one may choose to study, in the $\mathfrak{T}_1$-geometry, only those $\mathfrak{T}_1$-invariants that are not $\mathfrak{T}$-invariants, reserving the latter for the $\mathfrak{T}$-geometry.

3.5.7 Projective geometry

To continue the process begun in 3.5.6, one may consider the case where $\mathfrak{T}$ is the group of projective transformations of the plane. A projective transformation, from the analytic standpoint, is by definition a transformation which replaces a point (x, y) by a point (x', y') according to the rule:

$$x' = \frac{ax + by + c}{dx + ey + f}$$

$$y' = \frac{gx + hy + i}{dx + ey + f}$$

where a, b, c, $\cdots$ are real numbers and satisfy the condition that the determinant

$$\begin{vmatrix} a & b & c \\ d & e & f \\ g & h & i \end{vmatrix} \neq 0.$$

The group of affine transformations of the plane is that subgroup of the group of projective transformations for which $d = e = 0$. Now even parallelism of lines is no longer an invariant of the larger group; however, *incidence* of points and lines (that a point p and a line L are incident means that p is on L), for example, is an invariant. For an excellent elementary discussion of projective geometry (including a description and invariance proof of one of its most important invariants, the "cross ratio" of four points), the reader is referred to Courant and Robbins [C-R; 165ff].

3.5.8   Topology

As a branch of geometry,† the recently developed field of *topology* is based on a group $\mathfrak{T}$ whose elements, called *topological transformations* or *homeomorphisms*, are extremely general; a topological transformation is applicable to any topological space (3.5.2), and is merely a (1-1)-mapping (see IV 3.2.3.1) such that both the mapping and its inverse preserve limit points. For the layman, a topological transformation is therefore often roughly described as any deformation of a configuration that does not "tear" but is otherwise unrestricted; a circle may thus be deformed into an ellipse, a triangle, a polygon of any number of sides—but not into two non-intersecting circles (because of the "no tearing" condition) nor into a figure eight [because of the "(1-1)" character of the transformation]. Analogously, topology of the plane is sometimes facetiously called "rubber-sheet geometry." These descriptions are very unprecise, of course, as a topological transformation is something much more general, its true definition being that previously given in terms of preservation of limit points.

As for topological invariants, clearly distance is not an invariant, nor is any number which is a function of length, such as the cross ratio of projective geometry. However, to take a very simple case, the fact that two points, when deleted from a circle, separate it into two pieces is a topological invariant of the circle; for, no matter what the topological transformation T, the "transform" $T(C)$ of a circle C always has this property. Another, related topological property of

---

† It is hardly possible any longer to confine topology, as a branch of mathematics, to geometry in the Klein sense. Its early development by Riemann, Poincaré, Brouwer, Veblen, and others was geometric and quite classifiable within the Klein program. However, as it has most recently developed, topology has been adapted to all parts of mathematics, virtually any collection of mathematical objects being a "topological space" in some sense or other, with great advantages of simplification of method and breadth of perspective. Some have compared the rapidly growing role of topology in mathematics to the role which has been played by group theory.

the circle is that deleting *one* point from it does *not* "disconnect" it. The reader who has studied the theory of functions of a complex variable will recall the "simply connected regions" of the plane and the method of inducing simple connectedness by means of "cross cuts." Simple-connectedness and the minimum number of cross cuts needed to produce simple-connectedness are purely topological invariants.

3.5.9   Remarks. Although the Klein program formed an important landmark in the history of mathematics, serving to clear up many geometric misconceptions, arranging the mass of geometric material then existent in neat compartments, and pointing the way to new types of geometries,† what is today called "geometry" cannot be confined within its limits.‡ Nevertheless, the notion of a transformation group continues to be of great importance and to serve as a means of classification of geometries of the classic type.

4 Concluding remarks

With the discussion of these fundamental algebraic and geometric ideas we bring to a close our résumé of what may be called the foundations of classical mathematics. The ideas that form the content of this and the foregoing chapters are derived from the end result of centuries of mathematical thought and evolution, and constitute what we may consider the basis of the type of mathematics—algebra, geometry, analysis, etc.—that is commonly taught in universities at the present time.

In the following chapters we shall inquire more closely, from various points of view, into the source, validity, and acceptability of what has gone before.

SUGGESTED READING

Albert [Al; I, II, XI]   Kerschner and Wilcox [K-W; VII,
Baumgartner [Ba]   XX]
Bell [B₁; III–VI] [B₄; III–IX]   McCoy [Mc]
Birkhoff and MacLane [B–M]   Northrop [N; VIII]
Campbell [Ca; II–V]   van der Waerden [Wa]
                      Weyl [b]

† To invent a new geometry it was necessary only to find a new type of transformation group $\mathfrak{T}$ and a space to which it was applicable; such a "synthetically" produced geometry would perhaps be of little significance to the progress of mathematics, of course.

‡ Regarding geometries outside the scope of transformation group classification, see Veblen and Whitehead [V-W; 31–33].

PROBLEMS

1. Do the natural numbers and their reciprocals, with $\times$ as operation, form a group?

2. Let G be a set with three distinct elements 1, x, y, and an operation whose operation table is:

	1	x	y
1	1	x	y
x	y	1	x
y	x	y	1

Does G form a group with respect to this operation? If not, which of the axioms for a group fail to hold?

3. Form a group of order 6 analogous to the group of 1.2.1.3. Relate it to the regular hexagon.

4. Prove Theorem 1.3.4 without using the commutativity of i.

5. Show that, if in axioms 3 and 4 of 1.2 the expressions "$x \circ i = x$," "$x \circ x^{-1} = i$" are replaced by "$i \circ x = x$," "$x^{-1} \circ x = i$," respectively, then the new axiom system is equivalent to the old (cf. Problems 11 and 12 of Chapter II).

6. Show that, if only one of the two changes in axioms 3 and 4 indicated in Problem 5 is made, then the new axiom system is not equivalent to the old.

7. Show that, if axioms 3 and 4 of 1.2 are replaced by the statement of Theorem 1.3.5, then the new axiom system is equivalent to the old.

8. Show that, if G is of finite order n, then axioms 3 and 4 of 1.2 may be replaced by the right- and left-hand cancellation laws (1.3.2, 1.3.4.1).

9. Why are the elements of G in 1.2.1.4 restricted by the relation $ad \neq bc$?

10. Show that all groups of order 3 are isomorphic.

11. Exhibit two operation tables such that every group of order 4 has one of them for its operation table.

12. In any group we may represent $x \circ x$ by x^2, $x \circ x \circ x$ by x^3, and so on. If a group G has an element g such that, for every $x \, \varepsilon \, G$, there is a $k \, \varepsilon \, N$ such that $x^k = g$, then G is called *cyclic*. Show that for every $n \, \varepsilon \, N$ there exists a cyclic group of order n.

13. Show that the real numbers mod 1 do not form a system $(X, +, \times)$ as defined in 2.1.

14. Do the real numbers mod 1 satisfy the Laws of Signs as embodied in Theorems 2.2.2 to 2.2.4?

15. Show that the ring of integers mod 4 is not a field. What can one say in this respect about the integers mod p, where p is a prime?

16. If r is an element, not 0, of a ring R, and there exists $x \, \varepsilon \, R$, $x \neq 0$ such that $r \times x = 0$, then r is called a *zero-divisor* of R. Show that a necessary and sufficient condition that a ring R be an integral domain is that it have no zero-divisors.

17. Construct addition and multiplication tables for a field having four elements, in which $1 + 1 = 0$.

18. Show that the set of all real numbers of the form $a + b\sqrt{2}$, where $a,b \, \varepsilon \, F$, with $+$ and $\times$ in the ordinary sense, is a field.

19. Prove that no proper subset of F is a field (if $+$ and $\times$ have their usual meaning in F).

20. Show that, for any two elements x and y of a system $(X, +, \times)$, the number $[(-x) \times y] + [x \times y] + [-(x \times y)]$ is both $(-x) \times y$ and $-(x \times y)$ and hence $(-x) \times y = -(x \times y)$.

21. Show that the ring of all continuous, single-valued real functions is not an integral domain.

22. Using the notation of 2.3.6, show that, if A is an ideal of X, then the operation $\times$ is uniquely defined for the cosets of X/A; i.e., if $x_1 \, \varepsilon \, A + x$, $y_1 \, \varepsilon \, A + y$, then $x_1 \times y_1 \, \varepsilon \, A + (x \times y)$.

23. Show that the integers form a subring, but not an ideal, of the ring of all polynomials in one variable x with integer coefficients (with $+$, $\times$ as usually understood).

24. Show that, if X is the polynomial ring of Problem 23 and I the subring of integers, then the cosets of X mod I (rel. $+$) do not satisfy uniquely an operation $\times$ as defined for the case if I were an ideal of X.

25. In Definition 2.7.1, replace the requirement that "$0 < x$, $0 < y$ imply $0 < x \times y$" by "$0 < x$, $0 < y$ imply $x \times y < 0$." What do the "Laws of Signs" become in the resulting system? Is this new "real number system" consistent?

P A R T   I I

Development of
Various Viewpoints
on Foundations

Up to this point our chief concern has been with what might be called foundation *material;* i.e., the ideas and methods which form the basis of the mathematics taught in most modern universities. Except for incidental remarks, there has been little formal criticism or philosophical speculation on the *nature* of the material.

In this second part, however, the discussion is no longer confined to the "orthodox," although much of what is included may justly be so labeled, or at least is of such a character that it is rapidly becoming so. Although the preceding chapters may have seemed, with few exceptions such as the Russell and Burali-Forti contradictions, to consist of what the "non-cognoscenti" would expect of mathematics— precise, logical ideas and methods of deduction—and to depict a situation which appears fairly "austere and serene," the fact is that in modern mathematics the austerity and serenity are mainly on the surface. At the heart of mathematical creation there is sharp disagreement as to the origin, meaning, and validity of mathematical notions. The remark in II 6.3 that it would be almost a miracle to get as many as five mathematicians to agree upon a definition of *mathematics*, was not an exaggeration; certainly with few exceptions no mathematician would seriously propose such a definition.† This is due to the nature of the subject; it is not a dead compendium of laws regarding "quantity" and "space," but a live, growing aspect of human culture that would quickly break the bonds of any confining definition.

During periods which have been conducive to abstract thought and intellectual freedom, such as those of ancient Greece and the European Renaissance, mathematicians and mathematical philosophers have speculated on the nature of their activities. In modern times, such

† By "definition" is meant the type of definition used in mathematics; see the second paragraph of Chapter III.

speculation has been particularly active in the Western European culture, and has led to sharply differing conclusions. It will be the function of this second part to describe some of the chief aspects of this development and its present status; not exhaustively (which would require volumes!), but enough to draw a general picture whose details may be filled in, wherever desired, by reference to the bibliographical material cited. The descriptions of the differing views of various individual mathematicians or "schools" will be as objective and impartial as possible. At times it may seem that "sides" are being taken; such an impression, however, will be due to the desire to present the advocate's point of view as advantageously as possible.

It will be impossible, as a matter of fact, to do justice to all points of view in a work of this size and nature. The available space is too limited, and probably many readers would not want to labor with all the details. The best that can be done is to include certain general ideas to the extent of *provocation;* that is, that the reader will be provoked into going to original sources (furnished in the citations to the bibliography) and forming his own conclusions on the merits of the case in hand. If I succeed in doing this, I shall have fulfilled my function of reporter and expositor!

VIII

The Early Developments

Some description of the development of the present-day situation has already been included in the earlier chapters. For instance, in Chapter I we remarked on the background and development of the modern axiomatic method. And in III 1 and III 2 the circumstances which led up to the invention of the set-theoretic contradictions and some of the resulting impact on mathematical thought were described. In the present chapter these matters will find their place in a systematic (although necessarily of an "outline" character) presentation, in approximately chronological order, of the origin and sources of the various schools of opinion now in existence.

1   The eighteenth-century beginnings of analysis

Any student of the history of mathematics is familiar with the discussions that followed the work of Leibnitz and Newton on the calculus. The literature of the time shows that many different concepts of the meaning of differentials were then current; and that the methods of proof then in vogue would for the most part be wholly unacceptable today. One prominent mathematician † of the period postulated that "A quantity, which is increased or decreased infinitely little, is neither increased nor decreased." One may wonder just what "infinitely little" meant; to the modern mathematician the phrase would be indicative of a lack of comprehension of the fundamental ideas of the calculus. It is probably not unfair to state that for a long time the calculus had no foundation. Each writer chose what seemed to him a "foundation" and built thereon. The period can be characterized as one of experimentation. Mathematicians were aware of the importance of the new theory (calculus), and in general showed remarkably good sense in developing it. As a matter of fact, we should not be unjustly critical of the pioneering work done at this time; rather,

† Johann Bernoulli.

189

our admiration should be evoked by the manner in which sound mathematical theory was erected on unsound bases.

For example, Lagrange tried to avoid the difficulties in the meaning of the differential by using the derivative exclusively. Instead of proceeding, like Johann Bernoulli and Euler, to set up expressions in dx and treating some of the occurrences of dx as zero, and others as "infinitely small" quantities, he calculated his derivatives by expanding functions in Taylor's series and then selecting the respective coefficients as (by definition) the derivatives. He attempted to show that any function can be so handled, which is of course incorrect; but he may be considered to have incidentally made a beginning on the theory of analytic functions.

When any attention at all was paid to divergence of series, it was as a rule of a desultory and unrigorous character. Even after Cauchy had given a rigorous foundation for the theory of infinite series, old habits prevailed. The notion of *limit*, so simple from the modern standpoint, remained fairly clouded in mystery throughout the eighteenth century. D'Alembert gave a good approximation to the modern definition (his definition gave Cauchy the starting point for his "Cours d'analyse"), but unfortunately the idea of "approach"—a quantity approaching another "nearer than by any given quantity"— led to such futile questions as "Can a variable *reach* its limit?"

As we shall see, modern "rigor" is not beyond reproach,† although it would hardly be possible for a "layman" to criticize, with justification, the present standards of rigor, such as happened in the eighteenth century when Bishop Berkeley attacked Newton's "fluxions." ‡

2 The nineteenth-century foundation of analysis

Early in the nineteenth century Cauchy placed the calculus on an essentially modern basis; Abel, Gauss, and Cauchy developed a rigorous treatment of infinite series; and later in the century Weierstrass worked at the "arithmetization" of analysis. A characteristic of the latter was the freeing of analysis from the intuitive geometric type of proof so prevalent at the time. For example, the geometric approach to continuous real functions leads naturally to the belief that such a function, representable by a "smooth" graph, certainly must have derivatives at *some* points at least. Weierstrass' famous counter ex-

---

† The handling of differentials is still a subject of discussion; see, for example, Randolph and Kac [a], Church [c], and Jackson [a].

‡ See the entertaining account in Struik's remarkable little history of mathematics [St; 178]. The reader may find it profitable to read the entire account of the beginnings of analysis in this book.

ample † dispelled this illusion. We must here keep in mind, however, that to "free" a theory of certain notions does not necessarily imply that those notions forever thereafter cease to be of use. Just as in the case of the undefined terms of an axiomatic system we find it extremely useful, and in practice necessary, to keep certain interpretations in mind, so in the development of calculus and function theory we find it advantageous to continue to use geometric interpretations. Now and then an exceptional student can "bypass" analytic geometry, going directly to the study of calculus; but customarily it is advisable first to take the course in analytic geometry, it being generally conceded that the teaching of calculus is greatly facilitated by the use of graphs. Strictly speaking, however, no analytic geometry is needed for either calculus or function theory.

We might recall here that we make similar concessions to pedagogy in the teaching of high school geometry, not striving to place it on a truly axiomatic basis but allowing the student to use "preconceived notions" such as "straight," "distance," "measure." In the teaching of calculus, we accept the geometric foundation of the sine function which the student has studied previously in his trigonometry course, and consequently we resort to a fictitious geometric proof that $\lim_{x \to 0}(\sin x)/x = 1$, before establishing the derivatives of the trigonometric functions. (In analysis, the latter are *analytically* defined, not geometrically.) Such pedagogic devices are entirely justifiable, of course, except that it is questionable whether the student should forever be kept insulated from the underlying "concessions." Certainly he should not be allowed to believe that he is receiving *dogma*.

The work of Weierstrass was paralleled by that of other researchers, especially Dedekind and Cantor. Dedekind's approach to the foundation of the real numbers has already been exemplified in the "Dedekind cut" (see VI 3.4 for instance), and contact has been made with that of Cantor in the characterization of the order type of the real number system by means of the separability principle.‡ Both Dedekind's methods and those of Cantor were based on an acceptance of the "actually infinite." We have seen, for example, how the Dedekind cut defines a single real number in terms of infinite classes of numbers.

Vigorous opposition to these ideas, especially to the ideas of Cantor (which we discussed in some detail in Chapters IV and V), were expressed by Kronecker.

† Riemann also possessed such an example (unpublished).

‡ Cantor designated the order type of $\{x \mid 0 \leq x \leq 1\}$ as "order type θ." Instead of the Dedekind cut axiom which we used in VI 1.4, however, Cantor employed the notion of "perfect set"; to define the latter would have necessitated employing the notion of limit point.

2.1   Kronecker's "intuitionism"

Kronecker was a contemporary and (ultimately) colleague † of Weierstrass at the University of Berlin, but their different notions of what constitutes mathematical existence did not make for harmony between them.‡ Because of their "prophetical" significance and relation to the present-day discussions on foundations, we shall outline briefly Kronecker's chief views:

2.1.1   In the first place, he *objected strenuously to "clouding" mathematics by basing the notions of finite set and of real numbers on the actually infinite.* Although he agreed that "arithmetization" was the correct approach, not only to analysis but also to all mathematics, his ideas of arithmetization ruled out all use of infinite sets (as in the Dedekind cut) in both definitions and number constructions. Much quoted is his remark,§ "The integers were made by God, but everything else is the work of man." Hence:

2.1.2   He asserted that *the natural numbers and operations with them are "intuitively founded,"* and that *algebraic numbers and operations with them can be based on the natural numbers and their properties; but that the real numbers are not capable of such a foundation.*

Here he was striking at the heart of the question of *what constitutes mathematical existence.* Previously there had been considerable reluctance, because of fear of ridicule or of ecclesiastical denunciation, to introduce certain concepts (as, for example, negative and imaginary numbers, and non-euclidean geometries), but evidently Kronecker's objections were based on a serious and deeper-lying philosophy. He seemed to fear that there was a danger of mathematics drifting into fantasy and mysticism. To him, the Cantor theory of transfinite numbers was not mathematics but mysticism; ‖ it started with the

---

† Weierstrass was professor at the University of Berlin for thirty years, commencing with the year 1856. Kronecker (whose private resources freed him of the necessity of seeking a salaried position) commenced his sojourn in Berlin in 1855, teaching informally at the university until finally accepting a professorship made vacant by Kummer's retirement in 1883.

‡ In a letter to Sonja Kowalewski, Weierstrass complained bitterly of the fate that compelled him to endure the "interesting, but not mathematics" type of comment which Kronecker frequently used in appraising Weierstrass' work and that of others.

§ Bell [B₁; 34] facetiously remarks that inasmuch as "he said this in an after dinner speech perhaps he should not be held to it too strictly."

‖ Cantor was aware that his work was in a sense (to cite Struik [St; 243]) "a continuation of the ancient scholastic speculations on the nature of the infinite" and "defended St. Augustine's full acceptance of the actually infinite."

assumption that infinite sets exist in mathematics—an assumption that to Kronecker was untenable.

The reader may be puzzled by the conjunction of this statement with the preceding statement that Kronecker accepted natural numbers and operations with them. But notice that we did not say *"the set* of natural numbers . . ."' The latter might be taken to imply an *already existing* "totality." In the latter sense, we recognize, for example, that

$$2,867,944,782,612,713,942$$

is the symbol for a natural number, although it is quite likely that no one has ever seen it before it appeared here in print! That is, it is an element of the "set of all natural numbers" which existed *prior* to our selecting this particular one of its elements for exhibition. Quite different is the conception of the natural numbers as a kind of constructible or "growing" collection which consists of a *beginning* set of numbers—1, 2, 3, 4, 5, 6, 7, 8, 9, 10, etc.—and a rule for deriving new elements of the "collection" (thus $10 + 1 = 11$; $11 + 1 = 12$; going as *far as we like or are able*). In the latter case no actual infinite is ever attained! And the above natural number is not a natural number because it is a member of some *already existing* totality, but because it can be exhibited as a result of the construction just indicated. If one objects that each and every natural number is so attainable and hence the existence of the "set of all natural numbers" again follows, it can be pointed out that this assumes an *infinity* of operations in order to construct each and *every* natural number. For the "finitist," only the "constructible" concept of the natural numbers is acceptable. By "intuitively founded" Kronecker evidently meant that we have an intuition of the natural numbers founded on our experience of time and the succession of events.

When informed of Lindemann's proof (1882) that π is a transcendental number, Kronecker is reported to have remarked that this was of interest, excepting for the fact that π does not exist!

This is perhaps an exaggeration, the evidence pointing rather to a rejection of the general notions of irrationals as set up by his contemporaries. In order specifically to avoid these and, indeed, avoid the use of all numbers except natural numbers (even negative integers!), Kronecker developed a modular arithmetic, employing congruences mod $x + 1$, or mod $x^2 + 1$ (to avoid use of the complex unit i), etc. (For a simple discussion of these matters, see Couturat [Co₂; 603–616].)

2.1.3   *All definitions and proofs should be "constructive,"* that is, a definition of a mathematical entity should permit one to construct the entity; for example, by giving a *rule* for its construction from mathematical elements already known to exist. (In particular, the "set of all real numbers" is not definable in this sense.) And, if a proof is given of the existence of a mathematical entity, then the proof should be "constructive"; i.e., one following the steps of the proof should thereby commence constructing the entity.

For example, most proofs of the Fundamental Theorem of Algebra are non-constructive, in that they show that the assumption of the existence of an algebraic equation having no root leads to contradiction. Such proofs give no inkling as to how to find the root. Generally, reductio ad absurdum existence proofs are of this nature, hence, from Kronecker's point of view, unacceptable.

Another type of existence proof to which Kronecker would have objected is that which relies on the Choice Axiom (III 6.3). An outstanding example of such a proof is that of the Well-ordering Theorem (V 5.1.4). In this proof it is assumed, on the basis of the Choice Axiom, that, for each subset S' of a given set S, there exists a representative element $x(S')$. But no rule is given for specifying $x(S')$, so that one is unable actually to well-order a given set by following the steps of the proof.

Like comments hold regarding the proof (V 3.1.6.3) that the set R (assuming its existence for the moment) has a basis. Before giving the rule for constructing such a basis, a well-ordering of R has to be provided! Yet from the existence of a basis one can prove many beautiful mathematical theorems.

2.1.4   *Arguments of a purely logical nature do not necessarily yield legitimate mathematical theorems.*   This is a natural corollary of the stipulation (2.1.3) that existence proofs must be constructive. Thus, to use again the example of the reductio ad absurdum proofs of the Fundamental Theorem of Algebra, such existence proofs are logically correct perhaps, but they are of no value as *mathematics*. For mathematics the proofs must provide a way of *finding* the roots asserted to exist.

We note here the first inkling of a possible limitation on the use of logic in mathematics. From a position of utter dependence on logic, one turns to a new criterion: *construction* on the basis of the natural numbers. One may still use logic—for example, one will prove *nonexistence* of an entity by the usual demonstration that assumption of existence leads to contradiction. But to squeeze *existence* out of such logical manipulation is not valid *mathematically*.

2.1.5   Thus Kronecker's meaning of the term "arithmetization" is quite literal! From the arithmetic of the natural numbers one constructs, by finite methods, the rest of mathematics. As we shall see, in "the rest of mathematics" we do not reach all that is commonly taught today, not even all the real numbers which are at the basis of present-day analysis!

Kronecker found, in his day, no supporters for his opinions. Otherwise, our discussion of his ideas would not have been relegated to a few paragraphs of a summary nature! No doubt this was due in considerable measure to the severe limitations they placed on both method and content, and the radical proposal which they contained regarding the purely *logical* as opposed to the *mathematical*. But still his ideas might have found more favor, and certainly would have been accorded more sympathetic discussion among his colleagues, if it were not for the advent of Cantor's theory of the transfinite.

2.2 Cantor's theory of the transfinite

During the period 1879–1897 Cantor published his investigations on the theory of sets, including the theory of cardinal and ordinal numbers. It is interesting to observe that he was led to his ideas by his researches in analysis, particularly in the theory of trigonometric series. We have already referred (footnote in connection with V 3.2.2.2) to his observation of the well-ordered sequence of derivatives of a given set of real numbers, for instance. Cantor's ideas, as applied to the foundations of analysis, form an extensive continuation of the work of Weierstrass.

Their fruitfulness in analysis, however, was almost eclipsed by their influence on mathematics in general. In geometry, for example, they made possible a new perspective. And in the new field of topology they became indispensable.

On all sides, then, Cantor's ideas bore fruit. Is it any wonder that the objections of Kronecker † were of no avail and that the Cantorian theory prevailed? It is true that some of the "fruit" was sour—Cantor himself was probably aware of the fact that care and discretion had to be used in "storming the infinite"—else one might transcend consistency entirely. But the good seemed by far to outweigh the bad. Consequently today we find the ideas of Cantor, especially his extensions of Weierstrass' treatment of the real number system, almost universally accepted and taught in the universities and colleges of the world. This, incidentally, partially explains the prominence which we have accorded them in the earlier chapters.

Before continuing in this vein, however, we should note another development that was taking place during the latter part of the nineteenth century, one which was to have considerable influence on present-day thought.

3 The symbolizing of logic

We have already had occasion to comment, in III 2.3, on the rise of "symbolic logic." In order that the nature of this development

---

† Cantor's ideas also met criticism, but, since most of this was based either on misunderstanding or on non-mathematical grounds, it received little attention from mathematicians.

may be clear, we recall that logic, as developed by the Greeks (particularly Aristotle), and by the scholastic philosophers of the Middle Ages, made little use of symbols. It is true that not infrequently symbols were used as a kind of shorthand. For example, the syllogism might be stated in the form, "If from A follows B, and A is true, then B is true." Here A and B stand for propositions of perfectly general character; the classical logicians understood well the generality of their logical laws. But such use of symbols is a far cry from a *calculus* of symbols, such as was introduced in mathematics in very early times.

3.1   Meaning and purpose of a symbolic logic

When we speak of *symbolic logic*, then, we mean something analogous to the use of symbols in mathematics. When we apply algebra to the solution of some concrete problem, we are employing a *symbolic calculus* in which the steps involved in solving the particular problem have all been provided for; little further thought need be expended, once the symbols of the algebra (x, y, $\cdots$) have been properly interpreted or adapted to the problem. In a simple case where only one symbol, x, receives a meaning, and, say, a quadratic equation results, the solution of the latter by the "quadratic formula" gives the desired result "ready made." So, in logic, we desire not only symbols to designate the entities (such as propositions and classes) with which we deal, but symbolic representation of *relations* (such as $\supset$, ε, $\subset$) and *rules for operating with them*. The reasoning involved in special problems should be provided for in the resulting calculus.

It was undoubtedly the example of what a good calculus of symbols had accomplished in mathematics that stimulated the search for a similar apparatus to employ for the *reasoning process*. The purpose of such an apparatus would be not simply a way of making reasoning —more specifically, the drawing of conclusions by the deductive process—an easier feat, but it was realized, in view of the example of mathematics, that (1) greater rigor and (2) broader perspectives would be attainable. Both of these aspects of the symbolic method are involved in the facility with which the mathematician sees new properties and relations in known theories, and the opening up of new avenues of research.

3.2   Influence of Leibnitz

Probably no one realized these facts better than Leibnitz, who, though neither he nor anyone else can be credited with *beginning* symbolic logic, was one of the prime movers in its direction. With Leibnitz's somewhat grandiose schemes for systematizing, and reducing to a few simple elements, all human thought we are not concerned here; but his recognition of the importance of a good symbolism, and in particular of instituting a calculus of reasoning (*calculus ratiocinator*), together with his subsequent propagandizing for it, were unquestionably a factor in stimulating the logicians of the eighteenth and nineteenth centuries.†

3.3   Boole's algebra of logic

What can perhaps properly be called a "foundation" for symbolic logic was laid in England in the first half of the nineteenth century, especially by Boole and De Morgan. In Boole's work we obtain for the first time a calculus of logic, specifically a calculus of sets, complete with rules of operation. It is properly called an algebra—not quite the modern form of "Boolean algebra," however—since all four elementary operations of algebra are defined. Subtraction had the same meaning as in III 3.3.2, and multiplication the same meaning as in III 3.3; but addition was somewhat different in that ‡ $x + y$ was defined only for x and y disjoint. Rules such as the commutative laws of addition and multiplication and distributive laws were given, as well as such peculiar laws as $x^2 = x$. The numbers 1 and 0 occupied special positions in that 1 designated the entire universe of elements (of which all sets are subsets); 0 designated the null set (our ∅ of III 3.4). The difficulties arising in the interpretation of such expressions as $x + 1$, x/y, $2x$, were circumvented by noticing that, if one treated the algebra as though the variables were restricted to the values 0 and 1, then all ordinary laws and operations were applicable. The result was, then, that if one carried through the algebra without worrying about interpreting the formulas derived,§ and used the devices worked out by Boole to reduce the resulting expressions, the end product would be both valid and capable of interpretation.‖

† The reader might consult the section on Leibnitz in Struik [St; 154ff].

‡ To denote sets we shall use here the usual symbols x, y, $\cdots$ of algebra rather than the capital letters (S, A, B, $\cdots$) of Chapter III.

§ These were usually incapable of interpretation.

‖ The student familiar with Boole's *Calculus of Finite Differences*, still used in present-day instruction (particularly of actuarial students), should understand this process perfectly. The algebraic operations with Σ, $\int$, etc., performed with meaningless formulas, but ultimately reduced to a form where they can be affixed to the functions under consideration, form a nice analogue of the logical algebra.

3.4 Subsequent development of the algebra

One of the principal changes subsequently made in Boole's algebra of logic was the interpretation (Jevons) of $x + y$ as defined in III 3.3. This enabled one to write $x + x = x$ and thus eliminate the $2x$ which had no interpretation. And, to get rid of other non-interpretable formulas, division was altogether eliminated (Peirce). The inclusion symbol, $\subset$, of III 3.1.2 was introduced by C. S. Peirce. The monumental treatise of Schröder [Sch], published in 1890, more or less brought this development to a final satisfactory form.

It would take us too far afield to exhibit the details † of the Boole-Schröder algebra; and it is essential only that we sketch the background of the present-day uses of symbolic methods. Before leaving the subject matter of this section, however, we should note one other item of importance for the sequel. This is the distinction between *proposition* and *propositional function* introduced by Peirce and Schröder. The former may be represented by a statement involving only constants, and that is always true or always false; the latter by a statement that involves certain variables for some values of which it may be true, for others false. A substantial portion of the contribution of Peirce and Schröder was devoted to developing the calculi of propositions and propositional functions.

4 The reduction of mathematics to logical form

By the latter half of the nineteenth century, mathematical thought had matured to the point where it was recognized that mathematics could be developed along "pure" or abstract lines, with no reference to material reality. Undoubtedly the acceptance of conflicting (euclidean and non-euclidean) geometries and the consequent denial of one of the tenets of Kantian philosophy had a good deal to do with this evolution. And, too, the ideas of Leibnitz and the subsequent development of logic along formal lines must have exerted an influence. In addition, both Peirce and Schröder had begun to apply their logical calculus to arithmetic.

4.1 Frege's arithmetic

The first work of a definitive character, so far as basing mathematics on logic is concerned, was that of Frege. In his *Begriffschrift* [Fr₁] he introduced the notion of "propositional function"—called by him

---

† The reader might consult Couturat's little book [Co₁]. Also see Birkhoff and MacLane [B-M; XI]. Regarding Peirce's work, see Keyser [a] and works cited therein.

"Function," the term "propositional function" being due to Russell (see Chapter IX)—and a complete system of basic formulas for propositions in terms of implication and negation (compare the comment of Hilbert-Bernays [H-B; 64f]). Frege's *Die Grundlagen der Arithmetik*, published in 1884 (now available in parallel paged German and English translation [Fr]), is a landmark in the development of the modern logical foundations of mathematics, being the first attempt to base mathematics on pure logic; specifically, to found, on the notions of primitive logic, both definitions of number and laws of arithmetic. To quote Frege's own appraisal of the work † [Fr; 99ᵉ], "Arithmetic thus becomes simply a development of logic; and every proposition of arithmetic a law of logic, albeit a derivative one." This work (in which, incidentally, the "Frege-Russell" definition of number given in IV 4.1 first appeared) was not accorded proper credit until Russell called attention to its true worth and significance.

4.2 The Peano school

Of a somewhat different type was the work of Peano and his colleagues. Instead of trying to *base* mathematics on logic, they analyzed the methods of mathematics and tried to *express* them in a form similar to that of the logical calculi. It could be characterized as a union of mathematics and a calculus of logic. Instead of trying to give "natural number" a *meaning* such as is embodied in the Frege-Russell definition, i.e., reducing it to the logical notion of set, Peano treated the notion as undefined and set up essentially the axiom system which we gave in III 5.1.

However, as Peano formulated the axioms, they were stated in the logical symbols which constitute his "pasigraphy." For "number" the symbol "No" was used, $a+$ designated the successor of a, etc., and the analogue of axiom (2) of III 5.1, for example, was stated in the form

$$a \, \varepsilon \, \text{No} \, . \supset . \, a+ \, \varepsilon \, \text{No}, \ddagger$$

where ε corresponds to the symbol denoting "is an element of" which we introduced in III 3.1. (The introduction of this symbol ε, implying a recognition of the necessity for making a distinction between ε and $\subset$, was an important innovation, incidentally.) The derivation of theorems becomes an algebraic process, only symbols and formulas being employed; each theorem is stated as a symbolic formula. The

† By permission of Basil Blackwell.

‡ Literally translated: "If a is a number, then $a+$ is a number"; the symbol $\supset$ denoted implication.

reader can consult Peano's *Formulaire* [P₃] for details, especially Volume V.†

This method of deriving mathematical theorems as symbolic formulas from a given set of axioms stated as formulas, using what corresponds to a logical calculus for the derivation, finds its counterpart in the so-called "formal systems" of modern mathematical logic, to which we come later. It reduces mathematics to a strictly "formal" process, with no direct reference to any "real" interpretation of the symbols involved. It has the advantages that accrue from avoiding errors due to varied interpretations of terms or unsuitable connotations, such as are frequently made in the use of ordinary language, as well as from rendering the steps of a proof more precise and less vaguely dependent upon logical rules. It has its opponents among those who dislike such formality and divorcement from "reality." It does, however, represent an important development in the relations between mathematics and the methods of symbolic logic, as well as in the evolution of mathematics itself, and has had an influence on both mathematics and logic which continues to the present day.

5   Introduction of antinomies and paradoxes

Another development of great importance, which occurred at the end of the nineteenth century and the beginning of the twentieth, was the introduction of the contradictions to which the "unrestricted" theory of sets leads (cf. III 1.1, III 2, IV 4.2.7, V 3.2.3). That this new theory, so beautiful and fruitful, should lead to such logical consequences came as a profound shock to many mathematicians. Frege (who lived until 1925), for example, considered that all his work, based on the theory of sets, was jeopardized. Many mathematicians, as a result of the antinomies, as well as of later developments in the foundations, have ceased to work on aspects of mathematics which depend upon an unqualified acceptance of set theory. Poincaré characterized the theory of sets as "a disease from which mathematics will some day recover." Others, more courageous perhaps, or more convinced of the ultimate validity of the theory of cardinal and ordinal numbers, set out to correct the errors into which mathematics had drifted. Prominent among these was Russell, whose use of the "logistic" method we shall discuss presently; also Zermelo, who attacked the problem of providing a set theory free of contradiction by trying to furnish a consistent axiom system which would avoid the "too large" sets.

† The volumes of the *Formulaire* were published between 1894 and 1908, and essentially represent a series of reports by Peano and his collaborators.

6 Zermelo's Well-ordering Theorem

The publication of Zermelo's proof of the Well-ordering Theorem (Zermelo [a]) in 1904 added fuel to the discussion, since even those mathematicians who would grant the existence of the set R were, in many cases, loath to admit the possibility of its being well-ordered. There was no question of any contradiction here; it was a question of admissible methods and existence. Already the question of what constitutes mathematical existence had arisen in connection with Kronecker's views, and the appearance of contradiction in set theory had revived some of the ideas expressed by Kronecker. This was particularly to be noted in Poincaré's writings.

7 Poincaré's views

Poincaré's reaction to the Zermelo theorem was one of complete rejection. His basis for this was the *lack of definition* of representative elements involved in the use of the Choice Axiom, which we have already stated (in 2.1.3) would have been opposed by Kronecker. In a way, Poincaré can be considered a follower of Kronecker in his philosophy of mathematics. Of Poincaré's views we should mention specifically the following:

7.1 *Every mathematical concept should be capable of explicit (finite) definition.*

7.2 *Existence of a mathematical entity should be verifiable by a finite procedure.*

7.3 *Most of the concepts and conclusions of the Cantor theory of sets should be excluded from mathematics.*

In 7.1 to 7.3 Poincaré was clearly in agreement with Kronecker. Kronecker did not have the antinomies before him as a guide in attacking the problem of definition, however, as Poincaré did. Poincaré's reaction to them was:

7.4 *Non-predicative definitions should not be employed.* By a *non-predicative definition* is meant a definition of an entity E which defines E in terms of a class of which E is an element. It not infrequently happens that, in order to specify a certain real number, for example, we determine a class to which we know it belongs, and then we define the number in terms of this class. Thus we define the maximum of a continuous function, which has been defined over a closed interval, as the greatest of all its values. Such a definition is non-predicative.†

But it seems impossible to give up this type of definition entirely, especially in the theory of sets. To reject sets defined non-predicatively would, to be sure, bar such self-contradictory and non-predicatively defined sets as the set of all sets and the well-ordered set of all ordinal numbers. But the cost appears too great unless some modification can be introduced to retain the apparently legitimate uses of this type of definition.

7.5   *Poincaré rejected and ridiculed attempts to base mathematics on logic.* He asked, "If . . . all the propositions [which mathematics] enunciates can be deduced one from another by the rules of formal logic, why is not mathematics reduced to an immense tautology? The syllogism can teach us nothing essentially new, and, if everything is to spring from the principle of identity, everything should be capable of being reduced to it. Shall we then admit that the enunciations of all those theorems which fill so many volumes are nothing but devious ways of saying A is A?" [Po; 31.‡] Someone has written "Logic is barren, whereas mathematics is the most prolific of mothers." Poincaré exclaims "Logic is no longer barren; she has brought forth a contradiction!" (in reference to the Russell antinomy).

He believed that attempts to place the method of mathematical induction on a contradictionless basis were doomed to run into a vicious circle, in that the induction procedure would of necessity be used in the proof of freedom from contradiction. For mathematical induction, he felt, is forced on us by our intuition. Nevertheless he granted— and in this he agrees with the Formalists (Chapter XI) rather than the Intuitionists—that, in general, proof of freedom from contradiction, as in the case of a geometry, is adequate basis for assertion of mathematical existence.

During the first decade of the present century a discussion took place between Poincaré and Russell which fortunately took the form of a series of articles in the French periodical *Revue de metaphysique et de morale.*§ These are available for the reader familiar with French.

---

† It is amusing to note that, soon after Poincaré made known his opposition to the non-predicative type of definition, one of his colleagues pointed out to him a situation in one of his (Poincaré's) own articles, where he had used this objectionable type of definition. (Unfortunately, Poincaré was able to point out how it could be avoided in this case!)

‡ Quoted with permission of Science Press.

§ Probably many of Russell's early ideas on the relations between mathematics and logic were formed during this exchange.

Poincaré's *Foundations of Science* is available in English translation [Po].

7.6   Many of Poincaré's French colleagues were equally vehement in voicing their opinions concerning "le grand débat." Their views make interesting reading; some will be found in Note IV of the appendix to Borel [Bo; 150–160]. In particular there are included there five letters interchanged by Borel, Hadamard, Lebesgue, and Baire (loc. cit., pp. 150ff) which were prompted by the appearance of Zermelo's Well-ordering Theorem.† Also see Menger [a].

8   Zermelo's set theory

In Section 5 we mentioned the reactions of Russell and Zermelo to the introduction of the antinomies. Because of the scope of Russell's work we defer its exposition to the next chapter; we close this chapter with some details concerning Zermelo's axioms for set theory.

8.1   Zermelo conceived the idea of providing an axiom system, similar to those used in geometry, in which the undefined terms would be *set* and ε. (Compare *point* and $<$ as used in the simple order axioms, II 7.) The aim would be to provide a consistent system of axioms in these terms, so that, if the only sets used in practice actually constituted *models* of the axiom system, no contradictions would result; and such that, while not permitting the "too large" sets in the models, would allow large enough sets for all ordinary purposes of mathematics.

8.2   The manner in which Zermelo carried out this idea (see Zermelo [c]) was substantially as follows: ‡

With the undefined term *set* and binary relation ε between sets, the terms *subset* $(A \subset B)$, *disjoint* and relation $=$ between sets may be defined essentially as in III 3.1.2, 3.1.3, and 3.6. If a relation $x \varepsilon M$ holds between sets x and M, we call x an *element* of M. The first five axioms are:

I. If a, b, and A are sets such that $a \varepsilon A$ and $a = b$, then $b \varepsilon A$.§

II. If a and b are distinct sets, then there exists a set, denoted by $\{a, b\}$, such that $a \varepsilon \{a, b\}$, $b \varepsilon \{a, b\}$, and, if $x \varepsilon \{a, b\}$, then x is either a or b.

---

† These appeared originally in the *Bulletin de la société mathématique de France*, 1904.

‡ For our elementary exposition we are following the first formulation of Fraenkel [F₂; 58ff], which differs in minor respects from Zermelo's. Fraenkel's axioms, as translated by R. L. W., are used with permission of B. G. Teubner.

§ The necessity for this axiom rests on the undefined character of ε.

III. If $\mathfrak{M}$ is a set and $M \,\varepsilon\, \mathfrak{M}$ for at least one set M, then there exists a set $\mathfrak{SM}$ whose elements are the elements of all the elements of $\mathfrak{M}$, and only these. (In symbols, $x \,\varepsilon\, \mathfrak{SM}$ implies $x \,\varepsilon\, M$ for some M such that $M \,\varepsilon\, \mathfrak{M}$; and, if $x \,\varepsilon\, M$ such that $M \,\varepsilon\, \mathfrak{M}$, then $x \,\varepsilon\, \mathfrak{SM}$.)

IV. If M is a set, then there exists a set $\mathfrak{U}M$, called the *power set* of M, whose elements are the subsets of M, and only these. [Thus $\mathfrak{U}M$ is the analogue of the set 2^M defined in IV 3.2.3.4.]

V. If M is a set and P a property having significance for the elements of M, then there exists a subset $M(P)$ of M whose elements are all those elements of M that have property P, and only these.

By the term "significant property" in axiom V is meant a property such that, if $x \,\varepsilon\, M$, then either x has property P or it does not. Thus, if M is the set of all natural numbers, P may be the property of being odd, or it may be the property of being prime. If M is the set of all real numbers, P could be the property of being algebraic, even though there exist numbers about which we do not at present know whether they are algebraic or not! If M is the set of natural numbers and P is the property of being red, then P is not a significant property for the elements of M. (That the use of this notion in the axioms is objectionable was recognized by Fraenkel and others. For further comment on this axiom see Section 9.)

Since the next axiom (VI) involves the null set and product set of a given set, we prove the following theorems which introduce and establish their existence:

8.2.1   Theorem.† *If there exists any set at all, then there exists a unique set $\emptyset$ called the null set, which has no elements and is a subset of every set.*

Theorem 8.2.1 follows from axiom V if, for given set M, we let P be the property of *not being an element* of M; and from the definition of subset (cf. III 3.1.3–3.1.4).

8.2.2   Theorem. *If M is a set, then there exists a set $\{M\}$ whose only element is M.*

Proof.   Given a set M, there exists the set $\emptyset$ by 8.2.1. And by axiom IV there exists the set $\mathfrak{U}\emptyset$, which evidently is a set $\{\emptyset\}$ having exactly one element, namely $\emptyset$.‡

† In Zermelo's formulation (see Zermelo [c]), the existence of the sets $\emptyset$ and $\{M\}$ (cf. 8.2.2) was postulated along with $\{a, b\}$ in axiom II.

‡ We have to distinguish between the set $\emptyset$, which has *no* elements, and the set $\{\emptyset\}$, which has *one* element. Similarly, we have to distinguish, for any set M whatsoever, between M and $\{M\}$; the former may have many elements, whereas the latter has only one.

Thus, no matter whether M is $\emptyset$ or not, there exist two distinct sets M and N, and hence by axiom II the set $\{M, N\}$. If we let P denote the property of being "equal to $(=)$ M," then from axiom V we get $\{M, N\}(P)$ to be $\{M\}$.

8.2.3   Theorem. *If M is a set different from $\emptyset$, whose elements are disjoint sets, then there exists a set $\mathfrak{P}M$ whose elements are those subsets of $\mathfrak{S}M$ that have exactly one element in common with each element of M. If $\emptyset \, \varepsilon \, M$, then $\mathfrak{P}M = \emptyset$.*
Proof. The set $\mathfrak{S}M$ exists by axiom III, and the set $\mathfrak{U}\mathfrak{S}M$ by axiom IV. Let P be the property of having exactly one element in common with each element of M. Then by axiom V the set $\mathfrak{U}\mathfrak{S}M(P)$ exists, and is the desired set $\mathfrak{P}M$. If $\emptyset \, \varepsilon \, M$, no element of $\mathfrak{U}\mathfrak{S}M$ has property P and in this case $\mathfrak{P}M$ is $\emptyset$.

8.2.4   We can now state the next axiom which, it will be noted, is another form of the Choice Axiom:

VI. If M is a set different from $\emptyset$, whose elements are disjoint sets, and $\emptyset \, \not\varepsilon \, M$, then the set $\mathfrak{P}M$ is different from $\emptyset$.

8.2.5   It will be noted that all the axioms I to VI, as well as Theorems 8.2.1 to 8.2.3, are of the "If . . . , then . . ." form. None of them is an assertion of *existence;* in other words, none of them gives us permission to assume that any sort of set exists, a priori.

One way to remedy this defect is to assert the existence of some set; for example, we might add the axiom, "There exists at least one set." Or we might be more explicit and state the existence of the set $\emptyset$ (cf. footnote to Theorem 8.2.1). In either case, we would then have postulated the existence of sets with any finite cardinal number. For, if M is a set, then $\emptyset$ exists by Theorem 8.2.1, and the set $\{M\}$ with exactly one element exists by Theorem 8.2.2. Axiom II provides the set $\{\emptyset, \{\emptyset\}\}$ with two elements. And so on.

However, the existence of an infinite set would not follow from the axioms unless a stronger existence axiom is added. For this purpose we might use:

VII. There exists a set Z having the following properties: The set $\emptyset$ is an element of Z, and, if $x \, \varepsilon \, Z$, then $\{x\} \, \varepsilon \, Z$.†

With this axiom it is provable ‡ that there exists a set Z_0 of the type postulated in this axiom which is a subset of *every* set Z of the type

† This is VII b of Fraenkel [F₂; 99].
‡ See Fraenkel, loc. cit.

postulated here. The set Z_0 is a "smallest" set of this type; in other words, its elements are $\emptyset$, $\{\emptyset\}$, $\{\{\emptyset\}\}$, $\{\{\{\emptyset\}\}\}$, etc. Its similarity to the set of natural numbers (which has the smallest transfinite cardinal number $\aleph_0$) is evident.

8.2.6   Even with axiom VII, the existence of sets with arbitrarily large cardinal number is not assured. Although from the set Z_0 (defined in 8.2.5) we obtain, by virtue of axiom IV, the set $\mathfrak{U}Z_0$ of cardinal number $2^{\aleph_0} = c$; and (denoting $\mathfrak{U}Z_0$ by Z_1) a set $Z_2 = \mathfrak{U}Z_1$ of still larger cardinal number—in fact, then, a sequence of sets $Z_0, Z_1, \cdots,$ $Z_n, \cdots$ such that, for each n, $\overline{\overline{Z}}_n < \overline{\overline{Z}}_{n+1}$; no set of cardinal number greater than *all* the numbers $\overline{\overline{Z}}_n$ is assured. In the "unrestricted" set theory (see Problem 18 of Chapter IV) we obtain such a number by first forming the set $Z = \{Z_0, Z_1, \cdots, Z_n, \cdots\}$, then the set $T = \mathfrak{S}Z$. Then $\overline{\overline{T}} > \overline{\overline{Z}}_n$ for all n. But, with axioms I to VII alone, the "set" Z is not postulated as a *set* by these axioms!

From the standpoint of consistency, perhaps this is desirable. The axioms seem to provide all sets of the type ordinarily used, without going so far as to permit "too large" sets of the self-contradictory type such as the "set of all sets" or the "well-ordered set of all ordinal numbers." However, we may go even further, providing for the existence of such sets as the set T of the preceding paragraph by strengthening the assertions of the axioms. The details of this we do not go into here. The reader will find them, together with extended commentary, in Fraenkel [F_2; 114–115].

8.2.7   Relations and functions. In order to introduce the notion of cardinal number on the basis of the above axioms,† it is necessary to set up the relation of (1-1)-correspondence. It is possible to go further, however, since by introducing the notion of *ordered pair* we may set up general binary relations between sets and hence the concept of function. This may be done by the Wiener-Kuratowski method ‡ as follows:

8.2.7.1   Definition. If x and y are distinct sets, then the *ordered pair* $[x, y]$ is the set $\{\{x\}, \{x, y\}\}$.

Note that, if x and y exist, then $\{x\}$ exists by Theorem 8.2.2, $\{x, y\}$ exists by axiom II, and consequently the set $\{\{x\}, \{x, y\}\}$ exists by axiom II; thus the ordered pair $[x, y]$ exists. The symbol $[x, y]$ can

---

† The discussion in 8.2.5 and 8.2.6, in which sets of various cardinalities were mentioned, was of course "extra-axiomatic" and not *within* the system.

‡ See Wiener [a] and Kuratowski [a].

be extended to the case where $x = y$ by making the convention that $\{x, x\}$ is the set $\{x\}$.

On the basis of Definition 8.2.7.1 it is easy to set up definitions of binary relations, correspondences, and functions, the latter two in substantially the same manner as was done in II 4.4.1 and IV 3.2.3.1. A *binary relation* in a set S can be defined as a collection $\Re$ of pairs $\{\{x\}, \{x, y\}\}$, where $x,y \, \varepsilon \, S$. For each such pair we may write, for example, $x < y$, or $x \Re y$, to indicate that the pair $\{\{x\}, \{x, y\}\}$ is an element of $\Re$.

9   Amendments to the Zermelo system

We have already referred (8.2) to the objectionable use of the notion "significant property" in axiom V. As we pointed out in III 3.2.1, set and property are interchangeable notions. Hence to introduce into the axioms for sets the idea of "property" as though it were an intuitively known concept is clearly unsatisfactory. In the first place, it is tantamount to favoring one of two equivalent notions by accepting it as a kind of "universal" while subjecting the other to axiomatic treatment. And, in the second place, to sneak an equivalent notion into the axioms under the guise of a "universal" smacks of a vicious circle procedure [Fraenkel calls it a "jellyfish" ("quallenhaft") device].

9.1   The problem of how to eliminate this defect from the axiom system was attacked by both Skolem (see Skolem [a]) and Fraenkel ([F₁; 285ff], [F₂; 103ff]). As they reformulated the offending axiom, the "properties" admissible for determining subsets are defined by formulas built up from formulas of the type $x \, \varepsilon \, M$. Thus Fraenkel commences with elementary set-functions consisting of (1) any fixed given set, (2) the (variable) set x, (3) the set $\mathfrak{S}x$ (axiom III), and (4) the set $\mathfrak{U}x$ (axiom IV); and (5) if $\varphi(x)$ and $\psi(x)$ are set-functions, then so are $\{\varphi(x), \psi(x)\}$ and $\varphi(\psi(x))$. Axiom V is then restated as follows:

V′. Given a set M and two functions $\varphi(x)$ and $\psi(x)$; then there exists a subset $M′$ of M which has as its elements exactly those elements x of M such that $\varphi(x) \, \varepsilon \, \psi(x)$.

For example, if M and A are given sets, then the assignment of meanings $\varphi(x) = x$, $\psi(x) = A$, with M as in V′, proves the existence of the set $A \cap M$.

Further details will be found in Fraenkel (loc. cit.).

For axiom systems for set theory containing further improvements, one may consult papers of von Neumann [a, b], Bernays [a], and Gödel [G]. (See also Ackermann [a].)

ADDITIONAL BIBLIOGRAPHY

Bell [B$_3$; 553ff] Lewis [Le; I–III, VI]
Fraenkel [F$_1$; V] Menger [a]
Skolem [b]

IX

The Frege-Russell Thesis: Mathematics an Extension of Logic

In this chapter we again pick up the logical thread which had its origin in ancient Greece, and was strengthened by the introduction of symbolic methods during the last two centuries by Leibnitz, De Morgan, Boole, and others. As we saw in the last chapter, despite the criticism of Kronecker, the set-theoretic approach became more and more popular and was freely used by Weierstrass, Cantor, and Dedekind in the founding of analysis. Frege, and Peano and his colleagues, attempted to make the relations of logic and mathematics even more intimate, using symbolic methods to construct what seemed to them a firmer and more rigorous foundation of mathematics.

1 The Frege-Russell thesis

Early in the present century a new shift of emphasis occurred; from being a method or a *tool* for the construction of mathematical theory, logic was advanced as a progenitor of mathematics. What is variously called the "logistic thesis," or the "Frege-Russell thesis," viz., that mathematics is derivable from, or an extension of, logic, was presented in extensive detail in the *Principia Mathematica* of Whitehead and Russell [P.M.].†

This thesis was not entirely new; its germ can be found in the writings of earlier logicians and mathematicians. Thus Jevons remarks:‡ "I hold that algebra is a highly developed logic, and number but

† Hereafter we shall denote the *Principia Mathematica*, 2nd ed., by P.M. (See Whitehead and Russell [P.M.].) This was preceded by Russell's book, *The Principles of Mathematics* [R₂], which, as explained in the Preface to P.M., was to have been the first volume of P.M. As the writing of P.M. progressed, however, it became clear that revisions, etc., of material contained in *The Principles of Mathematics* necessitated the writing of a completely new work.

‡ As quoted by Frege; cf. Frege [Fr; 22ᵉ]; used here with permission of Basil Blackwell.

logical discrimination." Frege held † that ". . . inferences which on the face of it are peculiar to mathematics, such as that from n to $n + 1$, are based on the general laws of logic"; and ‡ ". . . essential for mathematics . . . is the recognition of its close connection with logic. I go so far as to agree with those who hold that it is impossible to effect any sharp separation of the two."

To Peano and his followers, however, the use of symbolic logic would seem to have been purely a means to an end. Logic, to them, was the *servant* of mathematics; a servant that mathematics admittedly could not dispense with. It was probably inevitable that a school of thought should arise that would conceive of this dependence on logic as the outward evidence of a relationship that was more like that of parent to child than servant to master. (See VIII 4.1.)

1.1 Background of the thesis

We can hardly do better here than let the chief protagonists of this theory speak for themselves: "[This work, i.e., P.M.] has arisen from the conjunction of two different studies, . . . On the one hand we have the work of analysts and geometers, in the way of formulating and systematizing their axioms, and the work of Cantor and others on such matters as the theory of aggregates. On the other hand we have symbolic logic, which, after a necessary period of growth, has now, thanks to Peano and his followers, acquired the technical adaptability and the logical comprehensiveness that are essential to a mathematical instrument for dealing with what have hitherto been the beginnings of mathematics. From the combination of these two studies two results emerge, namely (1) that what were formerly taken, tacitly, or explicitly, as axioms, are either unnecessary or demonstrable; (2) that the same methods by which supposed axioms are demonstrated will give valuable results in regions, such as infinite number, which had formerly been regarded as inaccessible to human knowledge. Hence the scope of mathematics is enlarged both by the addition of new subjects and by *a backward extension into provinces hitherto abandoned to philosophy"* (P.M., Preface).§

1.2 Axioms of logic as a basis

The ideal goal of this "backward extension" was a set of "primitive" axioms of logic, statements that the logician would call "true," on which one could base the whole of mathematics. In this way the

---

† Loc. cit., IVe; quoted by permission of Basil Blackwell.
‡ Loc. cit., IXe; quoted by permission of Basil Blackwell.
§ The italics are mine; quoted with permission of Cambridge University Press.

main thesis might be considered established. Numbers, for instance, would be so defined as to have unique meanings; "1" would emerge as what we ordinarily think of as "unity," and not merely as a candidate for the initial element of a sequence as postulated in the Peano axioms (which might equally well be "0," "2," "3," or . . . , as "1," so far as the Peano axioms are concerned). At the same time, one would attempt so to construct the theory as to eliminate contradictions such as had appeared in the theory of sets and which had threatened the foundations of Frege's † work.

In what follows we shall give a sketch of the manner in which this program was carried out in P.M., together with some subsequent developments. Only enough detail will be given (1) to illustrate the general procedure which was followed and (2) to furnish a basis for the later discussion of intuitionist logic as well as of the modern "formalistic" approach to logic and mathematics.

2 Basic symbols; propositions and propositional functions

Much as in the axiomatic method, one starts with certain ideas that are left undefined, and with certain assumptions analogous to axioms. However, while recognizing this, Russell and Whitehead provide an auxiliary explanation of the "meanings" of these basic ideas. This is necessary, particularly since they are not dealing with such matters as euclidean geometry, for example, where one can usually assume that a reader is already familiar with the fundamental ideas in some form or other, as well as with just what the ultimate purposes are. The explanations are accompanied by the proviso that they "do not constitute definitions, because they really involve the ideas they explain."

2.1   Primitive ideas

The most elementary notion employed in P.M. is that of *proposition;* as used therein, it appears to be a *statement* that involves only definite or constant notions; thus "the sun is bright" or "this ink is

† Whitehead and Russell make clear their debt to Frege: "In all questions of logical analysis, our chief debt is to Frege. Where we differ from him, it is largely because the contradictions showed that he, in common with all other logicians ancient and modern, had allowed some error to creep into his premises; but apart from the contradictions, it would have been almost impossible to detect this error." And to Cantor: "In Arithmetic and the theory of series, our whole work is based on that of Georg Cantor." And, although the geometric portion of P.M. was never completed, the geometric (as well as axiomatic) work of "v. Staudt, Pasch, Peano, Pieri, and Veblen" is acknowledged. (Quotations from P.M., Preface, by permission of Cambridge University Press.)

black" are propositions. They are similar to the constants of elementary algebra or the points of geometry. But statements such as "x is red" or "x is a father of y" are not propositions since they contain *variables*. "Variable" is used much as in mathematics, every variable having associated with it a valid "domain of values." Statements that contain variables and which become propositions when specific values, i.e., constants, are substituted for all variables, are called *propositional functions*.

To propositions are assigned "truth-values," the truth-value of a proposition being *truth* if it is true, and *falsehood* if it is false.

These notions (cf. VIII 3.4 and VIII 4.1) embody concepts whose nature is not generally agreed upon even today by logicians and philosophers, who point out that in P.M. they seem not to be used consistently. With good reason, one may insist that to confine the notion of "proposition" and "propositional function" to actual sentences is reminiscent of the early status of the concept of "function" in mathematical analysis as an expression of a certain kind containing variables. In P.M. it is stated (p. 92),† for instance, that by "elementary propositional function" is meant "an expression containing an undetermined constituent, i.e., a variable, or several such constituents, and such that, when the undetermined constituent or constituents are determined, i.e., when values are assigned to the variable or variables, the resulting value of the expression in question is an elementary proposition."

Probably the majority of logicians would hold that a proposition is the "meaning" expressed by the sentence embodying it, so that "This table is small" and "Dieser Tisch ist klein" are the same proposition although their forms are different. And it is quite possible that this is the view intended in P.M.

2.2 Basic symbols

Propositions are denoted by small Latin letters, usually p, q, r, etc. Propositional functions are denoted variously: Thus φx denotes a function with a single variable x.‡ By φp one might indicate a propositional function whose variable p is replaceable by propositions. The assertion of the truth of a proposition or propositional function is indicated by the symbol $\vdash$. Thus

$$\vdash . p$$

† Quoted with permission of Cambridge University Press.
‡ Parentheses are avoided to a large extent in P.M.

asserts the truth of the proposition p. All axioms are assertions, and hence preceded by the symbol $\vdash$.

Most of the parentheses, brackets, etc., are replaced by dots on the line; e.g., "$.\, p \vee q\, .$" instead of "$(p \vee q)$." For brackets enclosing parentheses, a "double dot" : is used. And generally a larger number of dots indicates an "outside" parenthesis, a smaller number an "inside" parenthesis. Hence, if one encounters : in a formula, it indicates a bracket enclosing everything to the next double dot : or to the end of the expression. (Cf. pp. 9ff, 16ff of P.M.)

Negation is represented by the $\sim$ already used in II 3.1; thus $\sim p$ represents a denial or *falsity* of a proposition p. The and/or symbol $\vee$ is used as in III 3.3.1. The result of the application of $\sim$ or $\vee$ to propositions is again a proposition (if p is a proposition, then $\sim p$ is a proposition, etc.). In case p is a variable (i.e., undetermined) proposition, then $\sim p$ is a propositional function.

2.2.1   Implication. P.M. uses $\supset$ for implication, which is *defined* in terms of the basic symbols as follows:

(2.2a) $$p \supset q\, .\, =\, .\, \sim p \vee q \qquad \text{Df}$$

The Df stands for "definition" and in conjunction with $=$ denotes "is defined to mean." Both $=$ and, ultimately, $\supset$ are usually set off by dots. Expression (2.2a) can be read "p implies q is defined to mean that either p is false or q is true."

This definition of implication may at first seem strange, since in ordinary affairs of life we so commonly assume that in the statement "p implies q" or, as more commonly put, "If p, then q," the "antecedent" p is necessarily connected in some way with the "consequent" q. Thus, it would hardly seem natural to assert that "if water flows downhill, then light is bright." For in this case there is no apparent connection between antecedent and consequent. Nevertheless, if p is the proposition "Water flows downhill" and q the proposition "Light is bright," then $p \supset q$ (see 3.5—especially 3.5.3). For in view of the meaning of $\vee$, the expression "$\sim p \vee q$" is considered true whenever (1) p is true and q is true, (2) p is false and q is either (i) true or (ii) false; the only case ruled out by (2.2a) is that where p is true and q is not true. What one is interested in, here, is truth-value; whether there is some necessary connection between p and q is not of importance. The truth-value of $p \supset q$, like the truth-values of $p \vee q$ and $\sim p$, depends on the truth-values of the constituent propositions p, q; in the case of $p \vee q$, the truth-value is truth if the truth-value of either

p or q is truth. In order to distinguish it from other types of implication, (2.2a) is called *material implication* (cf. 3.8).

If we examine the kind of implication that we use in mathematics, we find that it actually corresponds to the "material" type. Consider, for example, the axiom system O'' obtained by adjoining to the simple order axioms (II 7) the axiom, "There exist two and only two distinct points in C," and changing the "If" part of axiom 3 to "If x, y, z are distinct." The new axiom 3 is not independent in the resulting system. For suppose we let p denote the statement "There exist three distinct points x, y, and z such that $x < y$ and $y < z$," and q the statement "$x < z$"; then the new axiom 3 states "If p, then q," or "p implies q." Now, in view of the new axiom, p is false, or, as we sometimes put it, "p cannot be satisfied," or "p is vacuously satisfied"; and whatever the statement "p implies q" may be, under these conditions we take it as valid in the system. In other words, if p is false, we accept that p implies q, no matter whether q is true or false.

2.3 The primitive propositions

The axioms of what may be called the *propositional calculus*, which forms the initial portion of P.M., and which P.M. calls "primitive propositions" (see P.M., p. 96), are as follows:

1	$\vdash : p \vee p \,.\, \supset \,.\, p$
II	$\vdash : q \,.\, \supset \,.\, p \vee q$
III	$\vdash : p \vee q \,.\, \supset \,.\, q \vee p$
IV	$\vdash : p \vee (q \vee r) \,.\, \supset \,.\, q \vee (p \vee r)$
V	$\vdash :.\, q \supset r \,.\, \supset \,: p \vee q \,.\, \supset \,.\, p \vee r$

(The dots after $\vdash$ always indicate range, which includes everything following the dots until either an equal number of dots is encountered preceding a symbol $\supset$, or the end of the expression.) These axioms may be read as follows:

I. If p is true or p is true, then p is true.

In P.M., I is called the "principle of tautology."

II. If q is true, then p or q is true.

P.M. calls II the "principle of addition"—to a true proposition any alternative may be added and the resulting proposition is true.

III. If either p or q is true, then either q or p is true.

This is obviously the commutativity of v; in P.M. it is called the "principle of permutation."

IV. If p is true, or either q or r is true, then q is true, or either p or r is true.

This is clearly a type of associative law.

V. If q implies r, then "p or q" implies "p or r." Notice the similarity to the monotonic law of real number arithmetic (VI 2.2.4). P.M. calls V the "principle of summation."

These "principles," from the logistic standpoint, are "primitive logical truths," and constitute a system sufficient for the theory of deduction.† They must, however, be accompanied by rules for determining *their own consequences*.

3 Calculus of propositions

Axioms I to V constitute, in their symbolic form, what would today be called a set of basic *formulas*. Formulas of a similar character proved from them would correspond to "theorems."

3.1 Manner of proving theorems

Inasmuch as the system so constituted is supposed to embody a "theory of deduction," it raises what seems at first sight to be a paradoxical question, viz., What kind of deduction shall we use to deduce the properties of deduction? The answer is that we give two simple rules for calculation of formulas from formulas. These rules, to be sure, appear again in the form of *formulas—within* the system, that is—thus playing two roles. They are:

(1) Substitution of a formula A for *all* occurrences of a proposition p in a given formula. (For example, substitution of $p \vee q$ for p in I gives $(p \vee q) \vee (p \vee q) \,.\, \supset \,.\, (p \vee q)$.) ‡

(2) Modus ponens: "Anything implied by a true proposition is true." (That is, if A is a true formula, and $A \,.\, \supset \,.\, B$ is true, where B is a formula, then B is a true formula.)

---

† As a matter of fact, I to III and V constitute such a system, since Bernays [b] showed that IV is derivable from them. Regarding the independence of these postulates, see Henle [a].

‡ This rule is not explicitly stated in P.M., but is employed throughout. Cf. Russell [R₁; 151f].

3.2 Some sample proofs

We insert here some examples of how formulas are derived from the "primitive propositions." In particular, we show through the following sequence of lemmas how to derive the Law of the Excluded Middle.

3.2.1 $\qquad \vdash : . \, q \supset r . \supset : p \supset q . \supset . p \supset r$

Proof. Using rule (1), substitute $\sim p$ for p in V:

(3.2.1a) $\qquad \vdash : . \, q \supset r . \supset : \sim p \vee q . \supset . \sim p \vee r$

By (2.2a), $\sim p \vee q$ is the same as $p \supset q$. Hence (3.2.1a) becomes

$$\vdash : . \, q \supset r . \supset : p \supset q . \supset . p \supset r$$

3.2.1.1 It follows easily from 3.2.1 that, whenever we have propositions of the form $a \supset b$, $b \supset c$ asserted, and $a \supset c$ is to be proved, then the proof may proceed as follows: Replacing p, q, r in 3.2.1 by b, c, a respectively gives

$$\vdash : . \, b \supset c . \supset : a \supset b . \supset . a \supset c$$

$$\vdash : b . \supset . c$$

Then by rule (2) we get

$$\vdash : a \supset b . \supset . a \supset c$$

$$\vdash : a . \supset . b$$

Again by rule (2),

$$\vdash : a . \supset . c$$

3.2.2 $\qquad \vdash : p . \supset . p \vee p$

Proof. Substitute p for q in II.

3.2.3 $\qquad \vdash . \, p \supset p$

Proof. In 3.2.1, substitute $p \vee p$ for q, and p for r:

$$\vdash : : p \vee p . \supset . p : \supset : . p . \supset . p \vee p : \supset . p \supset p$$

By virtue of I, $p \vee p . \supset . p$ is a true proposition. Hence, by rule (2), we get

$$\vdash : . \, p . \supset . p \vee p : \supset . p \supset p$$

which in turn gives, by 3.2.2 and modus ponens,

$$\vdash . \, p \supset p$$

3.2.4 $\qquad \vdash . \sim p \vee p$

Proof. This is merely a restatement of 3.2.3, by virtue of Definition (2.2a).

3.2.5 $\vdash . p \vee \sim p$ (Law of the Excluded Middle)

Proof. By III, with $\sim p$ and p substituted for p and q respectively,
we get

(3.2.5a) $\vdash : \sim p \vee p . \supset . p \vee \sim p$

But $\sim p \vee p$ is true by 3.2.4; hence by modus ponens (3.2.5a) and 3.2.4
give

$$\vdash . p \vee \sim p$$

3.3   The reductio ad absurdum

The type of proof which involves showing a proposition p false,
by showing that p leads to absurdity, is embodied in the assertion:

3.3.1 $\vdash : p \supset \sim p . \supset . \sim p$

Proof. In I substitute $\sim p$ for p to get

$$\vdash : \sim p \vee \sim p . \supset . \sim p$$

Then by (2.2a) this becomes the desired assertion.

3.3.2   As a matter of fact, there is a more general form for "reductio
ad absurdum," of which 3.3.1 is a special case, namely:

$$\vdash : p \supset q . \supset : p \supset \sim q . \supset . \sim p$$

3.4   The double negative

An important principle of classical logic is that the double negative
of a proposition is equivalent to the proposition. As soon as equivalence is defined, this may be derived from the primitive propositions
and the Law of the Excluded Middle as follows:

3.4.1 $\vdash . p \supset \sim(\sim p)$

Proof. In 3.2.5 substitute $\sim p$ for p:

$$\vdash . \sim p \vee \sim(\sim p)$$

Then by Definition (2.2a) this becomes the desired assertion.

3.4.2 $\vdash . p \vee \sim\{\sim(\sim p)\}$

Proof. In V replace q and r by $\sim p$ and $\sim\{\sim(\sim p)\}$ respectively:

(3.4.2a) $\vdash :. \sim p . \supset . \sim\{\sim(\sim p)\} . \supset : p \vee \sim p . \supset . p \vee \sim\{\sim(\sim p)\}$

In 3.4.1 replace p by $\sim p$:

(3.4.2b) $\qquad \vdash\ :\, \sim p\, .\, \supset\, .\, \sim\{\sim(\sim p)\}$

Relations (3.4.2a) and (3.4.2b), together with modus ponens, give

$$\vdash\ :\, p \vee \sim p\, .\, \supset\, .\, p \vee \sim\{\sim(\sim p)\},$$

which, with 3.2.5 and modus ponens, gives the desired assertion.

3.4.3 $\qquad\qquad \vdash\ .\, \sim(\sim p) \supset p$

Proof. In III replace q by $\sim\{\sim(\sim p)\}$:

$$\vdash\ :\, p \vee \sim\{\sim(\sim p)\}\, .\, \supset\, .\, \sim\{\sim(\sim p)\} \vee p$$

This, together with 3.4.2 and modus ponens, gives

$$\vdash\ .\, \sim\{\sim(\sim p)\} \vee p$$

Definition (2.2a) yields the desired assertion.

3.5 Miscellaneous theorems

The following exemplify other theorems important in the applications of the theory of deduction.

Frequently used is the type of argument which proves a proposition p by showing that the assumption of its falsity implies p. This is embodied in the P.M. calculus of propositions by:

3.5.1 $\qquad\qquad \vdash\ :\, \sim p \supset p\, .\, \supset\, .\, p$

Proof. From 3.4.1 and 3.2.1 (in the latter we substitute p for q, $\sim(\sim p)$ for r, and $\sim p$ for p), we get

$$\vdash\ :\, \sim p \supset p\, .\, \supset\, .\, \sim p \supset \sim(\sim p)$$

Substituting $\sim p$ for p in 3.3.1 gives

$$\vdash\ :\, \sim p \supset \sim(\sim p)\, .\, \supset\, .\, \sim(\sim p)$$

Hence by 3.2.1.1 we have

$$\vdash\ :\, \sim p \supset p\, .\, \supset\, .\, \sim(\sim p)$$

Application of 3.4.3 and 3.2.1.1 completes the proof.

A useful formula, also, is the following:

3.5.2 $\qquad\qquad \vdash\ :\, p\, .\, \supset\, .\, p \vee q$

Proof. Axioms II and III (with II in the form $p\, .\, \supset\, .\, q \vee p$, etc.) together with 3.2.1.1 give the desired relation.

A feature of the Russell-Whitehead system, often called "paradoxical," is the theorem that a false proposition implies every proposition:

3.5.3 $\vdash \, : \sim p \, . \supset . \, p \supset q$

Proof. Substitute $\sim p$ for p in 3.5.2 and apply (2.2a).

Another favorite device in mathematics is to prove that a proposition p implies a proposition q by showing, instead, that the falsity of q implies the falsity of p. The basis for this is the theorem:

3.5.4 $\vdash \, : p \supset \sim q \, . \supset . \, q \supset \sim p$

Proof. In axiom III replace p by $\sim p$ and q by $\sim q$, giving

$\vdash \, : \sim p \lor \sim q \, . \supset . \, \sim q \lor \sim p$

Application of (2.2a) gives the desired assertion.

Note that 3.5.4 takes the form stated in words prior to 3.5.4, if we change p to $\sim q$ and q to p (and apply 3.4.3).

In the Russell-Whitehead system (as a natural concomitant of its type of implication—cf. 3.9) is the assertion that a true proposition is implied by *any* proposition:

3.5.5 $\vdash \, : q \, . \supset . \, p \supset q$

Proof. In axiom II replace p by $\sim p$ and apply the definition of implication (2.2a).

3.6   The logical product

An important detail of the Russell-Whitehead propositional calculus is the non-independence of the logical product, indicated by a dot . and the symbols $\sim$, $\lor$. In P.M. (p. 109), the symbol . is defined as follows:

(3.6a) $p \, . \, q \, . = . \sim(\sim p \lor \sim q)$ Df

In words, (3.6a) becomes "p and q are both true if and only if it is false that either p is false or q is false."

3.6.1   A consequence of Definition (3.6a) is the equivalence, in the P.M. calculus of propositions, of the Law of the Excluded Middle and the Law of Contradiction. The latter has the form:

3.6.2 $\vdash \, . \sim(p \, . \, \sim p)$

In words, 3.6.2 states that it is false that a proposition is both true and false. To derive 3.6.2 from (3.6a) and the Law of the Excluded Middle (3.2.5), note that, by 3.2.3, Definition (3.6a) gives

$$\vdash\ :p\ .\ q\ .\ \supset\ .\ {\sim}({\sim}p\vee{\sim}q)$$

and hence, by 3.5.4 and modus ponens,

$$(3.6.2a)\qquad\qquad\vdash\ :\ {\sim}p\vee{\sim}q\ .\ \supset\ .\ {\sim}(p\ .\ q)$$

Since, by 3.2.5, $\vdash\ .\ {\sim}p\vee{\sim}({\sim}p)$, we get the desired relation by replacing q by ${\sim}p$ in (3.6.2a).

3.6.3   Note that combination of 3.5.3 and 3.6.2 furnishes the basis of the much-quoted assertion that, *if a logical system contains a contradiction—i.e., an assertion* $\vdash\ .\ A\ .\ {\sim}A$, *where A is a formula—then all propositions are provable in the system.*

3.7   Sheffer's "stroke" symbol

In closing this section, we might point out some developments which should prove of great interest to the student of mathematics. In II 4.10 we commented upon the effect of changing the undefined terms of an axiom system. Since P.M. was first published, with its two undefined symbols (or "logical constants") $\sim$ and $\vee$ and five axioms (later reduced to four axioms by Bernays—cf. 2.3), it has been shown that *one* undefined symbol and *one* axiom are sufficient.

The symbol referred to is / and is called "stroke." It was introduced by H. M. Sheffer [a], and its intuitive meaning can correspond to either (1) total rejection (employed by Sheffer, loc. cit.), or (2) incompatibility. To be more specific, p/q would mean, in case (1), that *both* p and q are false—in the previous symbols, ${\sim}p\ .\ {\sim}q$; and, in case (2), that *at least one* of the propositions p, q is false—in the previous symbols, ${\sim}p\vee{\sim}q$. In either case, ${\sim}p$ would be defined as p/p, whereas (1) would require that we define $p\vee q$ to mean $(p/q)/(p/q)$, and (2) that $p\vee q$ mean $(p/p)/(q/q)$. The intuitive meaning (2) is generally preferred, however (as leading to somewhat simpler forms).

Thus, treating the new symbol / as undefined, we would define the P.M. symbols $\sim$ and $\vee$ as follows:

$$(3.7a)\qquad\qquad {\sim}p\ .\ =\ .\ p/p\qquad\text{Df}$$

$$(3.7b)\qquad\qquad p\vee q\ .\ =\ .\ (p/p)/(q/q)\qquad\text{Df}$$

Since $\supset$ and . are defined in terms of $\sim$ and v, it is clear that by means of (3.7a) and (3.7b) they are definable in terms of / alone. For example,

(3.7c) $$p \supset q . = . p/(q/q)$$

If meaning (1) had been selected for /, then $p \supset q$ would have had to be defined as $\{(p/p)/q\}/\{(p/p)/q\}$. The simpler form (3.7c) is one of the reasons for preferring meaning (2).

That axioms I to V may be replaced by a single axiom in terms of / was shown by J. Nicod [a]. This axiom is a single formula in terms of propositional symbols p, q, $\cdots$ and the stroke /, and is not a "fictitious" combination of separate axioms of the sort discussed in II 3.6. It does, however, have the disadvantage of being rather complicated, so that it is probably better to found the system of P.M. on the basis outlined previously. Also see the comment of Hilbert-Bernays [H-B; 64–65] and the work of Tarski referred to therein.

3.8 Other types of "implication"

In dealing solely with propositions whose "truth-values" are of concern to us, Definition (2.2a) seems to embody the most generally accepted type of implication. It is not, however, the only kind definable, nor, when only the forms or structure of propositions are under consideration (with no attention paid to their content or "truth"), is it necessarily the most desirable.

The first attempt at an alternative type of implication was made by C. I. Lewis. This resulted in a theory of deduction which he called *strict implication*. A new undefined concept, denoted by $\Diamond p$, which may be read "p is possible," was introduced. The relation of strict implication was then defined thus:

(3.8a) $$p \mathbin{-\!3} q . = . \sim\!\Diamond\,(p . \sim\!q) \qquad \text{Df}$$

The formula $p \mathbin{-\!3} q$ may be read "p strictly implies q." Between this type of implication, and $p \supset q$, as defined in (2.2a), which may now be read "p materially implies q," the following relation holds:

(3.8b) $$p \mathbin{-\!3} q . \mathbin{-\!3} . p \supset q$$

(The "converse" implication does not hold.) Using the interpretation of 2.2.1, if p is "Water flows downhill," and q is "Light is bright," then, although $p \supset q$ holds, $p \mathbin{-\!3} q$ does not hold.

The paradoxical properties of material implication proved in 3.5.3 ("A false proposition implies every proposition") and 3.5.5 ("If a proposition is true, then it is implied by every proposition") do not hold for strict implication. (See, however, Halldén [a].)

It is maintained by some authors (see, for example, Carnap [Car$_1$; 254ff]) that the p and q in $p \dashv q$ should denote *names* of sentences, the important aspect of this relation being the *deducibility* of q from p, not the truth-values; while in $p \supset q$ the p and q are *sentences* whose truth-values are of primary importance, the resulting compound sentence thus expressing a proposition about the subjects of the component sentences. From the former one deduces the latter simply by stating "If p then q" with p and q replaced by the sentences named. Another way of looking at the difference indicated is to note that, when we write $p \supset p$ "materially," we mean that "if p is true, then p is true," where p is an actual sentence, whereas when we interpret it "strictly" it means that "every sentence is deducible from itself" without regard for any particular sentence. It seems evident, however, that this interpretation of strict implication is not in accord with Lewis' intentions, else p and q would have variable meanings in such formulas as (3.8b).

For further details regarding strict implication, the reader is referred to Lewis and Langford [L-L; 122ff]. In all, Lewis studied five different systems of deduction (see Lewis and Langford [L-L; 492ff]), remarking (loc. cit., pp. 501–2), "Prevailing good use in logical inference—the practice in mathematical deductions, for example—is not sufficiently precise and self-conscious to determine clearly which of these five systems expresses the acceptable principles of deduction."

Regarding the general problem, the reader is also referred to Tarski [T; 23ff], Emch [a], Lewis [a], Curry [Cu].

4   Forms of general propositions

A feature of the calculus of propositions which was not emphasized above is the *unanalyzed* character of the primitive entities, i.e., propositions, involved. Nowhere do we ask anything about the intrinsic form of a proposition p; all that matters is the truth-value of p. In the case of propositional functions, on the other hand, the form of a proposition is of importance. For example, a propositional function may have only one variable, and be symbolized as $\varphi(x)$; but some propositional functions may involve several variables, being symbolized by such expressions as $\varphi(x, y)$, $\varphi(x, y, z)$ (as we shall see below, on the latter we base a theory of relations). Furthermore, it becomes necessary, especially in order to avoid the set-theoretic contradictions (such as "set of all ordinary sets," "set of all sets") to pay attention to the category or range of things for which the variables may stand.

4.1   Apparent (or bound) variables

Basic in the study of propositions formed from propositional functions are the "For all" and "There exist" types of propositions. These (introduced in the first edition of P.M. as primitive ideas) are respectively symbolized as follows:

(4.1a) $\qquad\qquad\qquad\qquad (x) \, . \, \varphi x$

(4.1b) $\qquad\qquad\qquad\qquad (\exists\, x) \, . \, \varphi x$

In these expressions φx is a propositional function of a variable x, the latter having (in each case) a specified range. The intuitive meaning of (4.1a) is "φx is true for all values of x (in the latter's range)"; or, briefly, "For all x, φx is true." And (4.1b) means "There exists an x, such that φx is true."

The occurrences of x in these expressions is compared to that of x in $\int_0^1 x^2 \, dx$; as the latter is a constant, the appearance of x is called only "apparent," and in P.M., x is called an *apparent variable* in (4.1a) and (4.1b). Another term for this is *bound variable*. The occurrence of x in φx itself may be called that of a *free variable*.

The extension to functions of more than one variable is made in an obvious fashion.

4.2   Usually a proposition must be more precisely represented than in the general forms (4.1a), (4.1b). Thus, the proposition "All men are mortal" may be analyzed as follows: Let φx stand for "x is a man" and ψx stand for "x is mortal." Then "All men are mortal" is expressed symbolically by the formula

$$(x) \, . \, \varphi x \supset \psi x.$$

Similarly, the proposition "There exists an animal which has three legs" may be represented by

$$(\exists\, x) : \varphi x \, . \, \psi x,$$

where φx stands for "x is an animal" and ψx for "x has three legs."

The details regarding the various combinations—for example,

$$(x)\varphi x \, . \, \supset \, . \, (x)\psi x$$

—that may be formed by use of the basic constants $\mathbf{v}$, $.$, $\supset$, we shall not go into. In order to extend the theory to expressions containing apparent variables, not only must the various forms which these may take be studied, but also the equivalences resulting from such use of basic constants must be investigated. For example,

$$\sim\{(x) \cdot \varphi x\} \cdot = \cdot (\exists x) \cdot \sim\varphi x$$

$$\sim\{(\exists x) \cdot \varphi x\} \cdot = \cdot (x) \cdot \sim\varphi x$$

The use of $\vee$ is more complicated, since there are various cases; for example,

$$(x) \cdot \varphi x \cdot \vee \cdot p : = \cdot (x) \cdot \varphi x \vee p$$

where p is a proposition. And

$$(x) \cdot \varphi x \cdot \vee \cdot (\exists y) \cdot \psi y : = : (x) : (\exists y) \cdot \varphi x \vee \psi y$$

[The treatment of these general propositions and relations by the general calculus of propositions is handled differently in the two editions of P.M. Cf. the Introduction to the second edition.]

5 Classes and relations

It was remarked in III 3.2.1 that the notion of set could be replaced by that of property, a set being considered to consist of all things which have some given property. A similar notion is at the basis of the treatment of sets, or classes as they. are called in P.M.

Consider a propositional function φx. Then by $\hat{x}(\varphi x)$ we may denote the class of all things x such that φx is true. In the symbolism of III 2, $\{x \mid \varphi x\}$ is evidently the same as $\hat{x}(\varphi x)$, and we could obviously use the former symbol here. But as it is more commonly used by logicians, we shall in the present discussion employ the latter symbol.

5.1 Avoidance of contradiction

Although, from the standpoint of mathematics, the main purpose of developing the theory of classes is to define [see IV (4a)] number and set up arithmetic, it is necessary also to take care that the theory is so constituted as to avoid the contradictions to which the "unrestricted" theory of sets leads (cf. III 2, V 3.2.3).

Let us suppose that C denotes the class determined by the function φx, and let us express this by the relation

(5.1a) $C = \hat{x}(\varphi x).$

That y is an element of C we may denote by the usual ε: $y \varepsilon C$. That y is not an element of C we may denote by $y \sim\varepsilon C$.

Now the x in the function φ defining C should have a definite range. Thus, if φx is the propositional function "x is a professor of mathematics," we would not substitute "New York" for x. A value of x

which we should particularly avoid in assertion of either truth or falsity is the class C itself; for C is only a symbol which was defined (5.1a) in terms of φ (compare VIII 7.4). It is violation of this principle that gives rise to such contradictions as that of the "set of all sets that are not elements of themselves." For, if $\sim \varphi C$, and hence $C \sim \varepsilon\, C$, is a permissible assertion, then we may define

$$S = \hat{C}(C \sim \varepsilon\, C).$$

Then either (1) $S \;\varepsilon\; S$ or (2) $S \sim \varepsilon\, S$. But (1) $S \;\varepsilon\; \hat{C}(C \sim \varepsilon\, C)$ implies $S \sim \varepsilon\, S$; and (2) $S \sim \varepsilon\, \hat{C}(C \sim \varepsilon\, C)$ implies $\sim(S \sim \varepsilon\, S)$; i.e., $S \;\varepsilon\; S$.

Furthermore, no statement containing a bound variable should be allowed as a value of that variable. For suppose, for example, that φx stands for "x is a rule" and ψx for "x has an exception." Then the statement "All rules have exceptions" becomes, in the symbolism of the calculus of propositional functions,

(5.1b) $(x) : \varphi x \,.\, \supset \,.\, \psi x$

Now suppose that we consider (5.1b) itself a rule; denote it by R. Then, if R is allowed to be a value of x, we get

$$\varphi R \,.\, \supset \,.\, \psi R,$$

which implies a negation of (5.1b) and hence contradiction. (For a complete analysis of this contradiction, see Lewis and Langford [L-L; 442ff].)

5.2   Theory of types

To avoid such contradictions, P.M. introduced a "theory of types" for the handling of propositional functions. As it was presented in P.M., this theory involved the use of an axiom called the "Reducibility Axiom," at whose non-primitive and arbitrary character much criticism was directed. Some critics pointed out that the axiom, from a logical standpoint, is probably not true, and in any case renders void the contention that mathematics has been shown to be derivable from postulates of primitive logic. Whitehead and Russell were not unaware of this; thus in the Introduction to the second edition of P.M. they stated: "This axiom has a purely pragmatic justification: it leads to the desired results, and to no others. But clearly it is not the sort of axiom with which we can rest content." Subsequent attempts by Chwistek [a], Wittgenstein [Wt], Ramsey [Ra], and later logicians to eliminate or modify the use of the axiom have nullified this objection to a great extent, and the "simple theory of types" such as pioneered by Chwistek and Ramsey indeed renders pointless the axiom of reducibility.

5.2.1 Simple theory of types

Because of the parallel between (1) classes and (2) propositional functions, a type theory may be set up for either classes or functions. Because of our extended discussion of set theory in the earlier chapters, we shall choose the former.

A simple type theory, then, would consist of a hierarchy of levels, each level above the first encompassing a class type; specifically, on the first or 0-th level would be placed the elements of lowest order, what would be called "individuals," from which classes of the first level are formed. The classes of level 1 may be used as elements to form classes of level 2; and so on. In applying such a type theory, one follows the rule that the elements of a class are all to belong to a given level; in an expression $A \; \varepsilon \; B$, the symbol B may stand for a class of any level above the 0-th, but then A must be the symbol for a class (or an individual) of next lower level. Adherence to such a rule would, it will be noted, avoid such contradictions as that of Russell and "the set of all sets."

The parallel simple type theory for functions is set up analogously. To classes of the first level correspond propositional functions of the first level; to classes of the second level, functions of the second level (whose variables are, then, functions of the first level); etc.

5.2.2 Relations

From propositional functions of two or more variables may be formed relations: Thus, if φxy is a propositional function of two variables x, y, there corresponds a relation

$$(5.2.2a) \qquad\qquad \hat{x}\hat{y}(\varphi xy).$$

[Obviously one can think of this as the class of all pairs (x, y) satisfying the propositional function φxy.]

For example, if φxy is the propositional function "x is the father of y," then $\hat{x}\hat{y}(\varphi xy)$ would denote the relationship of fatherhood; in particular, if x_1 and y_1 are particular (constant) individuals bearing this relationship, one could write

$$x_1 \quad \hat{x}\hat{y}(\varphi xy) \quad y_1$$

in which formula (5.2.2a) is used as the symbol for the relationship.

5.2.3   Extension of the type theory

With the introduction of relations, it becomes necessary to extend the theory of types in order to accommodate functions of several variables. For the theory of classes, it is sufficient to designate the primary "individuals," and thence the classes of first, second, . . . , levels, as in 5.2.1. But, where two or more variables are involved, these may not all be of the same type.

In P.M., a so-called "ramified" type theory was introduced which would enable one to avoid not only the set-theoretic contradictions, but also the "semantical" contradictions such as that of Grelling (see Problem 1 of Chapter III) and Richard (see Problem 25 of Chapter IV). In this ramified theory, propositional functions of the same type were divided into "orders" according to the occurrence of functions as bound variables. Thus, on the first level, propositional functions, φx, where x is an individual (0-th level), would be designated as of first order, but $(\varphi)\psi(\varphi, y)$, in which a first-order function occurs as bound variable, would be designated as a second-order function. Unfortunately the resulting theory necessitated at this point the introduction of the "Reducibility Axiom" mentioned above, which asserted that every propositional function is formally equivalent † to a "predicative function" (i.e., a propositional function whose variables are individuals or functions of next lower type). And, as remarked above, this axiom was criticized on various grounds. The work of later logicians makes it apparent, however, that the axiom is by no means necessary. Ramsey [Ra] made the distinction between the set-theoretic contradictions and the contradictions of semantic type, and gave an alternative theory sufficient to avoid the former while maintaining the non-essentiality of the latter so far as mathematics is concerned.

The current use of the theory of types probably stems from the formulation of Carnap [Car; 19ff]. He denotes class types by symbols $t0$, $t1$, $t2$, $\cdots$, where 0 is the type of an individual. If in a relation xRy we call x the "first member" and y the "second member," then a relation whose first member is of type tm and second member of type tn is designated as of type $t(mn)$. Here, the m and n may denote not merely numbers, but combinations of numbers, etc. Thus, if m denotes the type of an individual and n a relation of type $t(02)$, then the relation itself would be designated as of type $t(0(02))$. Analogous conventions are made for relations involving three variables, four variables, etc. For classes, if the elements of a class have type tm, then the type symbol of the class is $t(m)$. Thus, if the elements

† Functions are called "formally equivalent" if they are true or false for the same values of their variables.

of a class are relations of type $t(02)$, then the class is of type $t((02))$. For $t(0)$ we may write $t1$, for $t(1)$ write $t2$, as before.

In employing this theory of types, it is stipulated that all values of a given variable must have the same type. In particular, all elements of a given class must have the same type; if the class is of type $t(m)$, then its elements must be of type tm, no "objects" of any other type than those of type tm being even considered as allowable candidates for elements of the class. (Thus no class C can stand in either relation $C \, \varepsilon \, C$ or $C \sim \varepsilon \, C$, each of these possibilities being ruled out.) Likewise all first elements of a relation must be of the same type, viz., type tm if the relation is of type $t(mn)$. [Exceptions are made in the case of class inclusion, such as $A \subset B$, class intersections, $A \cap B$, etc., where it leads to no difficulty if A, B are allowed to vary in type; strictly speaking, a special symbol, such as $\supset_{(mn)}$ should be used if A and B are of type $t(mn)$, for example.]

For further details, Carnap's work (loc. cit.) may be consulted. See also Hilbert-Ackermann [H-A; 152ff], and Church [e]. For a critique of the classical methods of constructing the continuum of real numbers, and alternative methods, see the work of H. Weyl [We]; also see the elementary expositions of Weyl [a] and Quine [b].

5.3   When the concepts of class and relation have been adequately developed, it is possible to proceed to the definition of cardinal number and to ordinary arithmetic. From our earlier discussions of number it can easily be surmised how we would go about doing this, without entering into the bothersome details.

Before leaving the subject, however, we should emphasize something that becomes apparent in the above discussion, namely, that in dealing with a symbolic logic we operate at different language levels. Thus, in discussing P.M., we have the language symbolized in terms of p, q, v, $\sim$, etc., as well as the language ("metalanguage") in which we discuss the former language, set up our rules of syntax, etc. For example, the symbols 0, 1, etc., used in discussing the theory of types, are in the metalanguage; later they appear in the arithmetic as it evolves from the theory of classes and relations, but now in the language of our formal logic.

Also, since mathematics contains geometry, it would be necessary, after arithmetic has been set up, to introduce geometry by the usual methods of coordinates. The geometric part of P.M. never appeared, however. Shortly after Whitehead's death, Russell [b] wrote: "Whitehead was to have written a fourth volume on geometry, which would have been entirely his work. A good deal of this was done, and I hope still exists. But his increasing interest in philosophy led him to think other work more important. He proposed to treat a space as the field of a single triadic, tetradic, or pentadic relation, a treatment to which, he said, he had been led by reading Veblen."

By way of an interesting historical footnote, we might add that in the same connection Russell pointed out the importance of Whitehead's contribution to P.M., attributing to him entire responsibility for the treatment of apparent variables, for instance; and commenting "Neither of us alone could have written the book; even together, and with the alleviation brought by mutual discussion, the effort was so severe that at the end we both turned aside from mathematical logic with a kind of nausea."

6 Concluding remarks

Whether the Frege-Russell thesis—that mathematics is an extension of logic—has been established or not is a matter of opinion. Obviously, an affirmative opinion would seem to assume that one is satisfied in his mind as to what mathematics is; indeed, the affirmation of the thesis does, in a way, assert a definition of mathematics, inasmuch as one points to P.M., or one of its more modern counterparts, and says "What you can thus and so derive from this system, using the rules assigned for such derivation, is mathematics." Furthermore, the meanings of the natural numbers are made precise, immutable, and fixed; no ambiguity remains as to what 2 stands for (except a "type" ambiguity), as there does when one bases his arithmetic on an axiom system such as that of Peano.

However, it is perhaps safe to say that generally the working mathematician tends to prefer a standpoint analogous to that of the Peano school (VII 4.2), a tendency further exemplified in the work of Hilbert and his followers, which we discuss in the sequel. Nevertheless, it may be a matter of pure choice whether one will base his theory of the natural numbers on the Peano system, or proceed as in the "logistic" manner. For one may set up a model for the former within a system of set theory, and then identify "numbers" with the elements of the set-theoretic model; any statement about the objects of the Peano system will then hold if and only if it holds for the numbers constructed from sets. In this manner the two ways of thinking about numbers are rendered equivalent.

ADDITIONAL BIBLIOGRAPHY

Black [Bl]   MacLane [a]
Eaton [E; Part III]   Rosenbloom [Ros]
Journal of Symbolic Logic   Russell [R₁]

X

Intuitionism

It is frequently stated that there are three present-day "schools of thought" regarding the origin and nature of mathematics: Logisticism, Intuitionism, and Formalism. This should not be interpreted to mean that the class of all mathematicians can be subjected to a class decomposition, relative to an equivalence relation denoting membership in the same "school" (as in II 8.5)! Probably the great majority of mathematicians spend little, if any, time speculating on the question of membership in a "school of thought." They are either too busy doing research at the higher levels of their fields, or (in many cases) disdainful of such a question.

Nor is this so-called division into "schools" even to be considered a decomposition of the relatively small body of mathematicians and philosophers who make research in the foundations their main occupation. They, too, are usually found to have their differing shades of individual opinion. Rather, it represents an attempt at classification of *thought tendencies*. It may be impossible to say of a given mathematician that he accepts the "logistic thesis" or is a "formalist"—he may lean to a little of both! But, as a thesis which evolved in the course of mathematical thinking and more or less culminated in P.M., "logisticism" or "logicism" for instance represents a philosophical stand regarding the nature of mathematics which one may wholly, partially, or in modified form select as his personal philosophy of mathematics. It did not evolve full-blown in P.M. Leibnitz, for instance, showed tendencies in this direction and would probably have gone even further, to judge from his stand on the basic importance of a "logistics." However, the first clear-cut statement, as well as mature development and exposition of the general thesis, certainly occurs in P.M.

In this chapter and the next one, we shall discuss the other two "schools" named above, viz., Intuitionism and Formalism. Associated with them in current thinking as respective "founders" of the schools are the Dutch mathematician, L. E. J. Brouwer, and the same D. Hilbert whose work in the foundations of geometry we mentioned in I 1.2 and in later sections. They bear to their respective "schools" much the same position that Russell bore to his; and a considerable part of our discussion will be based on their personal writings, or writings done under their personal influence by students or colleagues. Of course neither *began* the train of thought which culminated in his "school." Before Brouwer there was Kronecker; before Hilbert there was Peano.† Their works do present forthright formulations of philosophies regarding the nature of mathematics which had hitherto been only vague speculations for the most part, however. Although Brouwer's first writings on the foundations appeared in the first decade of the present century (antedating P.M.), their major and most influential portion was published during the third decade. A like comment holds for Hilbert's work on the general foundations.

1 Basic philosophy of Intuitionism

In our discussion of Kronecker's views in VIII 2.1, we emphasized his insistence on the notion of mathematics as a construction on the basis of the "intuitively given" natural numbers. This notion is the kernel of Intuitionism as it is generally understood ‡ today. And the consequences of this thesis, particularly in set theory and logic, will be shown below so the results can be contrasted with the "classical" concepts treated in Part I.

Before going into such details, however, let us review briefly the underlying philosophy of present-day mathematical Intuitionism. The most striking aspect of it is probably what we might call its *self-sufficiency*. It is *self-generating*, relying in no way on other philosophies

---

† Although Hilbert and Peano were contemporaries, Peano's "formalism" was a forerunner of the general symbolic procedures adopted by Hilbert in his "Grundlagen."

‡ We may as well remark here that, as a philosophy, Intuitionism has undoubtedly been misinterpreted in many of its details. This is quite probably not due to carelessness on the part of interpreters in general, however, but rather to the complicated nature of the basic definitions of Intuitionism as presented by Brouwer. Of recent years much of this unfortunate misunderstanding has been cleared up, owing in large measure to the investigations and expositions of Brouwer's students and colleagues (such as, for instance, A. Heyting; see especially Heyting [He]). The present author is quite aware, let it be made plain, of his own weaknesses of understanding and susceptibility to error; so the reader is admonished to take the following exposition "with a grain of salt" and, if sufficiently "provoked," to consult the bibliography cited herewith.

or logic. Its basic ideas are to be found in the *intuition*, which seems to be similar to the time (not the spatial) intuition of Kant. Specifically, it recognizes the ability of the individual person to perform a series of mental acts consisting of a first act, then another, then another, and so on endlessly. In this way one attains "fundamental series," the best known of which is the series of natural numbers.

This operation is not dependent upon the use of a language. To quote Brouwer (f; 86) in this regard: ". . . neither the ordinary language nor any symbolic language can have any other role than that of serving as a nonmathematical auxiliary, to assist the mathematical memory or to enable different individuals to build up the same set." As a consequence of this principle, mathematics is basically *independent of language*. For the *communication* of mathematics the usual symbolic devices, including ordinary language, are necessary, but this is their only function. This seems to make of mathematics virtually an *individual* affair rather than an organized or *cultural* phenomenon, and is perhaps the tenet of Intuitionism that it is most difficult to accept. For mathematics as it is known to most of us appears to be the result of the research of many different investigators who worked out and handed on their ideas by means of a symbolic faculty; without the latter not only would it be necessary to start a new mathematics with each generation, but also each individual would of necessity create his own mathematics. However, it is possible that the Brouwer thesis only requires that one set apart the basic ideas—the intuition of the natural numbers and the ideas regarding set-formation—from linguistic influences, while acknowledging the subsequent role of language in the development, on this basis, of mathematics as a cultural phenomenon. Whether this is a tenable doctrine or not is still debatable. (Compare Chapter XII.)

For the related insistence of Intuitionism that *mathematics is not dependent upon classical logic*, a stronger case can be made. Brouwer goes to considerable lengths to build his system without use of any logic other than what he can justify and found on his mathematics. Here the argument that mathematics is not dependent upon logic is supported by *doing*. There emerge general rules, supposedly intuitively arrived at, for the derivation of new theorems from old. And, as Heyting has shown, these can be presented in the form of a symbolic logic which he calls a *mathematical logic*. This mathematical logic is thus a subdomain of mathematics whose use outside of mathematics would be "senseless" (cf. Heyting [He; 13ff]). A brief description of it is given below (Section 7) in order that the reader may compare it with the classical type of logic as described in Chapters VIII and IX.

To summarize, the basic philosophy of mathematical Intuitionism is that, although historically mathematics was derived from the world of experience by means of the senses, in its abstract formation it is purely intuitive and not dependent upon logic or science. On the contrary, the latter depend upon and use the methods of mathematics. All mathematics may be derived from the fundamental series of natural numbers by "intuitively clear" constructive methods. Language and other symbolic apparatus are not mathematical tools, but (imperfect) means of communicating mathematical ideas.

2 The natural numbers and the definition of set

Kronecker was a strict finitist. To him, the "constructible" concept of the natural numbers, as described in VIII 2.1.2, embodied the only acceptable manner in which the natural numbers form a "set." Such a "set" is not a *set* in the Cantorian or generally accepted sense, which is that of an "already formed" or "already existing" totality. The reader may refer to the material in fine print in VIII 2.1.2, and compare with the following, which forms the opening paragraph of what may be taken as the "official" presentation of Brouwer's views: †

"At the basis of mathematics lies an unlimited sequence of symbols or finite symbol arrays, which is determined by a first symbol and the law which derives from each of these rows of symbols the next. For this purpose ‡ the sequence ζ, of (natural) numbers 1, 2, 3, 4, 5, $\cdots$ is especially useful."

The concept expressed here certainly seems to coincide with that of the finitist; "a first symbol and a law. . . ." Moreover, Brouwer bases his definition of *set* on the natural numbers; this definition is quite complicated:

"A *set* is a *law*, on the basis of which if an arbitrary natural number is repeatedly chosen, then each of these choices either generates a definite symbol array with or without termination of the process,§ or brings about stoppage of the process and rejection of its result; for every $n > 1$ following a non-terminating and non-stopped sequence of $n - 1$ choices, at least one natural number can be given which, if it is chosen as the nth natural number, does not bring about

---

† From here to the end of Section 5, the material is selected almost verbatim from Brouwer [a]; the only variations, aside from minor liberties of translation, being certain comments, interpretations, and examples.

‡ Meaning, presumably, "for the purposes of such a sequence."

§ Brouwer notes here that the possibility of the "termination of the process" can obviously be replaced by the possibility "that after a certain choice every further choice generates nothing."

stoppage of the process. Every sequence of symbol arrays generated in this manner by an unlimited sequence of choices (which is then generally not presentable in finished form) is called an *element of the set*. The common origin of the elements of a set M we shall usually designate briefly as *the set M*." †

It is to be observed that a set, according to Brouwer, is not a finished totality; rather it is a *law*, according to which *elements* ("of the set") can be constructed. Involved in the construction of an element is the sequence of natural numbers. Not even an element is necessarily presentable in finished form—the array of symbols constituting it is to be generated by an unlimited sequence of choices. Thus a real number, π for instance, is determined only to the extent to which the construction of its successive digits is carried out.

The laws determining finite sequences as unlimited sequences of symbol arrays of the kind found in the sequence ζ form special cases of sets whose elements are formed by the single symbols. The set of natural numbers, that is, the symbol arrays of ζ, will be designated by A.

As to the distinction between "finite" and "infinite" sets, Brouwer defines: "If for each n in ζ there is determined a natural number k_n, such that every time a natural number greater than k_n is selected as the nth choice, the process is stopped, then the set is called *finite*." As an example, he points out that the "unlimited" sequences of numbers of *one digit* form a finite set.

Two elements are called *equal* or *identical* if it is certain that for every n the nth choice for each element generates the same symbol array. Of just what this "certainty" consists, and its character, is not explained by Brouwer, but is presumably to be decided for the particular case. For example, if we were to present any two of the many well-known definitions of π, we could give a proof that the decimal developments of the two numbers so defined would agree in the nth digit for every n; and so the two numbers are equal. But suppose that N is a number defined as follows: N is a number such that $0 \leq N \leq 1$; in decimal form its nth digit after the decimal point, a_n, is 0, unless the nth digit of the decimal part of π is the first of a sequence of

† Compare this definition of *set* with that which some authors of elementary texts give for *function*. For example, in the Randolph-Kac *Analytic Geometry and Calculus* (New York, Macmillan, 1947) occurs the following: "We shall understand a function to be a rule whereby it can be told that for a given number either: A. No number is to be associated, or B. One and only one number is to be associated, and furthermore the rule tells what this associated number is." (Quoted with permission of The Macmillan Co.)

seven 7's—7777777—in which case the digit a_n is 1. We cannot say that N and 0 are equal, since we have no way of knowing that there does not exist a sequence of seven 7's in the decimal part of π. (Possibly there is such a sequence. Incidentally, π is now known, by computation in the ENIAC computer at Aberdeen Proving Ground, to 2035 digits; the result of the voluntary week-end work of four operators of the machine!)

Two *sets* are called *equal* or *identical* if for each element of either set "can be given" an equal element of the other set; and a set M is called a *subset* of a set N if for each element of M there "exists" an equal element of N. A subset M of N is *proper* if there can be given an element of N which cannot equal an element of M.

3 Species

On the basis of sets and elements, which he calls *mathematical entities*, Brouwer erects a hierarchy of concepts which he calls *species* (*Spezies;* compare the type theory of P.M., IX 4.3). A *species of the first order* is a *property* which only a mathematical entity can possess, in which case the entity is called an *element of the species of first order*. Thus the property of being prime is a species of first order, since it is a property only of natural numbers (which as elements of A are mathematical entities). And sets are themselves species of first order (since, if M is a set, then the property of being an element of M is possessed only by the elements of M—hence the latter are elements of a species, M, of the first order). Equality of species is defined in a manner similar to that for sets. A *species of second order* is a property which only a mathematical entity or species of first order can possess, in which case it is called an *element of the species of second order*. And similarly *species of the nth order*, as well as their equality, are defined for arbitrary number n. *Subspecies* are defined in a manner similar to that for subsets.

4 Relations between species

Equality was defined above, and the notions of subset and subspecies introduced. Two set elements are called *different* if it is *certain* that their equality is an impossibility. For example, the number N defined in Section 2 is not *different* from zero; thus we can say neither that N *equals* zero nor that N is *different* from zero. Similarly, two species are called different if it is certain that their equality is an impossibility. A species S is called *discrete* if it is possible to determine of each two elements of S that they are either equal or different. Thus any set which has both zero and the number N of Section 2 as elements cannot be called discrete.

4.1 Congruent species; semi-identical species

A species S is said to *project* † from a species S^1 if S has an element which is different from every element of S^1. Two species S and S^1 are called *congruent* if neither can project from the other (i.e., if every property impossible for elements of the one species is impossible for the elements of the other). As an example, Brouwer cites the case where S contains those numbers x, $0 \le x \le 1$, of which in binary form it is fixed how many zero digits precede the first digit 1, or that no 1 occurs, and where S^1 contains those for which it is fixed how many 1's precede the first zero digit, or that no 0 occurs. Note that the number N defined in Section 2, considered binary, is an element of S^1, but is not an element of S. However, we cannot say that N is *different from* (see above definition) every element of S. The property of being congruent is an "equivalence relation" as defined in II 8. (Brouwer does not use this terminology, remarking merely on the transitive character of the "congruence" relation.)

A subspecies of a species S is called *semi-identical* ‡ *with* S if it is congruent with S. Thus, the species denoted by S in the preceding paragraph is semi-identical with the species containing all numbers x of the unit interval $0 \le x \le 1$.

4.2 Union and intersection of species

Union (addition) of sets is defined as in ordinary set theory (III 3.3), and union of species is defined similarly. A like remark holds regarding *intersection* (product); see III 3. However, although the union of two sets is again a set, the intersection of two sets is not necessarily a set; as, for example (Brouwer, loc. cit.) if S is a set whose single ele-

---

† *Herausragen.* In the Brouwer exposition (loc. cit., p. 246) the symbols corresponding to S and S^1 are interchanged in the latter part of the definition. This is probably a misprint (if the terminology "project from"—meaning, literally, "sticks out from"—is to be at all natural).

‡ *Halbidentisch.* In this definition we set down what we presume Brouwer means by this term. As given in the Brouwer exposition (loc. cit., p. 246), the definition appears meaningless ("Eine mit M kongruente Teilspezies von N heisst auch *halbidentisch* mit N." One could surmise that the first M here should be N, which would conform to our definition above, and that M should be inserted after "Teilspezies." For Brouwer continues, "Dies ist z.B. der Fall, wenn M dieselbe Spezies wie im vorigen Absatz [the set S in the preceding paragraph of the text above—RLW] und N die Spezies der unendlichen Dualbruchentwicklungen des Einheitsintervalls vorstellt.")

ment is the number 0, and S' a set whose single element is the binary fraction N defined in Section 2.

4.3 Decomposition and separation of species

Two species S and S' are called *disjoint* (*elementefremd*) if they are *different* and if it is impossible for an element of S and an element of S', which are equal, to exist. If S' and S'' are disjoint subspecies of a species S, and if the union of S' and S'' is semi-identical with S, then we shall say that S is *composed by* ("zusammengesetzt") S' and S'', and we call S' and S'' *complementary species* of one another in S. This is, for example (Brouwer, loc. cit.), the case if S consists of all natural numbers, S' of all those natural numbers which, as exponents of the Fermat equation, render that equation solvable, and S'' of all those natural numbers which, as exponents of the Fermat equation, render it unsolvable.† If S' and S'' are disjoint subspecies of S whose union is *equal* to S, then we say that S is *separated into* S' and S'', and call the latter *conjugate separation-species* of S; and also say that S' (S'') is a *separable subspecies* of S. This is, for example (Brouwer, loc. cit., p. 247), the case if S consists of all natural numbers, S' of those numbers which have at most five digits, and S'' of those numbers which have more than five digits.

5 Theory of cardinal numbers

If there can be established a (1-1)-correspondence between two species S and S', that is, a law which makes correspond to each element of S an element of S' in such a way that equal and only equal elements of S correspond to equal elements of S', and every element of S' to an element of S, then we write $S \sim S'$, and say that S and S' *have the same cardinal number*, or are *cardinally equivalent*. (Brouwer cites the example of the set of all natural numbers and the set of all natural numbers except 1.)

If to every element of S is made to correspond an element of S' in such a way that equal and only equal elements of S correspond to equal elements of S', and the species of elements of S' that correspond thus to elements of S is semi-identical with S', then we say that S and S' are *cardinally semi-equivalent* (*halbgleichmächtig*).

---

† As the reader probably knows, Brouwer refers here to the equation $x^n + y^n = z^n$, which for $n = 2$ possesses such integral solutions as $x = 3$, $y = 4$, $z = 5$; but it is not known whether for $n > 2$ there exist such solutions. If, for a given n, such solutions exist, then Brouwer calls the equation "solvable."

5.1 Finite and infinite species and their cardinal numbers

A species is called *finite* if it is cardinally equivalent to the set of natural numbers of a certain initial segment † of the sequence ζ. A species is called *infinite* if it has a subspecies cardinally equivalent to *A*, and in particular *reducibly infinite* if the subspecies is separable. It should be noted that there is no basis for ascertaining that every set or species is either finite or infinite. On the other hand it is certain that a species cannot be both finite and infinite. For one can prove:

5.1.1   Theorem.‡ Principal property of finite species. *For every manner of representation of the (1-1)-correspondence between a finite species S and the set of numbers in an initial segment of ζ, the same initial segment is used.*

Proof. Let S_1 and N denote two "enumerations" of S, such that S_1 uses up the initial segment 1, 2, $\cdots$, k of ζ, and N uses up an initial segment that includes 1, 2, $\cdots$, k. Let S_2 denote the enumeration derived from S_1 by exchanging in S_1 the elements which correspond to 1 in S_1 and N. Then S_2 uses up the same initial segment 1, 2, $\cdots$, k of ζ as S_1, while in both S_2 and N the same element of S now corresponds to 1.

Next let S_3 be the enumeration derived from S_2 by exchanging in S_2 the elements which correspond to 2 in S_2 and N. Then S_1 and S_3 use the same initial segment 1, 2, $\cdots$, k of ζ, while S_3 and N have the same elements corresponding to 1 and 2.

Proceeding in this manner, we obtain finally a last enumeration, S_i, which uses the same initial segment of ζ as S_1, and at the same time has the same elements corresponding to 1, 2, $\cdots$, k, respectively, as N. But S_i contains all elements of S, and consequently the elements of N corresponding respectively to 1, 2, $\cdots$, k contain all elements of S; in other words, N has no elements corresponding to an element of ζ greater than k.

5.1.2   Cardinal numbers of finite sets. As a consequence of this theorem, Brouwer states that we can denote the *cardinal number* of a finite species by the last number of the sequence ζ which is used in an enumeration of the species. The cardinal number of a species having no elements is called *null* and denoted by 0. These are evidently to be taken as definitions of "cardinal number" for finite species,

---

† That is, section; see V 3.1.1. Note that Brouwer's "finite" corresponds to the "ordinary finite" defined in III 4.1.1.

‡ Compare with Theorem III 5.2.1.

since Brouwer gives no general definition such as that of Russell-Frege.

5.1.3   *A proper subspecies of a finite species S cannot be cardinally equivalent to S;* for the supposition of such an equivalence would lead to a contradiction of Theorem 5.1.1. And in particular *a finite species cannot also be infinite.*

5.1.4   Theorem. *Every reducibly infinite species S has a proper subspecies which has the same cardinal number as S.*

Proof. Let S' be the separable subspecies of S that is cardinally equivalent to A; the elements of S' may evidently be denoted by symbols $x_1, x_2, \cdots, x_n, \cdots, n \varepsilon A$. Let S'' be the subspecies of S such that S' and S'' are conjugate separation-species of S. The correspondences (x_n, x_{n+1}), $n = 1, 2, \cdots, n, \cdots$ and (x, x) for x an element of S'' constitute a (1-1)-correspondence between S and a proper subspecies of S.

The reader will note that the proof just given is formally identical with the latter part of the proof given in III 5.3. The debatable first part of the proof of III 5.3 is avoided in Brouwer's system, however, since he has defined "infinite" to imply the existence of the analogue of the set S_1 of III 5.3.

5.2   Denumerable sets

As in the classical theory (as given in Chapters III to V), the simplest example of an infinite set is the set A. Brouwer states (loc. cit., p. 249, § 3) that he will denote the "cardinal number" of this set by a (no explicit definition of "cardinal number" is given). Species which have the same cardinal number as A are called *countably infinite;* since no confusion would result, we may use the same term *denumerable* as we used in the classical case. Hence *every infinite species has a denumerable subspecies.*

Again, as in the classical theory (with the new meaning of "set," however), the set of integers, the species of the rational numbers, and the species of the algebraic numbers are each denumerable. The proof of the denumerability of the species of the algebraic numbers is worth noting, but will not be repeated here for lack of space (see Brouwer, loc. cit., pp. 249–250). Also, a species which can be separated into a denumerable species of denumerable species is itself denumerable.

5.3   The cardinal number c

As another example of an infinite set, Brouwer offers the set C of unrestricted sequences of natural numbers, whose cardinal number he denotes by c. Although this set is not reducibly infinite, it has a cardinally equivalent proper subspecies. The species C_n each of whose elements consists of n unrestricted sequences of natural numbers has the cardinal number c. And as in the classical theory, this fact permits a relation of cardinality between points of a line and points of n-dimensional euclidean space (for details see Brouwer, loc. cit., pp. 251–252).

5.4   Other types of equivalence between species

The notion of cardinal equivalence does not, according to Brouwer, exhaust the possible types of equivalence relations between sets. In the classical theory, it was shown that, if A and B are sets such that there exist (1-1)-correspondences between A and a subset of B, and between B and a subset of A, then there exists a (1-1)-correspondence between A and B (Bernstein Equivalence Theorem, IV 4.2.3). Brouwer defines:

5.4.1   Definition.   Two species S and S' (and likewise the corresponding cardinal numbers s and s') are called *equivalent* if by some law L_1 there is made to correspond to every element of S an element of S' so that to equal and only to equal elements of S equal elements of S' correspond; and if by some law L_2 there is made to correspond to every element of S' an element of S so that to equal and only equal elements of S' equal elements of S correspond.   This equivalence is expressed by the formula $s = s'$.

5.4.2   Definition.   If for species S and S' such a law as L_1, defined in 5.4.1, exists, but no such law as L_2 can possibly exist, then we write $s < s'$ (or $s' > s$) and say that S (s) is *smaller than* S' (s'), and S' (s') is *greater than* S (s).

5.4.3   Definition.   If we know that to every element of S there corresponds an element of S' such that to equal elements and only equal elements of S do equal elements of S' correspond, then we write $s \leqq s'$ (or $s' \geqq s$), although in this case *there need not necessarily one of the relations $s < s'$, $s = s'$ hold.*

It will be noted that we have here a denial of the Law of the Excluded Middle; since, if such a law as L_1 of 5.4.1 exists, then, according to the Law of the Excluded Middle, either such a law as L_2 exists (and hence $s = s'$) or such a law as L_2 does not exist (and hence *cannot* exist in the classical sense, so that $s < s'$).

In particular, the set C is greater than the set A; $a < c$. If K is the species of *lawfully defined* unlimited sequences of natural numbers (i.e., each element of K is defined by some law, as opposed to the un-restricted nature of the elements of C), then C is also greater than K. The "equivalence" possibilities are not yet exhausted. Because of the distinction between equality and semi-identity, we can define:

5.4.4   Definition.   A species S (and likewise its cardinal number s) is said to *outrank* a species S' (and its cardinal number s') if to every element x of a certain subspecies S_1 of S there corresponds an element y of S' in such a way that the species S_1' of such elements y is semi-identical with S'; we also write $s \overset{\circ}{\geqq} s'$. In the case where S_1' is iden-tical with S', the species S (and its cardinal number s) is said to *en-velop* the species S' (and its cardinal number s'), and we write $s \overset{\cdot}{\geqq} s'$. (Evidently $s \geqq s'$ implies $s \overset{\cdot}{\geqq} s'$.) In the case where S_1 is identical with S, we write $s \overset{\cdot}{\geqq} s'$ and say S (s) is *superposed on* S' (s'). In case S_1 is identical with S, and S_1' with S, we write $s \overset{\cdot\cdot}{\geqq} s'$ and say S' (s') is *covered by* S (s).

If S outranks S', but the converse is impossible, then we write $s \overset{\circ}{>} s'$ and say that S (s) is of *greater extent* than S' (s'). If $s \overset{\circ}{\geqq} s'$ and $s' \overset{\circ}{\geqq} s$, then we write $s \overset{\circ}{=} s'$ and say that S and S' (s and s') are of *equal extent*. If $s \overset{\cdot}{\geqq} s'$, but it is impossible that $s' \overset{\cdot}{\geqq} s$, then we write $s \overset{\cdot}{>} s'$ and say that S (s) has *greater breadth* than S' (s'). By $s \overset{\cdot}{=} s'$ is meant that $s \overset{\cdot}{\geqq} s'$ and $s' \overset{\cdot}{\geqq} s$. The relations $\overset{\cdot\cdot}{>}$ and $\overset{\cdot\cdot}{=}$ are de-fined analogously; in place of "extent" and "breadth" we may use "dimension" for these relations. If S' is covered by S, but the con-verse is impossible, then we shall write $s \overset{\cdot\cdot}{>} s'$ and say S has *greater weight* than S'. The relation $\overset{\cdot\cdot}{=}$ is defined in obvious fashion.

5.5   Types of countability

Corresponding to the above types of equivalence (and non-equiva-lence), Brouwer defines various types of countability. Denoting, for arbitrary species S, the cardinal number by s, we say S is *countable* (*abzählbar*) if $s \leqq a$. If in particular S is known to be in (1-1)-corre-spondence with a *separable* subspecies of A, then Brouwer calls S *zählbar*. (Inasmuch as the possibilities of adequate English terms seem to be nearly exhausted, we shall give only the German terms to distinguish the shades of meaning.) If $s = a$, then S is called *nach-zählbar*. And corresponding to the relations $s \overset{\circ}{\leqq} a$, $s \overset{\cdot}{\leqq} a$, $s \overset{\cdot\cdot}{\leqq} a$, $s \overset{\cdot\cdot}{\leqq} a$ the terms *auszählbar*, *überzählbar*, *durchzählbar*, and *aufzählbar*, respectively, are employed by Brouwer.

5.5.1   Examples.   Denoting by d_ν the νth digit after the decimal point in the decimal development of π, let us set $m = k_n$ if with d_m it happens for the nth time that $d_m d_{m+1} \cdots d_{m+9}$ forms a sequence

0123456789. Denote by S_1 the species of those *even* natural numbers n for which it is impossible that they be indices of symbols k_n, and by S_2 the union of S_1 with the species of odd natural numbers. Then S_1 and S_2 are both *countable*, consequently also *auszählbar* and *überzählbar*; neither S_1 nor S_2 is *zählbar*; S_2 is *nachzählbar* but S_1 is not; neither S_1 nor S_2 is *durchzählbar* or *aufzählbar*. Brouwer remarks that, wherever we here assert the negative of a type of countability for an S_i, it is to be understood that this means that the present state of our knowledge affords no basis for asserting that S_i has the type of countability in question.

If we denote by S_3 the set of non-stopped choice-sequences (cf. the definition of *set* in Section 2) which results when the choice of 3, 4, $\cdots$ always leads to stoppage of the process of choosing, while *after* a choice of 1 either 1 or 2 can be chosen without stoppage of the process, but *after* a choice of 2 only the number 2 can be chosen without stoppage of the process, then S_3 is *not countable;* hence it is neither *zählbar* nor *nachzählbar*, likewise neither *überzählbar* nor *aufzählbar*, but it is *auszählbar* and *durchzählbar*.

Let us denote by $S(\pi)$ the species which has the decimal part of π as single element, by S_4' the species of those decimals which exhibit infinitely many pairs of successive equal digits, and by S_5' the species of those decimals that contain a sequence 0123456789. If S_4 and S_5 are the intersections, respectively, of $S(\pi)$ and S_4', and of $S(\pi)$ and S_5', then S_4 and S_5 are both countable, and consequently *auszählbar* and *überzählbar*; neither is *nachzählbar*; S_5 is *zählbar* but S_4 is not; and neither S_4 nor S_5 is *durchzählbar* or *aufzählbar*.

If S_6 denotes the species of those natural numbers n for which the nth and $(n + 1)$th digits of the decimal part of π are equal, then S_6 is countable and *zählbar*, but not *nachzählbar;* but it is *aufzählbar*, consequently also *auszählbar*, *überzählbar*, and *durchzählbar*.

Further investigation of the relations between the possible types of "countability" has been made by Heyting [a].

5.6   Other cardinal numbers

With regard to the possibility of cardinal numbers "higher" than c, nothing seems to have been done in the intuitionist mathematics. The possibility of a "species of all subspecies of a given species" seems in general excluded by the difficulty of finding suitable defining properties, for instance. And, similarly, the diagonal procedure (IV 3) is in general not definable.

This does not mean, of course, that higher cardinal numbers are not definable. In any case, however, one obviously must distinguish between the cardinal numbers of intuitionist mathematics and those of the classical type as expounded in Chapter IV.

6   Order and ordinal numbers

As might be expected, in view of the above description of Brouwer's set theory, the treatment of order and ordinal numbers is quite different from that expounded in Chapter V. For a description of it, the reader is referred to Brouwer [b]. In that work, incidentally, Brouwer gives a definition of "continuum" which is very similar to the one given in VI 1.4 above, where use is made of the "Dedekind cut."

The theory of well-ordered species is given in Brouwer [c]. It is probably unnecessary to remark that for Intuitionism the theorem of Zermelo to the effect that "every set has a well-ordering" (Theorem V 3.1.6.1) is devoid of sense. To form well-ordered species two "generating operations" are permissible: addition of a finite number of known well-ordered species, and addition of a fundamental series of known well-ordered species. Consequently every well-ordered species is countable. The introduction of "null" elements renders the theory even less analogous to the classical theory. (Cf. Heyting [He; 27].)

For recent work of Brouwer concerning "partial order," and related types of order with applications to the continuum, one may consult Brouwer [d, e].

7   The intuitionist logic

In mathematics as it is usually taught in present-day schools, logic of the classical type is assumed as a priori, and plays an important role in proofs of theorems. Of special importance is the Law of the Excluded Middle and its consequence that the falsity of the falsity of a proposition p implies p (see IX 3.4.3). Thus, to prove a "Theorem A," if one can demonstrate that the assumption of the falsity of A leads to contradiction, then A is true. For any proposition which leads to contradiction must be false; hence, if the falsity of A is false, then A is true by the principle cited above. In particular, Theorem A may be an assertion of the type, "There exists a natural number having property P." If property P is "evenness," one naturally proves the theorem by exhibiting an even number. But, in the event that property P is of such a character that no number having this property has been found, one may resort to the device of showing that the assumption of non-existence of such a number leads to contradiction and concluding that one has thereby proved Theorem A.

The intuitionist would not accept such a "proof" as this. The former proof—by *exhibition* of a number with the desired property

P—is of the constructive character demanded by the intuitionist. But the latter proof introduces into mathematics a new principle that is not capable of being founded on the ideas set forth above. If one examines the proofs given in Section 5, one sees that those of 5.1.1 and 5.1.4 involve no use of logic; however, 5.1.3 employs the argument that a certain two species cannot be cardinally equivalent since the supposition of such an equivalence would lead to contradiction of 5.1.1. Thus the intuitionist accepts the principle that any proposition which implies contradiction must be false. This does not involve a use of the Law of the Excluded Middle, however, nor its corollary that the falsity of the falsity of a proposition *p* implies *p*!

It appears, then, that the intuitionist accepts the Law of Contradiction, but not the Law of the Excluded Middle. Of course he accepts the Law of the Excluded Middle where it is "intuitively" clear; if *G* were a *finite* set of natural numbers, then he would say that it is intuitively clear that either *G* contained a prime number or that no element of *G* was prime (no matter how great the number of elements in *G*, so long as it is finite). But, if *G* were infinite, the intuitionist would not admit the assertion, unless, of course, a prime number is exhibited in *G* or it is shown that the assumption that *G* contains a prime number leads to absurdity (the latter being accepted as proving that no element of *G* is prime). To show that the assumption that *G* contains no prime number leads to contradiction would not be accepted as a proof that *G* contains a prime number, since this would constitute a replacement of the falsity of the falsity of a proposition by the proposition itself.

We saw in IX 3.6 that, as the P.M. propositional calculus is set up, the Law of the Excluded Middle and the Law of Contradiction are equivalent; a consequence of the interdependence of the logical constants $\sim$, ., and **v**. And from the material in IX 3.4 it follows that *p* and $\sim(\sim p)$ are equivalent. Since the intuitionist accepts none of these principles, it becomes an interesting problem to analyze, if possible, what can be described as the logical apparatus to which the intuitionist mathematics leads.

7.1   An intuitionistic symbolic logic

Such an analysis was first made by Heyting in 1930. We shall give sufficient indication of Heyting's system to enable the reader to compare it with the logistic calculus as described in Chapter IX. (We base our description on Heyting [He] and Kolmogoroff [a].)

Instead of commencing with *two* "logical constants" as in Chapter IX, namely **v** and $\sim$, and defining $\supset$ and the logical product (as in IX

3.6), *four* symbols, ∧, ∨, ¬, and ⊃, are immediately introduced, standing respectively for conjunction ("and"), disjunction ("or"), negation, and implication. These symbols are independent of one another; for example, $a ⊃ b$ is not the same as $¬a ∨ b$ [cf. IX (2.2a)]. Then "postulates" or fundamental "formulas" are stated, as was done for the propositional calculus in Chapter IX. We find, for example, the formula

$$⊢ :. \, a ⊃ b . ∧ . b ⊃ c : ⊃ : a ⊃ c,$$

where a, b, and c are propositions; also the following, which embodies the Law of Contradiction,

(7.1a) $⊢ . \, ¬(a ∧ ¬a)$

The formula which would embody the Law of the Excluded Middle cannot be derived from the system. However, the formula

(7.1b) $⊢ . \, ¬¬(a ∨ ¬a),$

which may be interpreted as the falsity of the falsity of the Law of the Excluded Middle, is derivable in the system! But, although

(7.1c) $⊢ . \, a ⊃ ¬¬a$

occurs in the system, $¬¬a ⊃ a$ does not occur, so the formula $a ∨ ¬a$ does not follow from the above. Since the formula $¬¬a ⊃ a$ is derivable from $a ∨ ¬a$, it follows, by conjunction of this fact with the remarks just made, that the Law of the Excluded Middle is equivalent to the formula $¬¬a ⊃ a$; see Brouwer [g; 252, footnote 4], who attributes this observation to P. Bernays.

Nevertheless, long strings of negations do not occur. For the formula

(7.1d) $⊢ . \, a ⊃ b . ⊃ . ¬b ⊃ ¬a$

occurs in the system, and if in this formula we replace b by $¬¬a$ and make use of (7.1c), we obtain

(7.1e) $⊢ . \, ¬¬¬a ⊃ ¬a$

(as observed in Kolmogoroff [a; 63]; the same proof, in ordinary language rather than in the symbolic form given here, occurs in Brouwer [g; 253], however). Conversely, if we replace a by $¬a$ in (7.1c), we obtain

(7.1f) $⊢ . \, ¬a ⊃ ¬¬¬a$

and from (7.1e), (7.1f) the equivalence of $¬a$ and $¬¬¬a$ is obtained.

It follows from the above that every string of negations $\neg\neg \cdots \neg a$ can be reduced to either $\neg\neg a$ or $\neg a$.

It is interesting to observe that Gödel, employing certain results of Glivenko, showed that, if the "logistic" symbols

$$a \cdot b,\ a \vee b,\ \sim a,\ a \supset b$$

are replaced by the following symbols, respectively,

$$a \wedge b,\ \neg(\neg a \wedge \neg b),\ \neg a,\ \neg(a \wedge \neg b),$$

then every formula of the "logistic" calculus becomes a valid formula in the intuitionistic logic! (See Gödel [b].)

7.2   The Kolmogoroff interpretation

The intuitionistic logic assumes a much more natural character, if instead of considering the above a *propositional* calculus, we conceive of a, b, c, $\cdots$, as denoting *problems*, and the calculus itself as a mode for solving problems—a "solution calculus." We can, indeed, following Kolmogoroff [a], approach the matter entirely independently, without any intuitionist presuppositions, purely as a question of formulating methods of solution of mathematical problems (such as, for example, problems in geometric construction).

From the latter point of view, we consider a, b, c, $\cdots$ as denoting problems to be solved, and interpret $a \supset b$ to mean the problem of deriving the solution of b from that of a (or "carrying back" the solution of b to that of a); more explicitly, $a \supset b$ means the problem "assuming that a solution of a is given, find a solution of b." By $a \wedge b$ we would indicate the problem of solving both a and b, and by $a \vee b$ the problem of solving at least one of the problems a and b. By $\neg a$ is indicated "assuming that a solution of a is given, obtain a contradiction." The symbol $\vdash$ is used as an indication of a problem to be solved for all values of the variables (problems) involved; thus,

$$(7.2a) \qquad\qquad \vdash . a \supset a \wedge a$$

means "for all a, show how to obtain a solution of $a \wedge a$ from a solution of a." Certain basic problems, such as (7.2a), are postulated—that is, considered solved—and solutions of others derived therefrom. For example, if $\vdash . p \wedge q$ is solved, then $\vdash p$ may be considered solved.

The development of the "solution calculus" turns out to coincide, symbolically, with the intuitionist propositional calculus. For instance, we will not expect to find $\vdash . a \vee \neg a$—the Law of the Excluded Middle—in the "solution calculus," since it would be tantamount to having established, for *all* problems a, either a method for solving a or a method for showing that the assumption of a method of solution for a leads to contradiction. As Brouwer asserts, the assumption of the universal validity of the Law of the Excluded Middle would be equivalent to assuming that every problem is solvable. What may be considered the intuitionist form of the Law of the Excluded Middle, (7.1b), is the symbolic formulation of a theorem of Brouwer which asserts that there cannot be given a provably unsolvable problem. It should be noted, incidentally, that the intuitionist logic does not *give permission* to assert the existence of a "middle third"; formula (7.1b) is, in a sense, as far as the logic goes in assertions regarding the general validity of the formula $a \vee \neg a$.

8　General remarks

Enough has been given above, no doubt, to demonstrate that Intuitionism is not a purely negative philosophy such as that of Kronecker. In the hands of Brouwer and his followers a sizable literature of intuitionistic mathematics has been built up. It is interesting to observe that Brouwer, after his early work on the foundations of mathematics during the first decade of the present century, published during the second decade a series of basic and very important articles in the then budding field of topology. But in the third decade he resumed constructive work in the intuitionistic foundations of mathematics, not only laying down the principles of his general theory, but also supplying new proofs of classical theorems which met the requirements of the intuitionist program. For example, in [i] he gave a new proof of the Jordan Curve Theorem † (which he had earlier (1910) proved in his topological papers but not from an intuitionist standpoint); also new proofs of the fundamental theorem of algebra were given both by him and by others. Mention has already been made above of his present researches into partial orderings.‡

8.1　Summary

In a positive way, then, intuitionism builds on the "intuitively given" sequence of natural numbers, using only constructive methods. In the theory of sets this necessitates conceiving of a set not as a ready-made "collection," but as a *law* by means of which the elements of the set can be constructed in a step-by-step fashion. In proofs of

---

† If C is a circle in a plane S, then C divides S into two connected parts, called domains, of which C is the common boundary. The Jordan Curve Theorem states that every topological transform $T(C)$ in S does likewise (cf. VII 3.5.8).

‡ For a review of the effects of intuitionistic thought on various mathematical theories, the reader is referred to Heyting [He; 22–29].

existence, the entity whose existence is to be proved must be shown to be *constructible;* it is not sufficient to show that the assumption of its non-existence leads to contradiction.

In attempts to set up a logic for intuitionist mathematics, the latter fact is recognized by not identifying the double negation with affirmation, or, what is equivalent, by suitably limiting the Law of the Excluded Middle. A corollary of this is that it is not affirmed that every mathematical problem is solvable. It develops that intuitionist mathematics produces its own type of logic, mathematical logic thus becoming a branch of mathematics, or an "applied mathematics." In the view of Brouwer, the chief protagonist of intuitionist mathematics, language or symbolism is not basic to mathematics. While it is recognized that mathematics had its origins in experience, its modern abstract formulation is the product of the pure intellect, and has intuitive, not merely formal, content. In particular, the symbolic logic discussed in 7.1 is not a mathematical tool; it serves, however, as a means of communicating the logic engendered by intuitionism.

8.2 Some specific examples

The number N defined in Section 2 furnishes a good example of the effect of the intuitionist philosophy on the real number continuum. Of this number it cannot be asserted that either it is equal to zero or it is different from zero. For to show the latter it is necessary to *exhibit* a sequence of seven 7's in π, and to show the former it is necessary to prove that the assumption of the existence of such a sequence leads to contradiction.

The Brouwer continuum is of such a character that a number is fixed only by successive rational approximations or a "closing down" process, such that, for any given number $1/n$, the value of the number is determinate within an error $< 1/n$. Of two numbers N_1 and N_2, it is possible that they are equal (as defined in Section 2), that they are definitely unequal (*entfernt*) as in the case of 3 and π, for example, or such that neither of these assertions can be made, as in the case of 0 and N above.

Or consider the number X which is equal to

$$(-1)^k/(10)^k,$$

where k is the number of the first decimal place in the decimal development of π where a sequence of digits 0123456789 commences; or, if no such number k exists, $X = 0$. The number X is certainly well-defined; but we do not know whether it is negative, positive, or zero! And the number $1 + X$, although certainly positive, is not expressible in the decimal system (since we do not know whether to start it with 1.000 . . . or with 0.999 . . .)!

As might be expected, in the light of these limitations and the nature of intuitionist set theory (as set forth above), the building up of analysis—calculus, theory of functions, etc.—in the intuitionist mathematics takes a form quite restricted in comparison with that of the usual analysis. The fundamental theorem of Bolzano, which states that, if $f(x)$ is a continuous single-valued real function over an interval $[a, b]$ such that $f(a) < 0$ and $f(b) > 0$, then there exists a value $\bar{x}$ of x such that $a < \bar{x} < b$ and $f(\bar{x}) = 0$, is lacking, as is also the related theorem on the attainment of its maximum value by a function continuous over an interval. Those portions of analysis which are constructible by actual computational methods are in general to be found in intuitionist mathematics.

Geometry of the analytic variety, subject to the limitations imposed on analysis, is possible in intuitionist mathematics. So, too, are geometries which are built on an axiomatic foundation, so long as the latter is realizable analytically.

In spite of whatever objections may be raised against intuitionist mathematics, it is generally conceded that its methods do not lead to contradiction. Such non-constructively conceived notions as "the set of all sets," "the set of all ordinal numbers," are obviously unattainable by intuitionist methods. But whether such a "state of health" has been achieved by "cutting off the leg to heal the toe" is a matter of opinion, evidently!

Its influence on other foundation philosophies will be touched upon in the sequel.

ADDITIONAL BIBLIOGRAPHY

Brouwer [h]   Menger [a, b]
Dresden [a]   Weyl [We₁; II]

XI

Formalism

In contrast to the intuitionist tenet that language and symbolism are not basic to mathematics, stands the formalist conviction that symbols and operations with them constitute the very heart of mathematics.

Hilbert's growing belief that the axiomatic method offers the most hopeful remedy for the "ills" of mathematics was a natural evolution from his early work on axioms for geometry. But, to insure a mathematics free of contradiction, the axiomatic method as used in his *Foundations of Geometry*, or as described above in Chapters I and II, could not suffice. Freedom from contradiction is guaranteed only by consistency proofs; and the proof of consistency by interpretation (II 1, 2) cannot be satisfactory in general, inasmuch as it usually only shifts the question to another domain of mathematics. Thus, in the case of the *Foundations of Geometry*, consistency is assured only if real number arithmetic conceals no inconsistencies; and a proof of this is still lacking! A different approach is therefore demanded.

Partly influenced, no doubt, by the work of Peano and his school, as well as by the Russell-Whitehead work (there is evidence that for a time Hilbert was greatly impressed by the thesis that mathematics can be derived from primitive notions of logic), Hilbert decided upon a *union* of the axiomatic and logistic methods. A reduction of mathematics to logic, even if successful, would still leave open the question of the consistency of that "logic." But perhaps by analyzing mathematical concepts and processes, both logical and otherwise, and representing them by an appropriate symbolism, as in a symbolic logic, one may be able to demonstrate that the formula for a contradiction can never be obtained from the fundamental formulas and the rules laid down for manipulating the symbols (such as substitution and *modus ponens*—see IX 3.1).

1　Hilbert's "proof theory"

Hilbert called the formal system thus inadequately described a "proof theory." As described by Hilbert (cf. Hilbert [b]), the fundamental idea of any proof theory is as follows: "Everything which constitutes mathematics today is rigorously formalized, so that it becomes a stack of formulas. These distinguish themselves from the ordinary formulas of mathematics only by the fact that besides the ordinary signs or symbols there enter also the symbols of logic, especially implication ($\rightarrow$) and negation ($^-$). Certain formulas which serve as foundation stones for the formal edifice of mathematics are called *axioms*. A proof is a figure, which must lie clearly before us as such; it consists of conclusions by means of the conclusion scheme

$$\frac{\begin{array}{c} S \\ S \rightarrow T \end{array}}{T} \qquad \text{(modus ponens)}$$

where the premise, S, is either an axiom (or axioms) or the end formula of a proof figure which occurred earlier in the development.† A formula is called *provable* if it is either an axiom or the end formula of a proof.

"To the ordinary, thus formalized mathematics, is added a, in a certain sense, new mathematics, a metamathematics . . . . In this metamathematics one works with the proofs of ordinary mathematics, these latter themselves forming the object of investigation." (Cf. IX 5.3.)

Now, if F stands for any formula in such a system, then a contradiction is obtained if the formula

(1a)　　　　　　　　　　$F \cdot \overline{F}$

(where . is the logical "and," and $\overline{F}$ is Hilbert's form of the negation of F) is provable. If one can show that no such formula as represented in (1a) is provable, then one has shown the "consistency" of the system. In particular, if the symbols and axioms are given mathematical meanings, then by following the proof methods allowed in the theory no contradiction can be obtained in the corresponding mathematical system.

In this connection it is interesting to note Hilbert's comments (Hilbert [b; 154–155]): "The infinite comes into the proof theory as soon as we introduce the ideas 'all' and 'there exists.' The former is

---

† Hilbert may have been oversimplifying here, since in the "Grundlagen" (2.1) modus ponens is not the only rule of inference required.

equivalent to an infinite 'and,' the latter to an infinite 'or.' From the Law of the Excluded Middle for finite sets we conclude that either all elements of a given finite set have a certain significant property P, or there exists one that does not have property P. . . . In ordinary mathematics we argue likewise in regard to infinite sets.

"But if we thoughtlessly apply to infinite totalities a procedure which is permissible in the finite case, then we open gate and door to errors. It is the same source of error that we see in analysis; in the latter field the carrying over, to infinite sums and products, of theorems which are valid for the corresponding finite sums and products is permissible only if special convergence conditions, etc., are satisfied. Similarly we cannot treat the infinite logical sums and products in the same manner as the finite, unless our proof theory reveals such treatment to be justified." Incidentally, these remarks, among others, were later cited by Brouwer [h], as evidence of the influence which Intuitionism has had on Formalism.

2 Actual development of the proof theory

As Hilbert's program developed, there first appeared (in 1928) the Hilbert-Ackermann *Grundzüge der theoretischen Logik* [H-A]. In essence preparatory to the larger work cited below, it is (as its title indicates) a formal treatise on logic in the tradition of Peano and Russell (calculus of propositions, calculus of predicates and classes, and both the narrower and extended functional calculi).

2.1 The *Grundlagen der Mathematik*

What may be considered the "Principia Mathematica" of Formalism is the Hilbert-Bernays *Grundlagen der Mathematik*, published in two volumes; volume I appeared in 1934 and volume II in 1939 [H-B]. Originally planned as a detailed exposition of the proof theory, with proofs of freedom from contradiction, its scope had to be enlarged as a result of unforeseen difficulties. (The first forty-four pages of volume I contain some very interesting and elementary discussions of the axiomatic method as applied to geometry of the plane and elementary number theory, and the arguments for its formalization.)

Since it would not be practicable to give here a detailed summary of this work, we shall be content with some remarks regarding methods, the ends actually achieved, and the work of later writers.

2.2 Metamathematical proofs

A question which has probably already occurred to the reader is: What is considered a *proof* in the metamathematics? For plainly the proofs embodied in the formal mathematics, which are to be justified in the metamathematical study, must not be duplicated in toto in the latter! Otherwise we would be traveling in a vicious circle. More generally, we may ask, What *methods of procedure* are used in the metamathematics? In seeking the answers to these questions, we are at first struck by the intuitionist-like character of the methods used— not that metamathematics and intuitionist mathematics turn out to be the same by any means—but the existence of an entity, for instance, is considered established only if it is constructible by finite methods. ¦ For example, existence of a number having a given property is established only by giving a method for constructing such a number! And all proofs have to be of a finite character that is "clearly perceptible" (*anschaulich überblickbar*). Also, the method of induction based on the natural numbers, which Intuitionism regards as basic, enters through definition by recursion.

2.3   Recursive definition

By a "number-theoretic function" is meant a function of non-negative integers, each of whose values is a non-negative integer. Such a function, for example, would be a function $f(x)$ which is 0 when x is even and 1 when x is odd; or a function $f(x, y)$ which is 2 when $| x - y |$ is even and 3 when $| x - y |$ is odd. A function $f(x, y_1, \cdots, y_n)$ is called *recursively defined* by the number-theoretic functions $g(y_1, \cdots, y_n)$ and $h(z, x, y_1, \cdots, y_n)$ if for all non-negative integers $y_1, \cdots, y_n$ the following relations hold:

$$f(0, y_1, \cdots, y_n) = g(y_1, \cdots, y_n)$$

$$f(x + 1, y_1, \cdots, y_n) = h(f(x, y_1, \cdots, y_n), x, y_1, \cdots, y_n).$$

If $h(z_1, \cdots, z_m)$ and g_i, $i = 1, \cdots, m$ are given functions, then the function $h(g_1, \cdots, g_m)$ is said to be formed from h and the g_i's by substitution.

A number-theoretic function f is called *recursive* (see Gödel [c] for the definition as stated here; usually now called "primitive recursive" †) if there exists a finite sequence of number-theoretic functions $f_1, f_2, \cdots, f_k$ such that f_k is f, and every f_i, $i = 1, \cdots, k$ is either (1) recursively defined from two of the preceding f_i's, (2) results from preceding f_i's by substitution, or (3) is a constant or a "successor function" $x + 1$.

† Regarding "general recursiveness," and its relations to "effective calculability" (Church) and the Turing [a, b] computing machine, see the citations to Kleene below.

For example, let $S(x)$ be the successor function; i.e., $S(x)$ is the integer $x + 1$ directly following x in the series of integers. And let $g_i^n(x_1, \cdots, x_n) = x_i$, $i = 1, 2, \cdots, n$, be the identity (or selector) function; i.e., it selects the ith integer from the n-ad $(x_1, \cdots, x_n)$. Then we may define a function $A(x, y)$ as follows:

$$A(0, y) = g_1^1(y)$$

$$h(z, x, y) = S(g_1^3(z, x, y))$$

$$A(x + 1, y) = h(A(x, y), x, y).$$

As the function $A(x, y)$ is recursively defined from the functions g_i^n and h, it is a recursive function by virtue of the sequence S, g_i^n, h, A. (The reader will recognize $A(x, y)$ as the sum $x + y$; compare the above with VI 3.1.1.)

Such recursive functions are of fundamental importance in both the Hilbert-Bernays theory and modern investigations of "formal systems," inasmuch as functions that are recognized metamathematically as recursive have their counterparts in the systems under consideration. (For further information see Kleene [a, b, c].)

2.4 Degree of success of the program

For certain elementary systems the proofs of consistency were successfully carried out, thus incidentally exemplifying what Hilbert would like to have done for a "complete" mathematics. For instance, the first application of the proof theory in the *Grundlagen* [H-B; § 6] to an infinite system is a proof that a certain elementary system of axioms concerning integers is consistent. This system embodies the calculus of propositional functions and the Peano axioms, but not the mathematical induction principle. In the proofs, the case which involves no apparent variables (IX 4.1) is first treated, and then extension is made to cases involving apparent variables. In connection with the latter it is shown how to reduce a formula to numerical formulas which can be shown true or false (cf. Section 3 below).

It is subsequently shown how to extend such reduction methods to the system obtained by adding the mathematical induction axiom to the other Peano axioms in the system. Unfortunately this does not give a consistency proof for the entire arithmetic of whole numbers. For it will be recalled that in developing arithmetic from the Peano axioms it is necessary to define $+$ and $\times$ (VI 3.1.1, 3.1.2); and in the proof theory this is done by means of recursive definition. Hence it becomes necessary to determine whether the addition of such recursive definitions introduces the possibility of contradiction. That contradiction is not introduced so long as the system embodies only the propositional calculus for free variables was established.

2.4.1   An example. As an example of a system shown to be consistent in the *Grundlagen* we give the following (System "D," vol. I, p. 357). Instead of $S(a)$, the symbol a' is used.

$$a = a,$$

$$a = b \to (A(a) \to A(b)),$$

$$a' \neq 0,$$

$$a' = b' \to a = b,$$

$$a + 0 = a,$$

$$a + b' = (a + b)',$$

$$A(0) \,\&\, (x)(A(x) \to A(x')) \to A(a).$$

The last of these axioms will be recognized as the counterpart of axiom 4 of III 5.1 (mathematical induction principle).

If to the above are added the following axioms

$$a \cdot 0 = 0,$$

$$a \cdot b' = a \cdot b + a,$$

then a formalization † of the arithmetic of integers results (this is Hilbert-Bernays' System "Z"). No consistency proof for this system was obtained. As a matter of fact, a decision procedure such as will be described in the next section, if found for this System "Z," would provide a method for solving the famous Fermat problem (X 1.3.3f)! Also, such unsolved problems as "Is every even number the sum of two prime numbers?" and "Is it true that there exist arbitrarily large prime numbers differing by 2?" would become solvable. For these problems may be formulated in the symbols of the above system.

However, the consistency of System "Z" is demonstrable by methods due to Gentzen (see Gentzen [a, b]) which depart from the finite methods of the proof theory, depending on transfinite induction (V 3.1.4). It is true that the transfinite induction employed is of a limited type, being over the section of the ordinals determined by the first Cantor ϵ-number (cf. Sierpinski [S$_1$; 203–4]); but of course

† It will be noted that this formalization does not embody the concept of "set," or even of a "sequence," however.

this has not the finite character demanded of metamathematical methods. (Cf. [H-B II; 360ff].)

It is interesting to note that, if one uses the Gödel transformation (cf. X 1.6.1), the question of consistency for the arithmetic of integers is reducible to that of the consistency of the Heyting calculus of intuitionist arithmetic; and for the consistency of the latter the Kolmogoroff (X 1.6.2) "problem-calculus" affords a proof by interpretation (as explained in II 2).

Whether the complete Hilbert program could be carried out was rendered very doubtful by results due to Gödel (which appeared in 1931, before the actual publication of the *Grundlagen*) and other authors.

3   Gödel's incompleteness theorem

The result of Gödel mentioned above may be roughly characterized as a demonstration that, in any system broad enough to contain all the formulas of a formalized elementary number theory, there exist theorems (formulas) that can neither be proved nor disproved within the system.   In particular, then, as Gödel pointed out, a system such as that of Principia Mathematica (see Chapter IX) must contain "undecidable" formulas, as must also certain axiom systems for set theory (such as the Zermelo-Fraenkel-von Neumann system) when formalized by the addition of the axioms and rules of conclusion of the calculus of logic.   The manner in which this was accomplished is described below.†

Consider a formal ‡ system whose primitive symbols consist of individual variables x, y, z, $\cdots$, functional symbols F, G, $\cdots$, and further symbols S, 0, $=$, $\sim$, $\supset$, $($, $)$.   In interpreting formulas constructed from these symbols we shall regard the individual variables as ranging over the natural numbers, while the functional symbols stand for properties and relations of numbers. S will denote the successor function (so that Sx is the number $x + 1$), while 0, $=$, and the logical connectives have their usual meaning.   Thus the formula §

$$(x)F(x) \, . \, \supset \, . \, (\exists\, y)(G(y) \vee (y = SS0))$$

† The material below and in Section 4 is based on lectures given by Professor Leon Henkin at the Mathematical Seminar, University of Southern California, November, 1949.   Attention is also called to an elementary exposition given by Rosser [b], and to Weyl [We₁; 219ff].

‡ Concerning formal systems in general, see Curry [a].

§ Symbols like $\vee$, $\wedge$ (for the logical product, analogous to the $\cdot$ of P.M.), $\exists$ may be regarded, in this system, as abbreviating formulas composed only of primitive symbols.   For example, $(A \vee B)$ would be taken as short for $((\sim A) \supset B)$, whatever the formulas A and B, while $(\exists x)A$ stands for $\sim((x)\sim A)$.

would be read: If every number x has the property F, then there exists a number y such that either y has the property G, or y is 2. In the formal system, incidentally, we shall denote $SS0$ by $\overline{2}$, $SSS0$ by $\overline{3}$, etc.

After setting up formal axioms and rules of inference for obtaining formal proofs of those formulas which express valid propositions about numbers, we proceed to "arithmetize" † the formal system as follows. We first assign to each primitive symbol a *coordinate* in the following manner (in the groupings below, symbols in the first line are within the system, and the numbers in the second line are the coordinates of the symbols directly above):

For the basic logical symbols we make the correspondences:

$$0 \quad S \quad \sim \quad \supset \quad (\quad) \quad =$$
$$2 \quad 3 \quad 4 \quad 5 \quad 6 \quad 7 \quad 8$$

For the individual variables (which can be denumerably infinite in number):

$$x \quad y \quad z \quad . \quad . \quad .$$
$$11 \quad 11^2 \quad 11^3 \quad . \quad . \quad .$$

For functions of the first order:

$$F_1 \quad G_1 \quad H_1 \quad . \quad . \quad .$$
$$13 \quad 13^2 \quad 13^3 \quad . \quad . \quad .$$

And so on, using powers of the $(n + 5)$th prime number for function symbols of the nth order.

To a formula in the system will correspond, then, a sequence of numbers, namely those corresponding to the successive symbols of the formula. Thus, to

(3a) $\qquad\qquad\qquad (x)F_1(x)$

will correspond the sequence

$$6 \quad 11 \quad 7 \quad 13 \quad 6 \quad 11 \quad 7$$

We can make a unique number correspond to the formula by taking the product of the successive prime numbers (in their natural order) with powers equal to the numbers of the symbols (in the order in which they occur). Thus to formula (3a) will correspond the number

$$2^6 \cdot 3^{11} \cdot 5^7 \cdot 7^{13} \cdot 11^6 \cdot 13^{11} \cdot 17^7$$

We shall call this the *Gödel number* of the formula.

† Note the similarity to the process of assigning coordinates to points in geometry.

Notice that the Gödel number can be computed as soon as a formula is given; and that, conversely, when a number is given we can determine (by factoring it into primes) whether or not it is a Gödel number, and if so to which formula it belongs.

Finally, to any sequence of formulas we may make correspond a unique number

$$(3b) \qquad 2^{n(1)} \cdot 3^{n(2)} \cdot \ \cdots \ \cdot p_k^{n(k)}$$

where $n(1)$, $n(2)$, $\cdots$, $n(k)$ are the successive Gödel numbers of the formulas of the sequence. We call (3b) the *sequence number* of the sequence of formulas. In particular, to every formal proof (i.e., proof within the system) corresponds a sequence number, since a formal proof of a formula F consists of a finite sequence of formulas each of which is an axiom, or derived from axioms and preceding formulas by the allowable rules of inference of the system, the last formula of the sequence being F itself.

By means of this arithmetization, statements about the formal system can be "translated" into sentences about numbers. For example, instead of saying that formula A consists of formula B plus other symbols added at the end, we may say simply that the Gödel number of B divides the Gödel number of A. In general, corresponding to each class, relation, or operation on formulas there is an associated class, relation, or operation on (Gödel) numbers.

Now it happens that many of the interesting classes and functions arising in this way are primitive recursive (2.3). Since all primitive recursive notions can be defined by formulas of our system, we see that in a sense the formal system can "talk about itself"! The meaning and some of the consequences of this fact will become evident as we proceed.

Outside the system (in the metamathematics, that is) let $B(x, y)$ denote that y is the sequence number of a formal proof in which the last formula has Gödel number x. And let $f(x, y)$ be the Gödel number of the formula obtained by replacing, in the formula having Gödel number x, each occurrence of the particular individual variable z by $\bar{y}$. Gödel shows that both B and f are recursive.

Now form the relation $B(f(x, x), y)$. This is also recursive; denote it by $G(x, y)$. Being recursively definable, it has a counterpart in the system which we denote by $\Gamma(x, y)$. Then the system contains the formula

$$(3c) \qquad \sim(\exists y)\Gamma(z, y).$$

Let the Gödel number of this formula be i.

A new formula is obtained by replacing z in (3c) by $\bar{\imath}$:

(3d) $\sim (\exists y) \Gamma(\bar{\imath}, y)$.

Let the Gödel number of (3d) be j. Note that

(3e) $j = f(i, i)$.

We now prove:

3.1   Theorem. *If a formal system, S, such as that described above, is consistent, then the formula* (3d) *is not provable in S.*

Proof. Suppose that it is provable in S, and let k be the sequence number of such a proof. Then $B(j, k)$ holds and, by virtue of (3e), $G(i, k)$ holds. But then $\Gamma(\bar{\imath}, \bar{k})$ is provable in S, for it may be shown that, whenever particular numbers are in some recursive relationship, the formula of the system which expresses this fact is formally provable. It then follows easily that $(\exists y) \Gamma(\bar{\imath}, y)$ is provable in S. Since our starting assumption was that (3d) is provable in S, it follows that S is not consistent. However, S was assumed consistent, so we conclude that (3d) is not provable in S.

Although ordinary consistency is sufficient to show that the formula

(3f) $(\exists y) \Gamma(\bar{\imath}, y)$

is also not provable,[†] Gödel used the assumption of "ω-consistency":

Definition. A formal system is ω-inconsistent if it contains a formula $\varphi(x)$ such that both

$$(\exists x) \varphi(x)$$

and

$$\sim\varphi(0), \ \sim\varphi(\bar{1}), \ \sim\varphi(\bar{2}), \ \cdots$$

are provable in the system. If no such formula exists, then the system is called ω-*consistent*. Evidently ω-consistency implies ordinary consistency (since inconsistency implies all formulas provable), but the converse does not necessarily hold.[‡]

3.2   Theorem. *If the formal system S is ω-consistent, then the formula* (3f) *is not provable in S.*

Proof. Suppose that it is provable. Then $B(j, k)$ cannot hold for any k, since otherwise (3d) is provable in S and S is inconsistent. Thus, for no k does $B(j, k)$ hold. That is, $B(f(i, i), k)$ holds for no k, implying that $G(i, k)$ holds for no k. Thus, for each natural number

† Compare Rosser [a].
‡ Cf. Gödel [c], p. 190.

k, $\sim\Gamma(\bar{\imath}, \bar{k})$ is provable in S. In particular, then, all formulas

$$\sim\Gamma(\bar{\imath}, 0), \qquad \sim\Gamma(\bar{\imath}, \bar{1}), \qquad \sim\Gamma(\bar{\imath}, \bar{2}), \quad \cdots$$

are provable in S. But, since (3f) is also provable, this implies that S is ω-inconsistent. We must conclude, then, that (3f) is not provable in S.

From Theorems 3.1 and 3.2 it follows that S contains a formula (3d) that is not provable, nor, if S is ω-consistent, is its negation provable in S. From this we get

3.3   Theorem. *If the system S is ω-consistent, then it cannot be complete.*

4   Consistency of a formal system

It is natural to ask if such a formal system S could be made complete by adding to its basic axioms either (3d) or its negation. The answer is no, since, so long as only formulas are added whose Gödel numbers constitute a primitive recursive set of numbers, the resulting system will remain incomplete. In such systems, then, consistency seems to imply incompleteness; that the converse holds is obvious, since an inconsistent system is always complete. As for systems with axioms whose Gödel numbers do *not* form a recursive set—they suffer from the embarrassing drawback that there is no effective test for deciding whether or not a given formula is an axiom!

Regarding consistency, Gödel showed that in a formal system such as S above, it is a recursive notion and hence expressible in the system. This can be done as follows: Since $B(x, y)$ is recursive, it has a counterpart $\beta(x, y)$ in the system, and we can let "Wid" denote

$$(x) . \sim(\exists\, y_1)(\exists\, y_2) . \beta(x, y_1) \wedge \beta(N(x), y_2)$$

[Here we have indicated by $N(x)$ the counterpart in S of the Gödel number of $\sim A$, where A is the formula with Gödel number x.] Gödel then showed that, if the system is consistent, the consistency is not provable within the system:

4.1   Theorem. *If S is a consistent system, then* Wid *cannot be proved in S.*

Proof. By paralleling within the system our proof of 3.1, we can demonstrate that

(4.1a) $\text{Wid} \supset \sim(\exists\, y)\beta(\bar{\jmath}, y).$

And, since $j = f(i, i)$, and hence $B(j, y) = B(f(i, i), y) = G(i, y)$, (4.1a) gives

$$\text{Wid} \supset \sim(\exists y)\Gamma(\bar{i}, y).$$

Now, if Wid were provable, we would then have at once that

$$\sim(\exists y)\Gamma(\bar{i}, y)$$

was also a formal theorem. But this contradicts Theorem 3.1.

5   Formal systems in general

Although it appears an impossibility to develop mathematics in a complete, consistent formal system, just as it would be impossible to axiomatize the whole of mathematics in a single system using the type of axiomatics described in Chapters I and II, we can reduce special parts of mathematics and logic to formal systems just as we axiomatize special parts of algebra and geometry. And this has been done with fruitful results. In some of these systems, analogues of the Gödel theorems have been shown to hold. In others, however, positive results have been obtained; decision problems are solvable (see below) and completeness demonstrable. For instances of the latter, the reader may be referred to Tarski's "A decision method for elementary algebra and geometry" [T₁] (cf. also references to other cases therein); also Henkin's [a, b] (in which also references to other cases will be found).

5.1   Decision procedures

Given a collection, C, of formulas, a *decision problem* for C is the problem of finding a method by which, given any formula, one can decide in a finite number of steps whether it is in C. If such a method exists, it may be called a *decision method* or *decision procedure* for C. To quote Tarski [T₁], "a decision method must be like a recipe, which tells one what to do at each step so that no intelligence is required to follow it; and the method can be applied by anyone so long as he is able to read and follow directions." The same author cites as an example the collection, A, of all true formulas (sentences) of the form "p and q are relatively prime" in the elementary theory of integers. For any particular sentence, such as "215 and 349 are relatively prime," Euclid's algorithm provides a method for deciding whether it is in A or not.

The important case, and the one in which we are most interested, is that where C consists of the set of all derivable formulas of a formalized system. The decision problem then becomes the problem of finding a decision procedure by which it can be decided of any particular formula whether it is true, false, or simply undecidable; that is, whether it or its negation follows from the formulas that have been adopted as axioms. Such a method may be called a *decision procedure for the system*. In some cases this problem is settled, in others not.

5.2 Precise formulation of the notion of decision procedure

The precise formulation of the notion of decision procedures had to await the development of the theory of general recursive functions and certain related concepts. The proposal to identify the intuitive notion of decision procedure with the mathematically precise concept of "lambda-definability" (equivalent to general recursiveness) functions was made by A. Church [d], who also developed the (diagonal) argument which demonstrates *the absence of decision procedures for a large class of formal systems*.

Before this, and therefore at a time when the notion of general decision procedure had not been made precise, Gödel published the "undecidable" formula described above (which played an important role in the development under discussion, of course). The significance of this, however, was not the same as that of the notion of decision procedure as applied to formal systems. A *single* formula may be undecidable in a given system, but provable (or disprovable) in another. On the other hand, the notion of a decision procedure is only significant with respect to infinite *sets* of formulas; and, if a particular set of formulas is shown to have no decision procedure, this gives information about all possible effective procedures, not merely about some particular formal system.

Thus the fact that there are undecidable formulas in a given system does not preclude the existence of a decision procedure which tells, in a finite number of steps, whether any given formula of the system is provable, disprovable, or undecidable. Thus Gödel's theorem does not entail Church's result concerning the non-existence of decision procedures.

The converse, however, holds (as pointed out, essentially, by Rosser), viz., if we know that every formula F is decidable in some system (i.e., either F or $\sim F$ is a formal theorem), then a decision procedure for the system consists simply in enumerating all formal proofs and hence all formal theorems. By hypothesis any formula F, or else $\sim F$, is bound to turn up after a finite number of steps of this enumeration, and at that time we have an answer as to whether F or $\sim F$ is derivable in the system.

Thus Church's demonstration that certain formal systems have no decision procedure may be considered to constitute a second proof of Gödel's theorem concerning the existence of undecidable formulas for those systems.

We shall not go further into the technical aspects of these matters; the reader interested in them may consult Church's paper [d], as well as the expository paper of Rosser [b].

6   Many-valued logics

Although it has not been our purpose to discuss logic *per se*, nor to attempt even a complete discussion of its relation to, and significance for, mathematics, there are some aspects of modern logic that would provide an interesting sequel to our discussion. One of these is the notion of a many-valued logic.

The logic of P.M. (Chapter IX) constitutes a *two-valued* logic, in that the truth-value of a proposition is assumed to be restricted to either "truth" or "falsity." In the discussion of the Heyting formulation of intuitionist logic, it was pointed out (X 7.2) that no assertion of a "middle third" is to be inferred from the non-acceptance of the classical Law of the Excluded Middle. In contrast to these logics, a *three-valued* logic would definitely make such an assertion, the possible truth-values of a proposition being "truth," "falsity" or (to use a purely arbitrary term) "plausibility." Similarly, one could introduce the notion of 4, 5, $\cdots$, or n-valued logics.

The first formulations of such logics were made by Lukasiewicz, Post, and Tarski. As one might expect, in these logics revised meanings have to be assigned to the primitive logical constants such as v, ∧, and ∼, and the corresponding propositional calculi may be presented in deductive systems similar to that for the two-valued calculus of P.M.

For further details, bibliography, etc., the reader may consult Lewis and Langford [L-L; VII], Frink [a], Rosser [d], and Rosenbloom [Ros; 51ff].

ADDITIONAL BIBLIOGRAPHY

Carnap [Car₂]   *Journal of Symbolic Logic*
Curry [a]   MacLane [a]
               Woodger [Wo₁]

XII

The Cultural Setting
of Mathematics

In the preceding chapters we have tried to give an introduction to the fundamental ideas and methods of mathematics. In Chapters I and II we described the axiomatic method as it is commonly used in modern mathematics, and in Chapters III to V we discussed the basic notions of set theory which we encountered in the actual use of axioms and which are fundamental in modern mathematics. In Chapters VI and VII we applied the axiomatic method and set theory to the definition of basic notions of analysis and algebra. The rigorous formalistic use of axioms, which we found emerging in the works of earlier mathematical logicians (Chapters VIII and IX) and reaching maturity in modern symbolic logic (Chapter XI), is rarely used in actual mathematical practice. To proceed purely formally, setting forth the basic axioms as formulas, and the allowable methods of proof as prescribed rules for deriving new formulas from old (cf. XI 1), would probably be impractical as a mode of either teaching or research, generally speaking. Purely formal methods, although indispensable for the investigation of the foundations (as in questions concerning completeness, consistency, and decision problems, for example), would perhaps hamper research in higher mathematics rather than facilitate it.

The situation may be compared to that existing between a "natural language" and a formal language; whereas a language commonly spoken, such as English, is full of ambiguities and illogicalities, its replacement by a formal language, if such were possible, would probably slow up social intercourse, and the formal language undoubtedly would eventually be contaminated by the same kinds of ambiguities and logical defects found in the natural language.

The formal type of axiomatics still serves as an ideal for the non-intuitionist, in which he may confidently feel that his theories may be dressed up if the time and patience necessary to accomplishing this

264

were put forth. Moreover, it would probably be a good exercise for every mathematics student, at some time in his career, to take a mathematical concept with which he is familiar and proceed beyond the "naive" axiomatic formulation as described in Chapters I and II to its complete formalization.

Regarding the effect of the controversies over the theory of sets and the contradictions to which it is liable, it is probably safe to say that the average present-day worker in the foundations is more interested in the problems to which they have given rise than in the choice or validity of an underlying philosophy; one can be either a follower of Russell or an intuitionist and be interested in the relations between the Russell logic and the intuitionist logic (cf. X 1.6), or in the conditions sufficient for the solvability of a given problem. It is to such problems as the latter that the modern worker in foundations devotes most of his interest. We have not, indeed, touched upon all the varieties of foundation philosophies to which past speculation has given birth; for further discussion on philosophic lines the reader is referred to the general literature in the subject. See, for example, Black [Bl], Fraenkel [F₂], Kattsoff [K], Maziarz [M], and Weyl [We₁; P. I], and their extensive bibliographies.

In contrast to the somewhat technical material given in the preceding chapters, we shall now give some attention to the general cultural setting of mathematics. After all, it is in the latter that mathematics was born and nurtured. Without the perspective which the cultural background affords, a proper appreciation of the content and state of present-day mathematics is hardly possible.

1   The cultural background

In order to avoid misunderstanding, we must make clear our use of the term "culture" above. We use it in the general anthropological sense, as exemplified in the terms "Chinese culture," "ancient Greek culture." In this sense, a culture is the collection of customs, beliefs, rituals, tools, traditions, etc., of a group of people such as an Indian tribe, or the people of a given region such as the United States. It is not the use of the term as in "a cultured person" that we have in mind.

As human beings we are born into cultures, and it is these that, acting on and interacting with our receptive nervous systems, determine the habits, beliefs, etc., that largely make up our "personalities." Most of what we take for granted is culturally determined. A culture, it should be noticed, is more than the habits, beliefs, skills, etc., of any single one of the persons living under its influence; usually it existed before he was born and will continue to exist after him, although it may undergo change during his lifetime. He possesses some of the "cultural elements," but not all of them. If he is born and brought up in a middle western town of the United States, he may belong to one of the branches of the Christian religion (usually depending on whether his parents did), talks English of the variety spoken in that region, perhaps learns a trade such as tool-making, gets married, has a family and dies. His best friend's experiences may parallel these, except that the friend's religion may be different and he may become a musician instead of a tool-maker.

Now the tool-making skill, the religions, the musical techniques, etc., were already present in the middle western culture before the above hypothetical persons were born, and will go on after them. As individuals these persons may contribute to the culture new ways of making tools, new techniques of piano playing or musical composition, but these, though "new," are the result of the interaction of the cultural elements concerned with the individual's own capacities. Thus, the musical composition will probably be written in the diatonic scale, and contain elements common to the fashions in composition of the time. The effect of the culture on the modes of dress, eating habits, recreation, etc., are too obvious to dwell upon.

2   The position of mathematics in the culture

So far as mathematics is concerned, both the tool-maker and his friend the musician will probably learn to count before entering primary school, study arithmetic in the primary school, and possibly elementary algebra and plane geometry in the secondary school. Probably neither will go any further in mathematics, and the musician will undoubtedly promptly forget all the algebra and geometry he has learned. Both will retain enough knowledge of arithmetic to enable them to do the ordinary computations required in borrowing money, using recipes, etc., and the tool-maker may remember such elementary geometry as is useful to him in his trade. As carriers of the mathematical tradition in their culture, however, they play only a minor role, viz., that of every parent who teaches his child to count and helps him with his "home-work" during the school years. Their conception of mathematics might be considered a modern version of that of the ancient Babylonian and Egyptian computers, to whom mathematics was a body of rules for handling quantitative problems arising in the workaday world.

The principal mathematical element in the culture, embodying the living and growing mass of modern mathematics, will be chiefly possessed by the professional mathematicians. True, certain professions, such as engineering, actuarial science, and statistics, which employ a great deal of mathematics, carry a sizable amount of the mathematical tradition, and in some of these, as in the case of physics, engineering research, and statistics, some individuals contribute to the growth of the mathematical element in the culture. But, in the main, the mathematical element of our culture is dependent for its existence and growth on the class of those individuals known as "mathematicians."

Now, if we compare mathematics with such cultural elements as language, religion, and dress, we notice a striking difference. For, although the latter elements are generally peculiar, in their various manifestations, to regional groups, mathematics seems to have a universality that knows no boundary lines. During the past half-century it has been customary to hold international mathematical congresses every few years. In attendance at these will be found mathematicians representing all manners of language, dress, and religion, as well as all shades of political opinion. But a Russian algebraist, a German algebraist, and an American algebraist all share the same algebra; and a Japanese topologist and an American topologist share the same topology. What differences exist between them generally have to do with details concerning new theories, rather than with the known parts of the subject which they share. This universality of mathematics seems to be one of its most distinguishing characteristics among the various cultural elements.

However, on closer study we shall find that (1) this universality did not always exist, (2) it is not so complete as it seems, and (3) its existence is easily explained in cultural terms.

3   The historical position of mathematics

If we look at the position of mathematics in the various cultures about the time of Christ, we find a radically different situation from that of the present. In the Greek culture, geometry and its attendant logical and dialectical devices were the principal elements of mathematics; they were accompanied by a number theory whose basic symbols were unique to the Greek culture and have been virtually forgotten today. Although the Romans were influenced by the Greek mathematics, they had their own system for writing numerals—a system much more cumbersome than the Greek for numerical manipulations, yet surviving to this day on monuments, title pages, and other odd places. On the other hand, in the Chinese culture, no geometry of the Greek type was known. Mathematics in China consisted principally of numerical computations and solution of algebraic equations. And, although there were evidently contacts between the Eastern and

Western civilizations from early Christian times onward, there are few instances of diffusion of mathematical ideas from one of these culture areas to another until relatively modern times. No geometry of the systematic logical type cultivated by the Greeks gained a foothold in China, where such geometric elements as existed seem to have been of the non-logical, "rule" type characteristic of the pre-Greek Egyptian geometry. Chinese mathematics evidently emigrated to Japan along with other elements of Chinese culture and there, despite the probable introduction during the seventeenth century of Euclid texts in the Chinese language, mathematics continued along the same traditional lines. In the seventeenth and eighteenth centuries we find mathematicians in Japan solving equations of degrees as high as 3000 and 4000! The major resistance to absorption of Western mathematical ideas was not broken down in Japan until the cultural innovations following the Restoration of 1868, when European mathematics began to flow in along with other cultural elements.

On the other hand, cultural conditions in the Mediterranean area during the flourishing of the Greek culture and for centuries thereafter were such that no systematic development of algebra was made. And it was left to the Arabs to preserve and transmit, via Africa and Spain, the Hindu-Arabic mathematics (and the system of enumeration which is universal today), along with Greek geometry.

It is frequently very difficult to determine why an element of a culture C_1, which might be very useful in a culture C_2, is not always accepted and integrated with C_2. Thus it was pointed out by Sarton (see Schaaf [S; 72–73]), for example, that although the metric system would have been highly useful to the industrial elements in English culture, it was not accepted by the latter. Incidentally, Sarton used this example to support a contention that mathematics is not always "economically" determined, but dependent to a large extent upon forces "interior" to us. So far as economics is only a single aspect of culture, Sarton was of course correct; but one can question the propriety of setting the economic aspects of English culture, by implication, "external" to us and other aspects "internal." Evidently there were present in the English culture other elements (perhaps national pride and resistance to innovations from without, for instance) which were stronger in their resistance to adopting the metric system than the attraction of the metric system for the industrial elements of the culture.

These observations (which could be augmented by many others if space permitted) teach us that mathematics is not something which is by its nature universal, absolute, or foreordained; rather is it subject to laws of development and influence from other cultural elements much as are arts and sciences in general. Of course we do not expect to find mathematics developing, under cultural influences, exactly like other cultural elements, any more than we expect to find different individuals reacting the same way to their environments. This is due partly to the nature of the subject and partly to its position in the complex of human activities, just as the development of the individual personality is due partly to inherent qualities and partly to the position of the individual in his society and culture.

4 The present-day position of mathematics

In contrast to the historical situation depicted above, mathematics occupies today a seemingly unique position. Although mathematicians speak various "natural languages" around the world, their mathematical language is practically universal. Thus, an algebraist can pick up an algebraic article in a journal published in any part of the world, and, after piercing the natural language barrier, find the same algebraic notions and, as a rule, algebraic symbols with which he himself works. The same generally holds in any branch of mathematics (although in a new branch there usually is a period when the terminology is a bit chaotic).

However, variations in symbols and terminology do occur, not only between mathematicians in different countries but also between groups in the same locality. Not infrequently differences of opinion have arisen regarding the direction further research should take and the important problems to be solved. Such differences lead, temporarily at least, to different "schools"—not foundations schools such as we described in the last three chapters, but schools which, while sharing essentially the same philosophy about foundations, do differ on subject matter and choice of method.

For example, it is well known that usually there are many different ways of solving a given problem. Indeed, once a problem is solved, many new solutions are likely to be found, perhaps of a simpler or more elementary character than the original solution. Of the possible solutions, some will be preferred by one group, others by another group. Perhaps some of the solutions are geometric, for instance; then the geometric-minded will usually prefer them. If some are of an algebraic nature, with no geometric elements entering in, they will almost certainly be preferred by mathematicians who have specialized in algebra. An instance of the latter kind was especially noticeable in topology a few years ago when some, called "set-theorists," preferred to use set theory as their chief tool while others preferred algebraic methods. (Today mixed methods prevail in topology.)

It is natural also to expect that differences will be found between groups living in widely separated (geographically) areas. Indeed, some mathematics still takes on a distinctly national character. French mathematics has long been known for its preference for function theory, English for interest in applied mathematics, German for foundations, and Italian for geometry. Today one frequently hears comment among mathematicians regarding the abstract character of recent mathematics in the United States—a trend which was perhaps somewhat retarded by the call for mathematicians to go into war work in 1941 and subsequent years.

Nevertheless, despite these variations (which are generally due to cultural influences), mathematics can today be considered to be distinguished by a universality foreign to most other human activities. Noteworthy, incidentally, is the growing number of mathematical papers embodying the results of modern mathematical research emanating from China and Japan in recent years—whose variety represents a surprising change from the classical arithmetic tendences mentioned in the preceding section.

5   What is mathematics from the cultural point of view?

The question What is mathematics? has probably received as much attention as any question of fundamental character—and as many answers. In view of the discussion of the last three chapters, it would be unlikely that the reader would expect that anyone could give a nice, compact answer that would find general acceptance. Certainly one should not expect an intuitionist and a formalist to agree on any definition of mathematics.

Here one must qualify the question, however. As it stands, no indication is given as to the type of answer expected. It is not the dictionary type of definition that is ordinarily desired in asking the question. More likely it is expected that one will give the sort of answer that philosophy has sought. And both philosophers and mathematicians have given answers, but none has found general acceptance! The trouble seems to lie chiefly in the assumption that mathematics is by nature something absolute, unchanging with time and place, and therefore capable of being identified once the genius with the eye sharp enough to perceive and characterize it appears on the human scene. And, since mathematics is nothing of the sort (although the layman will probably go on for centuries hence believing that it is), only failure can ensue from the attempt so to characterize it.

Is there any sense, then, in which the question can be answered? Probably only in that it is one of those questions that have to be answered by pointing; we point out what the thing to be defined is, at a certain time and place. We do not thereby assume any responsibility for the appearance of the same thing at another time or place. Thus, we can give a pretty fair answer as to what mathematics was in Greece in the year 100 B.C. And much of this Greek mathematics has evolved to become part of what we would call mathematics today—although we should not take this to mean that mathematics has a timeless character as so many have asserted, for it is not eternal; much of mathematics once accepted has since been rejected—is no longer mathematics, that is—or has completely changed in character. Although from a superficial point of view the Greek geometry seems still to be a part of mathematics, in a strict sense it is not (it does, perhaps, still exist in a certain form as, for instance, in the English culture owing to the use of Euclid as a textbook in the schools, but we speak here of the main stream of mathematics—which does include English *mathematics* of course). For, in the Greek culture, geometry was considered either an idealistic description of real space dictated by natural phenomena, or a doctrine imposed by a philosophy of absolutes; whereas in our culture the analogue of what the Greeks called geometry is only one of several co-existing geometries, each of which embodies only a special mathematical concept. In its modern axiomatic form (as described in Chapters I and II), it is something quite different from what the Greeks considered it. In this sense, then, the Greek geometry cannot be said any longer to constitute mathematics, any more than does the progenitor of man in the evolutionary scale any longer exist except through his descendant, modern man. Like comments hold for the notion of number. The natural number, as exemplified in the Frege-Russell concept [IV (4a)] of cardinal number, can hardly be considered that of the Pythagoreans, for instance.

When the question: What is mathematics? is considered a request for a criterion that will enable one to distinguish the principal mathematical element of a culture from other elements, then a satisfactory answer may become possible. We have to bear in mind that during the course of human history, as man came to recognize differences between certain activities, he found it convenient to assign them *names* in order to distinguish them from one another; and then ultimately, in a philosophic mood, he came to believe that *the names themselves had acquired a content and being of their own;* and so he set out to find just what this content was! And the result, as in the case of other abstractions, such as "mind," "life," "beauty," has often been a philosophic muddle! "In the beginning was the word" simply does not hold concerning mathematics—for first there had to be something to be called "mathematics"! In primitive cultures having only such rudimentary forms of mathematics as counting, no word for "mathematics" is found.

Why do we differentiate certain elements of the Greek and Chinese cultures from other elements of those cultures and call them "mathematics"? More generally, what enables us to go into any culture and pick out its "mathematical" elements? Obviously we use what we call "mathematics" *in our own culture* as a criterion; thus, so far as ancient cultures are concerned, we lump together everything numerical, geometrical, and algebraic under the name "mathematics·" Conceivably, however, what *we* call "mathematics" in an ancient culture might have been (and probably was) called, in the culture, by names that would correspond, in our language, to "astrology" or "theology." Inevitably *we are influenced and guided by what* we *call mathematics,* in our determination of the mathematical elements of other cultures. And consequently we may as well narrow down the question to "What is the cultural element called 'mathematics' in the world of 1952?" (Because of its essential universality, there is no need to say "in the United States" or "in France"—"in the civilized world" will do.)

One way to answer the question, impractical to be sure, is to gather into one library copies of all the "mathematical" material in the world and, having done so, answer "This is mathematics in 1952." We said "impractical." For not only would it be obviously impossible to make such a collection, but also selection of the items to be included would in many instances reflect tastes peculiar to the selector! Recall Kronecker's reported remark concerning Lindemann's proof of the transcendence of π. It is still not uncommon to hear one mathematician characterize the work of another by a contemptuous "It's not mathematics!" The position of the selector would not be unlike that of the zoologist who is asked to determine whether certain tissues are "animal" or have "life." The "border-line" cases alone would render the task of selection an impossibility. The best that could be done would be to place some items in a department labeled with a question mark, or with the notation "not generally accepted as mathematics, but accepted by some."

There is an interesting historical item in this connection, namely the first extant history of mathematics—that of J. E. Montucla, published in 1758. Montucla divided "mathematics" into two parts, the one "comprising those things that are pure and abstract, the other those that one calls compound, or more ordinarily physico-mathematics." The first part dealt with what we would today call "pure mathematics" probably, and the second with other concepts that could be formulated in mathematical terms. Thus, Montucla treated such subjects as mechanics, optics, astronomy, judiciary astrology, navigation, geography, and music. And for good measure he flung in some material on applications to the construction of observatories, ships, etc. He cites evidence to show that his inclusion of such topics had a precedent in early Greek histories of mathematics which included music and gnomonics (although otherwise devoted exclusively to geometry). The "division of labor" consequent to the growth of mathematics since Montucla's time has forced a change in our ideas of what constitutes mathematics!

Compare Montucla's history with a history of mathematics written during recent years, and notice the change. Although modern histories of mathematics still contain references to astronomy (since so many early "mathematicians" were what we would today call "astronomers"), these are only incidental and no special section is devoted to astronomy as a rule. Vestigial remains of older cultures are still found in our colleges, in the existence of "departments of mathematics and astronomy," despite the fact that today we have a special class of workers called "astronomers" to whom "mathematics" is a "tool," not a profession.

Actually, the variability of the subject matter covered by the term "mathematics" is today so pronounced that it can be quickly discerned by comparing a history written about 50 years ago with one written during the past few years. Take for instance the histories of Ball [B] and Cajori [Caj], which were written shortly before 1900. In Ball's first edition (1888) there is no mention of "logic"; in the fourth edition (1908) there is a remark concerning George Boole to the effect that he "was one of the creators of symbolic or mathematical logic." The index of this book contains no citation to any other reference to logic. Cajori's first edition (1893) contains four remarks of a similarly incidental nature concerning logic. The second edition (1919), however, contains four pages (407–410) of material concerning "mathematical logic" (not cited in the index, for some reason). Compare these books with Bell's *Development of Mathematics* [B₃], published in 1940. Here at least 25 pages are devoted to "mathematical logic," reflecting the development of the past half-century sketched in our preceding chapters. Obviously mathematical logic is coming to be considered part of mathematics (at least by non-intuitionists), although still referred to by some as an "application" of "mathematics." Another reflection of this development is to be found not only in recent writings but also in the fact that, whereas all the logic formerly taught in our colleges was done under the auspices of "philosophy" (pursuant to the Aristotelian tradition), today in contrast many mathematics departments contain men whose major work is devoted to logic and who teach courses embodying the developments in logic since the Renaissance.

We are compelled to conclude that the "absolute" type of definition traditionally sought for "mathematics" probably cannot be given. Cultural changes show no respect for abstract definitions! Susceptibility to definition may be a sign of senility.†

6 What we call "mathematics" today

From what we have said above, it is perhaps clear that we cannot give a definitive answer even to the modified question "What is mathematics in the world of 1952?" The best we can do is to "approximate." And, in the culturological approach, the first move should be to observe what those men whom we call "mathematicians" do. And, since mathematicians also eat, drink, play, etc., like other people, we had best qualify this by saying that we should observe what those men, whom we call mathematicians, do *as mathematicians*. As mathematicians they seem to be dealing with, or studying, abstract forms or structures and relations between them. As we understand cardinal number, for instance, it is a structural property of a set; if we say a set has *four* elements, we have said something about the structure of the set. If we say it is *linearly ordered*, we have assigned another structural property. Similarly, topological or other geometrical statements are statements about the form or structure of some set. In algebra we assign relations between elements or subsets of a set. And so on. The nice thing about this characterization of what mathematicians do today is that it includes symbolic logic, which may be said to be concerned with the forms of proof or of abstract reasoning.

Of course one would immediately ask how this is to be differentiated from art, for example. Art also is concerned with form or structure. However, while mathematics *abstracts* form, art usually *individualizes* it. The mathematician uses the abstract number 4, but the artist only paints four birds, four flowers, etc. Even "abstract art," so-called, is a process of individualization. Many mathematicians, incidentally, consider mathematics an art (see, for example, the articles of J. W. N. Sullivan and J. B. Shaw reprinted by Schaaf [S]). From

† Regarding the cultural nature of mathematics, see L. A. White [a]; the same paper is reprinted, in somewhat altered form, in White [Wh], to which we also refer the reader for a general discussion of the meaning of "culture." See also Wilder [b].

our point of view, when one abstracts the forms which one finds in painting, pottery, music, etc., one does mathematics. However, no definition would be sufficient to rule out border-line cases, even when applied only to the present. It is impossible to say with definiteness or assurance just where mathematics stops, and art, or physics, or . . . begins.

The abstract structures with which mathematics deals can be applied to individual special cases—just as when we apply "4" to marbles and say "4 marbles," or apply euclidean geometry to engineering. In this we merely reverse the operation of abstraction. There is nothing mysterious, as some have tried to maintain, about the *applicability* of mathematics. What we get by abstraction from something can be returned! Much so-called "applied mathematics," as a matter of fact, is really (pure) "mathematics," in that, although it has been suggested by some particular structure, it is in itself a study of abstract structure. A great deal of the work in modern physics and related subjects is really mathematics in so far as it is concerned with abstract structures.†

Other "border-line" cases arise in applications of the axiomatic method. Is such a setup as that of Woodger [Wo], in which genetics is placed in an axiomatic form, mathematics, or is it biology? It would seem as though it could be called either; as a study in abstract structure perhaps we should call it mathematics, but, as soon as the undefined terms "org," "cell," "genet," etc., used therein are given their biological meanings, then it should perhaps be called biology (and applied mathematics).

It would seem, then, that present-day mathematics is properly characterized as a living, growing element of culture embodying concepts about abstract structures and relations between these structures. And, as such, its content is variable and subject to cultural forces much as is any other cultural element. Even the symbols which are used for the expression and development of mathematics have variable meanings; a symbol which represented one thing to the mathematicians of the nineteenth century may represent something quite dif-

† Perhaps we should point out that we have not really fallen here into the error of setting up a definition into which we are now trying to herd various activities that are usually called by other names! The "physicists" (and others) to whom we refer are usually quite willing to agree that what they are doing, in the sense referred to, is "mathematics." We shall not attempt to define what "physicists" do; but we can agree either that some "mathematics" is also what we call "physics," or that physicists sometimes are "mathematicians," no matter how they are classified on the payroll!

ferent, owing to the evolution of mathematical thought, to mathematicians of the twentieth century. And, correspondingly, the mathematical element of our culture during the nineteenth century was something quite different from that of today, even though many of the symbols remain the same (consider the varied meanings of dy/dx since its introduction by Leibnitz!). The concepts held by mathematicians of the nineteenth century may still be called "mathematical," although many of them may not actually form part of present-day mathematics; properly speaking, such concepts are mathematical only in the sense that they did form part of mathematics at a certain time and place.

7 The process of mathematical change and growth

One of the most persistent illusions of the layman about mathematics is that mathematics is a fixed, immutable body of "truth" epitomized in such statements as "2 and 2 are 4." Often quoted is that favorite nineteenth century orator (whose address at Gettysburg eclipsed Lincoln's famous address of the same occasion, in the opinion of their audience): "In the pure mathematics we contemplate absolute truths, which existed in the divine mind before the morning stars sang together, and which will continue to exist there, when the last of their radiant host shall have fallen from heaven"—a pronunciamento which would appear to make of the mathematician an inspired prophet. In the same address, Everett quoted "an ancient sage" (probably Plato: "God geometrizes continually") as saying that "God is a geometer," an opinion which has lately been repeated by the astronomer Jeans.

Even professional mathematicians share the illusion. Thus, G. H. Hardy wrote [a; 4]: "It seems to me that no philosophy can possibly be sympathetic to a mathematician which does not admit, in one manner or another, the immutable and unconditional validity of mathematical truth. Mathematical theorems are true or false; their truth or falsity is absolute and independent of our knowledge of them." New mathematics, according to Hardy [Ha; 63–64], "which we describe grandiloquently as our 'creations,' are simply our notes of our observations"; in his view it is already a part of some "mathematical reality" "outside us" and we simply "discover or observe it." As Bell observed [a], "The impregnable strength of this creed is that it can be neither proved nor disproved." And, he might have added, its inevitable weakness lies in its utter inability to explain anything about mathematics.

The cultural viewpoint, by way of contrast, does explain much about mathematics. Evidently this opinion was shared by D. J.

Struik, who, in the Introduction to his history [St], apologized that lack of space forced "insufficient reference to the general cultural and sociological atmosphere in which the mathematics of a period matured —or was stifled. Mathematics has been influenced by agriculture, commerce and manufacture, by warfare, engineering and philosophy, by physics and by astronomy. The influence of hydrodynamics on function theory, of Kantianism and of surveying on geometry, of electromagnetism on differential equations, of Cartesianism on mechanics and of scholasticism on the calculus could only be indicated in a few sentences—or perhaps a few words—yet an understanding of the course and content of mathematics can only be reached if all these *determining factors* are taken into consideration." [Italics mine. RLW.]† A similar viewpoint seemed to be in the mind of D. Jackson when he wrote [b; 411]: "On the plane of social rather than individual psychology, there is a fascinating subject of inquiry in the relation between mathematical advances and the general consciousness of the age that produces them."

Like any other cultural element, mathematics grows by *evolution* and *diffusion*. Given a suitable juxtaposition of ideas, either in the mind of an individual or in the minds of a group, certain syntheses take place and new concepts come forth. Thus, one can trace the evolution of the concept of an abstract group in the writings of nineteenth century mathematicians in the same manner as one can trace the evolution of the theory of biological evolution in the works of Darwin's predecessors and his own, and contemporary, writings. Every research mathematician is familiar with the numerous instances of the simultaneous announcement of new theorems and theories by two or more mathematicians. This is an entirely similar phenomenon to that which occurs when a new invention is about to be made; when the cultural conditions are right, it will appear without fail. As Spengler stated [S; v. 2, 507], "a task that historic necessity has set *will* be accomplished with the individual or against him." Mathematics does not grow because a Newton, a Riemann, or a Gauss happened to be born at a certain time; rather, great mathematicians were made because the cultural conditions—and this includes the mathe-

---

† In an earlier paper Struik speaks of "sociological" determination of mathematics. However, the quotation from [St] given above (with permission of Dover Publications, Inc.) seems to indicate that what he actually had in mind was "culturological" determination. It is interesting to note that, in a book edited by W. L. Schaaf [S], the essay referred to is contrasted with the remarks of Sarton cited above; actually, however, Sarton and Struik appear to be substantially in agreement if their writings are suitably interpreted in terms of cultural influences.

matical materials—were conducive to developing them. There were just as great potential analysts and algebraists living during the Greek era as during the age which produced Weierstrass and Kronecker, but among other things the necessary analytic and algebraic elements were lacking in Greek culture. This is not to belittle the greatness of great men, but rather to mourn for those who were and are denied the opportunity to develop their talents. What great man, if honest with himself, has observed the passing chimney-sweep without remarking, "There, but for the 'concatenation of events,' go I."

We can, of course, agree that mathematics could not advance without "creative genius" being available; but we can still insist that the genius cannot operate in an intellectual vacuum, and that without proper cultural stimuli his "genius" will never become known. As the anthropologist Ralph Linton remarked [Li; 319] †: "The mathematical genius can only carry on from the point which mathematical knowledge within his culture has already reached. Thus if Einstein had been born into a primitive tribe which was unable to count beyond three, lifelong application to mathematics probably would not have carried him beyond the development of a decimal system based on fingers and toes."

How do "favorable" conditions for the development of mathematics come about? So far as the general sociological and cultural conditions are concerned, we can say that, in the first place, only in a culture which affords specialization of occupations can mathematics develop to any great extent. Much of early mathematics developed through the needs of a priesthood or for religious purposes (the earliest mathematical work in the United States worthy of note seems to have been in the hands of men trained by the Jesuits to calculate the correct annual date for Easter ‡). But the process of counting developed much earlier, being found in all primitive cultures (a fact that could be considered an argument for the intuitionist's insistence upon the counting process as the proper basis of all mathematics!). As the needs of agriculture, religion, navigation, etc., make demands, new mathematical tools are created, as witness the development of the rudiments of geometry in ancient Egypt. In commenting on the arithmetical and geometrical rules that Sumerian clerks applied ("true prototypes of the quantitative laws of modern science"), the British

† Quoted with permission of Appleton-Century-Crofts, Inc.

‡ See the Smith-Ginsburg [S-G; 3–4] history; this excellent little work, incidentally, shows a remarkable awareness of the cultural nature of mathematics.

anthropologist Childe remarks [Chi; 102] †: "Obviously we need not bother to ask the names of the laws' discoverers. They are too patently social products called forth by the needs of a society affected by the urban revolution and discovered with the aid of the spiritual equipment produced by the revolution." The point hardly needs belaboring, it would seem, in the face of the abundant historical evidence.

In the second place, an adequate symbolism must be available. This is necessary for two reasons: (1) All human activity, as distinguished from such general animal activities as eating and sleeping is based on symbolism, and, when of such an abstract nature as mathematics, it becomes a sine qua non. (2) Symbols are the vehicle for the communication and diffusion of mathematical ideas. No mathematician needs to be convinced of (1); indeed, much mathematical work goes into the construction of suitable symbolic apparatus. And, so far as (2) is concerned, it is in large measure responsible for the present-day universal character of mathematics.

Thirdly—and associated with the above—suitable means should be available for the diffusion of mathematical concepts. Given proper cultural conditions in various societies, if mathematical ideas are to diffuse from one society to another good means of communication must have been established. Greek and Chinese mathematics developed along such different lines chiefly because of the lack of diffusion of ideas from one culture to another at that time. In modern times, with fairly good means of communication, together with the establishment of mathematical journals, visits of scholars to foreign countries, international mathematical gatherings, etc., mathematics achieves its current practically universal character. Depending only upon the use of symbols, and not necessitating the possession of intricate tools or expensive apparatus, it can achieve a universality not so easily attained in other fields. Even in the face of such barriers to diffusion as are sometimes raised by the conflicts of international politics, mathematics has not, in any appreciable manner, developed different culture areas in modern times.

This is not to imply that mathematics has not been affected by such cultural forces as are comprised by recent political and social events. The influx to the United States of mathematicians fleeing from the Nazi philosophy and persecution of 1930–1945 has had a great influence on mathematics. The resultant contacts between leaders in their fields has led to syntheses of ideas that might not yet, if ever,

† Quoted with permission of Penguin Books, Ltd.

have occurred under the former conditions of cultural separation. Unfortunately on the other side of the ledger must be noted those losses, not only in the lives of brilliant mathematicians, but also in the breaking up of various groups who were active in mathematical research (Göttingen, Warsaw, etc.).

8   Differences in the kind and quality of mathematics

It needs to be emphasized that from the cultural point of view such differences in the development of mathematical ideas as occurred between the Greek and Chinese, as well as those slight differences between nations today, are due not to the "nature" or intrinsic qualities of the peoples involved, but to the cultures to which they are subject. From the cultural point of view the peoples themselves may be regarded as constants; it is the cultures into which they are born and to whose evolution they contribute that differ.   The mathematicians in a given culture possess a subculture—the mathematical subculture —which is affected not only by diffusion from other mathematical cultures, but also by the larger culture in which it is embedded.   If the larger culture makes demands such as those currently made in the United States by military developments, the subculture cannot avoid being affected.   Thus we find mathematicians today working on high-speed computers, and various applications (which will themselves inevitably give rise to new concepts), who otherwise would have followed a different course of mathematical development.

A curious illusion related to that which conceives of mathematics as a product of different "human natures" instead of different cultures is that which attributes to different "races" certain mathematical character.   Most mathematicians who remember the World War of 1939–45 will recall Nazi fulminations against "Jewish mathematics." Not so many are aware that no less a mathematician than Felix Klein (of Erlanger Program fame—cf. VII 3.5) harbored this delusion.   In a lecture delivered in 1893 in the United States,[†] he stated: ". . . it must be said that the degree of exactness of the intuition of space may be different in different individuals, perhaps even in different races. It would seem as if a strong naive space-intuition were an attribute pre-eminently of the Teutonic race, while the critical, purely logical sense is more fully developed in the Latin and Hebrew races.   A full investigation of this subject, somewhat on the basis suggested by

† *Lectures on Mathematics, Evanston Colloquium,* New York, Macmillan, 1894; the statement quoted is in Lecture VI, p. 46.

Francis Galton in his researches on heredity, might be interesting."
Even if Klein's observations were not due to chance or to misinterpre-
tation, to attribute them to such biological intrinsic factors as heredity
is hardly tenable. What would be of interest, perhaps, is a determination of the long-term cultural factors which lay at the basis of the
differences he noted (if, indeed, they did exist).

Certainly the direction that mathematics takes in a culture is
guided by the cultural needs or attributes—religious, philosophical,
agricultural, navigational, industrial, as well as mathematical—of the
culture. The different directions taken by Greek and Chinese mathematics were determined by the primitive cultural conditions prevailing in those cultures during their prehistorical periods. And, having
received an initial push in a certain direction, the mathematical sub-
cultures no doubt proceeded to a certain extent on their own momentum, operating mainly under evolutionary forces within (in the case
of Chinese mathematics) or under both evolutionary and diffusionary
forces (from other parts of the general culture; especially philosophy
in the case of Greek mathematics).

Today, mathematics grows under the influence of a complexity of
evolutionary and diffusionary forces. Many authors have emphasized
the *freedom* which a mathematician has in the choice of direction of
his research. Without going so far as Spengler's "freedom to do the
necessary . . . ," we still have to admit that only those mathematical
constructs can evolve and be destined to live that are so related to
the evolutionary development of mathematics as to prove fruitful in
their consequences in some way. The arbitrary setting up of postulational systems, for example, and calling them "mathematics" is not
necessarily creating mathematics.

The *importance* of a theory or a problem in mathematics is similarly determined, i.e., by its relation to the evolutionary development
of mathematics. However, what is not mathematics today (because
of its lack of relation to the existing mathematics) can one day become
mathematics!

We have mentioned some of the instruments of diffusion above—
journals, international and national gatherings, emigration of mathematicians under political or other pressure—but little about the nature of evolutionary forces. These forces present a difficulty, in that
they are not so easily detected and pointed out as are the diffusionary
forces. It seems reasonable, however, to expect that, once a new
branch of mathematics, offering a fertile field for research, is present

in the minds of a sufficient number of mathematicians, then that branch is going to grow along certain lines, irrespective (except for minor details) of the idiosyncrasies of the particular individuals possessing it.† Much overlapping of results ensues, and the activity in the subject reaches a maximum intensity, which is followed by a waning of interest, due perhaps to the most important and interesting problems having been solved, or perhaps to the branch having been absorbed in a more encompassing new branch of mathematics. Ultimately only scattered workers may be left in the original branch, the majority of the younger men in the field having become occupied with newer theories.

It will be noticed how similar this process is to that of *styles* or *fashions*. Various fashions arise in mathematics and pursue a course not unlike that of fashions in other parts of the culture. A mathematician of the early part of the century would probably be appalled by the mathematics of today. It is not uncommon to hear a mathematician who participated in the rapid development of classical analysis express his disdain for the subject matter and methods of modern mathematics. As in other fields of human affairs, the elders deplore the new fashions favored by youth! But the youth are no more to be blamed for the changes in fashion than are the women whose husbands complain about the changes in styles of clothes. Kroeber has shown that in fashions definite cycles occur, the changes being not in any way subject to the whim of fashion designers (who, like the Sumerian clerks, are "patently social products"). It is possible that, two thousand years hence, similar cycles may be discerned in the history of mathematics. (Although we are accustomed to think of mathematics as one of the most ancient of man's creations, the rapid development of mathematics under both evolutionary and diffusionary forces is a distinctly modern development.) Perhaps the abstract form assumed by modern mathematics is to be superseded by a form more like classical analysis, especially in its relations to the needs of other fields of knowledge. There are already signs that such may be the case, in the applications of mathematical (symbolic) logic, postulational methods, modern algebra, topology, etc., especially in the social sciences such as psychology and sociology. Where classical analysis found application and, indeed, origin in physics, chemistry, and other natural sciences, the new mathematics may find its applica-

† Compare: "Mathematical science, like all other living things, has its own natural laws of growth."—C. N. Moore, *Bull. Amer. Math. Soc.*, vol. 37 (1931), p. 240. Also Weyl [b; 538].

tions and many of its concepts in the social sciences.† Such a development would only be in agreement with our view of mathematics as a subculture of our general culture, developing not only under its own evolutionary momentum but also subject to forces, sometimes concealed, that affect it from without.‡

9   Mathematical existence

What is the effect of the cultural point of view on the question of mathematical existence? For example, what light does it throw on Kronecker's rejection of infinite sets (VIII 2.1.2)? So far as such an attitude is based on the desire to avoid possible contradiction, or even on an esthetic impulse to found mathematics in a manner free of certain principles, or the like, it may be held to have justification—or at least to provide room for argument. But, when such attitudes are based, as they frequently are, on a philosophy which conceives of mathematics as an ideal entity or as having an absolute nature which we endeavor to *discover*, much as the physicist or the explorer seeks natural data, then they appear to be unwarranted. For mathematics, like other cultural entities, is what it is as a result of collective human effort directed along evolutionary and diffusionary lines. And what it becomes will not be determined by the discovery of "mathematical truth" now hidden from us, but by what mankind, via cultural paths, makes it.

Consequently, if for sufficient reason, such as the discovery of new contradictions or of more pleasing alternative ideas, uncountably infinite sets are no longer used in mathematics, it will not be because they do not "exist"—they will continue to "exist" as much as they

† Those who think that a social "study" cannot be a "science" or an "exact science" until it is capable of being put into the same type of mathematical form as modern physics seem to be guilty of putting the cart before the horse. Much of classical mathematics, especially analysis, is due to the needs of physics or to physical influences, and to try to squeeze a modern social science into the same framework is unjustified. This is not to say that some classical analysis, such as is used in statistics for instance, may not find significant application in some aspects of social science. But the type of mathematics needed by the social sciences, if any, will be developed either as a result of direct need or of the simultaneous acting of hidden cultural forces. (Examples will continue to occur, of course, of mathematical materials which evolved along purely mathematical lines and of "no practical value," which later find application in another field; this is not to gainsay our main point, however.)

‡ Sarton remarks (see Schaaf's reprint [S; 71]): "On the basis of my historical experience, I fully believe that mathematics of the twenty-fifth century will be as different from that of today as the latter is from that of the sixteenth century." (Quoted with permission of G. Sarton and Harper and Brothers.)

ever did. They would merely cease to be considered "mathematical."
Similar remarks may be made concerning the Choice Axiom, well-
ordering, continuum hypothesis, etc. It is even conceivable that future political conditions might lead to such a pronounced separation
of cultures that one culture, C_1, will reject much of classical mathematics, such as the Cantor set theory—as it would if it adopted whole-
sale the intuitionist philosophy—while another culture, C_2, proceeds
along the lines of mathematical thought as it exists in the United
States today. There would then be no question as to which mathematics is the "true" mathematics—that of C_1 or of C_2—each having
been culturally determined and neither having any preferred claim to
"truth."

In short, mathematics is what we make it; not by each of us acting
without due regard for what constitutes mathematics in our culture,
but by seeking to build up new theories in the light of the old, and to
solve outstanding problems generally recognized as valuable for the
progress of mathematics as we know it. Until we make it, it fails to
"exist." And, having been made, it may at some future time even
fail to be "mathematics" any longer.†

† For an idea of the large amount and variety of new mathematics published
annually, the reader is advised to consult the files of *Mathematical Reviews* in any
mathematics library. This journal publishes abstracts of articles embodying the
results of current mathematical research—articles which have appeared in journals
throughout the world.

Bibliography

BOOKS AND MONOGRAPHS

Albert, A. A.
[Al]   *Modern Higher Algebra*, Chicago, Univ. of Chicago Pr., 1937.

Ball, W. W. R.
[B]   *A Short Account of the History of Mathematics*, London, Macmillan, 1888; 4th ed., 1908.

Baumgartner, L.
[Ba]   *Gruppentheorie*, Sammlung Göschen, No. 837, Berlin, de Gruyter, 1921.

Bell, E. T.
[B₁]   *The Queen of the Sciences*, Baltimore, Williams and Wilkins, 1931.
[B₂]   *The Search for Truth*, Baltimore, Williams and Wilkins, 1934.
[B₃]   *The Development of Mathematics*, New York, McGraw-Hill, 1940.
[B₄]   *Mathematics, Queen and Servant of Science*, New York, McGraw-Hill, 1951.

Birkhoff, G.
[Bi]   *Lattice Theory*, Amer. Math. Soc. Coll. Pub., v. 25, rev., New York, 1948.

Birkhoff, G. D., and Beatley, R.
[B-B]   *Basic Geometry*, Chicago, Scott, Foresman, 1941.

Birkhoff, G., and MacLane, S.
[B-M]   *A Survey of Modern Algebra*, New York, Macmillan, 1944.

Black, M.
[Bl]   *The Nature of Mathematics*, New York, Harcourt, Brace, 1934.

Borel, E.
[Bo]   *Leçons sur les théorie des fonctions*, 3d ed., Paris, Gauthier-Villars, 1928.

Bourbaki, N.
[B₁]   *Théorie des ensembles* [Actualités scientifiques et industrielles, No. 846], Paris, Hermann, 1939.

Cajori, F.
[Caj]   *A History of Mathematics*, New York, Macmillan, 1893; 2nd ed., 1919.

Campbell, A. D.
[Ca]   *Advanced Analytic Geometry*, New York, Wiley, 1938.

Cantor, G.
[C]   *Gesammelte Abhandlungen*, herausg. von Ernst Zermelo, Berlin, Springer, 1932.
[C₁]   *Contributions to the Founding of the Theory of Transfinite Numbers*, transl. by P. E. B. Jourdain, Chicago, Open Court, 1915.

Carnap, R.
[Car]   *Abriss der Logistik*, Vienna, Springer, 1929.
[Car₁]   *The Logical Syntax of Language*, New York, Harcourt, Brace, 1937.
[Car₂]   *Foundations of Mathematics and Logic*, Int'l Enc. of Unified Sc., v. 1, No. 3, Chicago, Univ. of Chicago Pr., 1939.

Childe, G.
[Chi] *What Happened in History*, New York, Penguin Books, 1946. (Orig. published in England, 1942, by Penguin Books Ltd.)

Church, A.
[Ch] *Introduction to Mathematical Logic*, Part I, Annals of Math. Studies No. 13, Princeton, Princeton Univ. Pr., 1944.

Chwistek, L.
[Chw] *The Limits of Science. Outline of Logic and Methodology of the Exact Sciences*, transl. by H. C. Brodie and A. P. Coleman, New York, Harcourt, Brace, 1948.

Courant, R., and Robbins, H.
[C-R] *What Is Mathematics?*, London and New York, Oxford Univ. Pr., 1941.

Couturat, L.
[Co₁] *L'Algèbre de la logique*, Scientia, Phys.-Math. Série, No. 24, Paris, Gauthier-Villars, 1905.
[Co₂] *De l'infinie mathématique*, Paris, Felix Alcan, 1896.

Curry, H. B.
[Cu] *A Theory of Formal Deducibility*, Notre Dame Math. Lectures, No. 6, Notre Dame, Indiana, 1950.

Dedekind, R.
[D₁] *Stetigkeit und irrationale Zahlen*, Braunschweig, Vieweg, 1872.
[D₂] *Was sind und was sollen die Zahlen?*, Braunschweig, 1888 (also appears in [D₃]).
[D₃] *Gesammelte mathematische Werke*, Braunschweig, Vieweg, 1932.

Eaton, R. M.
[E] *General Logic*, New York, Scribner, 1931.

Fraenkel, A.
[F₁] *Einleitung in die Mengenlehre*, 3d ed., Berlin, Springer, 1928. (Republished by Dover Pubs., New York, 1946.)
[F₂] *Zehn Vorlesungen über die Grundlegung der Mengenlehre*, Leipzig, Teubner, 1927.

Frege, G.
[Fr] *The Foundations of Arithmetic*, Oxford, Basil Blackwell, 1950.
[Fr₁] *Begriffschrift*, Halle, Louis Nebert, 1879.

Gödel, K.
[G] *The Consistency of the Axiom of Choice and the Generalized Continuum-Hypothesis with the Axioms of Set Theory*, Princeton, Princeton Univ. Pr., 1940.

Grelling, K.
[Gr] *Mengenlehre*, Leipzig, Teubner, 1924.
[Gr₁] *Die Paradoxien der Mengenlehre*, Stuttgart, Math. Büchlein, 1925.

Hardy, G. H.
[Ha] *A Mathematician's Apology*, Cambridge, England, The University Pr., 1941.

Heath, T. L.
[Hea] *The Thirteen Books of Euclid's Elements*, Cambridge, England, The University Pr., 1908.

Heyting, A.
[He] *Mathematische Grundlagenforschung. Intuitionismus. Beweistheorie.* Ergebnisse der Mathematik und ihrer Grenzgebiete, vol. 3, No. 4, Berlin, Springer, 1934.

Hilbert, D.
[H$_1$] *Grundlagen der Geometrie*, Leipzig, Teubner, 1899. (Published in *Festschrift zur Feier der Enthüllung des Gauss-Weber-Denkmals in Göttingen.*)
[H$_2$] *Grundlagen der Geometrie*, 7th ed., Leipzig, Teubner, 1930.
[H$_3$] *The Foundations of Geometry*, Chicago, Open Court, 1902. (English translation of [H$_1$], incorporating material from French edition, by E. J. Townsend.)

Hilbert, D., and Ackermann, W.
[H-A] *Principles of Mathematical Logic*, New York, Chelsea Publ. Co., 1950.

Hilbert, D., and Bernays, P.
[H-B] *Grundlagen der Mathematik*, vol. I (1934), vol. II (1939), Berlin, Springer. (Reprinted in lithoprint by Edwards Bros., Ann Arbor, 1944.)

Hobson, E. W.
[Ho] *The Theory of Functions of a Real Variable and the Theory of Fourier's Series*, vol. 1, 2nd ed., Cambridge, England, The University Pr., 1921; 3d ed., 1927.

Huntington, E. V.
[Hu] *The Continuum and Other Types of Serial Order*, 2d ed., Cambridge, Mass., Harvard Univ. Pr., 1917. [Originally published under the title *The Continuum as a Type of Order*, Annals of Math., vol. 6 (1905), pp. 151–184.]

Kamke, E.
[Ka] *Mengenlehre*, Sammlung Göschen, Berlin and Leipzig, de Gruyter, 1928.
[Ka$_1$] *Theory of Sets* (translation of 2nd ed. of [Ka] by F. Bagemihl), New York, Dover Pubs., 1950.

Kattsoff, L. O.
[K] *A Philosophy of Mathematics*, Ames, Iowa State College Pr., 1948.

Kershner, R. B., and Wilcox, L. R.
[K-W] *The Anatomy of Mathematics*, New York, Ronald, 1950.

Klein, F.
[Kl] *Elementary Mathematics from an Advanced Standpoint*, transl. by E. R. Hedrick and C. A. Noble, Part I, New York, Macmillan, 1932.

König, D.
[Kö] *Theorie der endlichen und unendlichen Graphen*, Leipzig, Akad. Verlagsgesellschaft, 1936.

Landau, E. G. H.
[La$_1$] *Foundations of Analysis; the Arithmetic of Whole, Rational and Complex Numbers*, transl. by F. Steinhardt, New York, Chelsea Publ. Co., 1951.
[La$_2$] *Grundlagen der Analysis*, Leipzig, Akad. Verlagsges. M. B. H., 1930.

Lewis, C. I.
[Le] *A Survey of Symbolic Logic*, Berkeley, Univ. of Calif. Pr., 1918.

Lewis, C. I., and Langford, C. H.
[L-L] *Symbolic Logic*, New York, The Century Co., 1932.

Linton, R.
[Li] *The Study of Man*, New York, Appleton-Century-Crofts, Inc., 1936.
Lusin, N.
[L] *Leçons sur les ensembles analytiques*, Paris, Gauthier-Villars, 1930.
McCoy, Neal H.
[Mc] *Rings and Ideals*, Carus Mathematical Monographs, No. 8, Math. Assoc.
of Amer., Buffalo, 1948.
Matthewson, L. C.
[Ma] *Elementary Theory of Finite Groups*, Boston, Houghton Mifflin, 1930.
Maziarz, E. A.
[M] *The Philosophy of Mathematics*, New York, Phil'l Lib., 1950.
Miller, G. A., Blichfeldt, H. F., and Dickson, L. E.
[MBD] *Theory and Applications of Finite Groups*, New York, Stechert, 1938.
Moore, E. H.
[Mo₁] *Introduction to a Form of General Analysis*, New Haven, Yale Univ. Pr.,
1910.
Newsom, C. V.
[Ne] *An Introduction to Mathematics*, Univ. of New Mexico Bull. No. 295,
Albuquerque, Univ. of New Mex. Pr., 1936.
Northrop, E. P., and other members of the College Mathematics Staff, University
of Chicago.
[N] *Fundamental Mathematics*, vol. 1, 3d ed., Chicago, Univ. of Chicago Pr.,
1938.
Pasch, M.
[Pa] *Vorlesungen über neuere Geometrie*, Leipzig, Teubner, 1882.
Pasch, M., and Dehn, M.
[P-D] *Vorlesungen über neuere Geometrie*, Berlin, Springer, 1926.
Peano, G.
[P₁] *I Principii di Geometria*, Logicamenta Esposti, Turin, Bocca, 1889.
[P₂] *Arithmetices Principia*, Turin, Bocca, 1889.
[P₃] *Formulaire de Mathématiques*, vols. I–V, Turin, Bocca, 1894–1908.
Pierpont, J.
[Pi] *Lectures on the Theory of Functions of Real Variables*, New York, Ginn,
1905, vol. I.
Poincaré, H.
[Po] *The Foundations of Science*, transl. by G. B. Halsted, Lancaster, Pa.,
Science Pr., 1946.
Quine, W. V.
[Q] *Mathematical Logic*, New York, Norton, 1940.
Ramsey, F. P.
[Ra] *Foundations of Mathematics*, London, Paul, Trench, Trubner, 1931.
Richardson, M.
[R] *Fundamentals of Mathematics*, New York, Macmillan, 1941.
Robinson, Gilbert de B.
[Ro] *The Foundations of Geometry*, Toronto, Univ. of Toronto Pr., 1940.
Rosenbloom, P. C.
[Ros] *The Elements of Mathematical Logic*, New York, Dover Pubs., 1950.

Russell, B.
[R₁] *Introduction to Mathematical Philosophy*, London and New York, Macmillan, 1919; 2nd ed., 1920.
[R₂] *Principles of Mathematics*, New York, Norton, 1903; 2nd ed., 1937.
Schaaf, W. L., editor.
[S] *Mathematics Our Great Heritage: Essays on the Nature and Cultural Significance of Mathematics*, New York, Harper, 1948.
Sierpinski, W.
[S₁] *Leçons sur les nombres transfinis*, Paris, Gauthier-Villars, 1928.
[S₂] *Hypothèse du continu*, Warsaw-Lwow, Monografje mat., vol. IV, 1934.
Smith, D. E., and Ginsburg, J.
[S-G] *A History of Mathematics in America before 1900*, Carus Mathematical Monographs, No. 5, Math. Assoc. of Amer., Buffalo, 1934.
Spengler, O.
[S] *The Decline of the West*, transl. by C. F. Atkinson, New York, Knopf; vol. 1, 1926; vol. 2, 1928.
Struik, D. J.
[St] *A Concise History of Mathematics*, 2 vols., New York, Dover Pubs., 1948.
Tarski, A.
[T] *Introduction to Logic*, New York, Oxford Univ. Pr., 1941.
[T₁] *A Decision Method for Elementary Algebra and Geometry*, Project RAND, publication R-109, Santa Monica, RAND Corp., 1948.
Veblen, O., and Whitehead, J. H. C.
[V-W] *The Foundations of Differential Geometry*, Cambridge, England, The University Pr., 1932.
Veblen, O., and Young, J. W.
[V-Y] *Projective Geometry*, New York, Ginn, 1910, vol. I.
[V-Y₂] *Projective Geometry*, New York, Ginn, 1918, vol. II.
van der Waerden, B. L.
[Wa] *Moderne Algebra*, 2nd ed., 2 vols., Berlin, Springer, 1937 and 1940; photostat reprint, New York, Ungar, 1943.
Weyl, H.
[We] *Das Kontinuum*, Leipzig, von Veit, 1918.
[We₁] *Philosophy of Mathematics and Natural Science*, Princeton, Princeton Univ. Pr., rev. ed., 1949.
White, L. A.
[Wh] *The Science of Culture*, New York, Farrar, Straus, 1949.
Whitehead, A. N., and Russell, B.
[P.M.] *Principia Mathematica*, Cambridge, England, The University Pr., vol. 1, 2nd ed., 1925; vol. 2, 2nd ed., 1927.
Wittgenstein, L.
[Wt] *Tractatus Logico-philosophicus*, New York, Harcourt, Brace, 1922.
Woodger, J. H.
[Wo] *The Axiomatic Method in Biology*, Cambridge, England, The University Pr., 1937.
[Wo₁] *The Technique of Theory Construction*, Int'l Enc. of Unified Sc., vol. 2, No. 5, Chicago, Univ. of Chicago Pr., 1939.
Young, J. W.
[Y] *Lectures on Fundamental Concepts of Algebra and Geometry*, New York, Macmillan, 1916.

Young, J. W. A., editor.
[Yo] *Monographs on Modern Mathematics*, New York, Longmans, Green, rev. ed., 1915.

PAPERS, ETC.

Ackermann, W.
[a] *Mengentheoretische Begründung der Logik*, Math. Ann., vol. 115 (1937–38), pp. 1–22.

Bachmann, F.
[Encyk] *Aufbau des Zahlensystems*, Encyklopädie der Math. Wiss., vol. I 1, Heft 2, 1939, pp. 1–28.

Bell, E. T.
[a] *Confessions of a mathematician*, Sc. Monthly, vol. 54 (1942), p. 81 (review of G. H. Hardy's "A Mathematician's Apology").

Bernays, P.
[a] *A system of axiomatic set theory*, Journ. Symb. Logic, vol. 2 (1937), pp. 65–77; vol. 6 (1941), pp. 1–17; vol. 7 (1942), pp. 65–89, 133–145; vol. 8 (1943), pp. 89–106; vol. 13 (1948), pp. 65–79.
[b] *Axiomatische Untersuchung des Aussagen-Kalkuls der "Principia Mathematica,"* Math. Zeit., vol. 25 (1926), pp. 305–320.

Bernstein, F.
[a] *Über die Reihe der transfiniten Ordnungszahlen*, Math. Ann., vol. 60 (1905), pp. 187–193.
[b] *The continuumproblem*, Proc. Nat. Acad. Sci., vol. 24 (1938), pp. 101–104.

Birkhoff, G. D.
[a] *A set of postulates for plane geometry, based on scale and protractor*, Annals of Math., vol. 33 (1932), pp. 329–345.

Borel, É.
[a] *Quelques remarques sur les principes de la théorie des ensembles*, Math. Ann., vol. 60 (1905), pp. 194–195.

Brouwer, L. E. J.
[a] *Zur Begründung der intuitionistischen Mathematik, I.*, Math. Ann., vol. 93 (1925), pp. 244–257.
[b] *Zur Begründung der intuitionistischen Mathematik, II.*, ibid., vol. 95 (1926), pp. 453–472.
[c] *Zur Begründung der intuitionistischen Mathematik, III.*, ibid., vol. 96 (1926), pp. 451–488.
[d] *Remarques sur la notion d'ordre*, Comptes Rendus Acad. Sci., Paris, vol. 230 (1950), pp. 263–265.
[e] *Sur la possibilité d'ordonner le continu*, ibid., pp. 349–350.
[f] *Intuitionism and formalism*, Bull. Amer. Math. Soc., vol. 20 (1913–1914), pp. 81–96 (transl. by A. Dresden).
[g] *Intuitionistische Zerlegung Mathematischer Grundbegriffe*, Jahresbericht d. Deut. Math. Ver., vol. 33 (1925), pp. 251–256.
[h] *Intuitionistische Betrachtungen über den Formalismus*, Proc. Akad. Wet. Amsterdam, vol. 31 (1928), pp. 374–379.
[i] *Intuitionistischer Beweis des Jordanschen Kurvensatzes*, ibid., vol. 28 (1925), pp. 503–508.

Cavaillès, J.
[a] *Sur la deuxième définition des ensembles finis donnée par Dedekind*, Fund. Math., vol. 19 (1932), pp. 143–148.

Church, A.
[a] *A bibliography of symbolic logic*, Journ. Symb. Logic, vol. I (1936), pp. 121–216.
[b] *Additions and corrections to A bibliography of symbolic logic*, ibid., vol. 3 (1938), pp. 178–212.
[c] *Differentials*, Amer. Math. Mo., vol. 49 (1942), pp. 389–392.
[d] *An unsolvable problem of elementary number theory*, Amer. Journ. Math., vol. 58 (1936), pp. 345–363.
[e] *A formulation of the simple theory of types*, Journ. Symb. Logic, vol. 5 (1940), pp. 56–68.

Chwistek, L.
[a] *The theory of constructive types*, Annales de la Société Polonaise de Mathématique, vol. 2 (1924), pp. 9–48; vol. 3 (1925), pp. 92–141.

Curry, H. B.
[a] *Some aspects of the problem of mathematical rigor*, Bull. Amer. Math. Soc., vol. 47 (1941), pp. 221–241.

Dresden, A.
[a] *Brouwer's contributions to the foundations of mathematics*, Bull. Amer. Math. Soc., vol. 30 (1924), pp. 31–40.

Dushnik, B., and Miller, E. W.
[a] *Partially ordered sets*, Amer. Journ. Math., vol. 63 (1941), pp. 600–610.

Emch, A. F.
[a] *Implication and deducibility*, Journ. Symb. Logic, vol. 1 (1936), pp. 26–35.

Faber, G.
[a] *Über die Abzählbarkeit der rationalen Zahlen*, Math. Ann., vol. 60 (1905), pp. 196–203.

Frink, O.
[a] *New algebras of logic*, Amer. Math. Mo., vol. 45 (1938), pp. 210–219.

Gentzen, G.
[a] *Die Widerspruchsfreiheit der reinen Zahlentheorie*, Math. Ann., vol. 112 (1936), pp. 493–565.
[b] *Neue Fassung des Widerspruchs-freiheitsbeweises für die reine Zahlentheorie*, Forschungen zur Logik und zur Grundlegung der exakten Wissenschaften, Neue Folge, Heft 4, pp. 19–44, Leipzig, 1938.

Gödel, K.
[a] *What is Cantor's continuum problem?*, Amer. Math. Mo., vol. 54 (1947), pp. 515–525.
[b] *Zur intuitionistischen Arithmetik und Zahlentheorie*, Erg. Math. Kolloqu., 1933, Heft 4, pp. 35–38.
[c] *Über formal unentscheidbare Sätze der Principia Mathematica und verwandter Systeme I*, Monats. für Math. u. Phys., vol. 38 (1931), pp. 173–198.

Hall, M. S., Jr.
[a] *The word problem for semi-groups with two generators*, Journ. Symb. Logic, vol. 14 (1949), pp. 115–118.

Halldén, S.
[a] *A note concerning the paradoxes of strict implication and Lewis's system S1*, Journ. Symb. Logic, vol. 13 (1948), pp. 138–139.

Hamel, G.
[a] *Eine Basis aller Zahlen und die unstetigen Lösungen der Funktionengleichung:* $f(x + y) = f(x) + f(y)$, Math. Ann., vol. 60 (1905), pp. 459–462.

Hardy, G. H.
[a] *Mathematical proof*, Mind, vol. 30 (1929), pp. 1–25.

Hartogs, F.
[a] *Über das Problem der Wohlordnung*, Math. Ann., vol. 76 (1915), pp. 438–443.

Helmer, O.
[a] *On the theory of axiom-systems*, Analysis, vol. 3 (1935), pp. 1–11.

Henkin, L.
[a] *Fragments of the propositional calculus*, Journ. Symb. Logic, vol. 14 (1949), pp. 42–48.
[b] *The completeness of the first-order functional calculus*, ibid., pp. 159–166.

Henle, P.
[a] *The independence of the postulates of logic*, Bull. Amer. Math. Soc., vol. 38 (1932), pp. 409–414.

Heyting, A.
[a] *De telbaarheidspraedicaten van Prof. Brouwer* (The countability-predicates of Prof. Brouwer), Nieuw Archief voor Wiskunde (2), vol. 16, no. 2 (1929), pp. 47–58.

Hilbert, D.
[a] *Über das Unendliche*, Math. Ann., vol. 95 (1925), pp. 161–190; also published in French translation in Acta Math., vol. 48 (1926), pp. 91–122.
[b] *Die logischen Grundlagen der Mathematik*, Math. Ann., vol. 88 (1922), pp. 151–165.

Huntington, E. V.
[a] *A complete set of postulates for the theory of absolute continuous magnitude*, Trans. Amer. Math. Soc., vol. 3 (1902), pp. 264–279.
[b] *A new set of postulates for betweenness, with proof of complete independence*, ibid., vol. 26 (1924), pp. 257–282.
[c] *Simplified definition of a group*, Bull. Amer. Math. Soc., vol. 8 (1902), pp. 296–300.

Jackson, D.
[a] *A comment on "differentials,"* Amer. Math. Mo., vol. 49 (1942), p. 389.
[b] *The human significance of mathematics*, Amer. Math. Mo., vol. 35 (1928), pp. 406–411.

Jones, F. B.
[a] *Connected and disconnected plane sets and the functional equation* $f(x) + f(y) = f(x + y)$, Bull. Amer. Math. Soc., vol. 48 (1942), pp. 115–120.

Keyser, C. J.
[a] *Charles Sanders Peirce as a pioneer*, Galois Lectures, Scripta Mathematica Library, no. 5, pp. 87–112; Scripta Mathematica, Yeshiva College, N. Y., 1941.

Kleene, S. C.
[a] *General recursive functions of natural numbers*, Math. Ann., vol. 112 (1936), pp. 727–742.
[b] *A note on recursive functions*, Bull. Amer. Math. Soc., vol. 42 (1936), pp. 544–546.
[c] *On the interpretation of intuitionistic number theory*, Journ. Symb. Logic, vol. 10 (1945), pp. 109–124.

[d] *Recursive predicates and quantifiers*, Trans. Amer. Math. Soc., vol. 53 (1943), pp. 41–73.

Klein, F.

[a] *A comparative review of recent researches in geometry*, Bull. N. Y. Math. Soc., vol. 2 (1892–3), pp. 215–249; transl. by M. W. Haskell.

Kneser, H.

[a] *Eine direkte Ableitung des Zornschen Lemmas aus dem Auswahlaxiom*, Math. Zeit., vol. 53 (1950), pp. 110–113.

Kolmogoroff, A.

[a] *Zur Deutung der intuitionistischen Logik*, Math. Zeit., vol. 35 (1932), pp. 58–65.

Kuratowski, C.

[a] *Sur la notion de l'ordre dans la Théorie des Ensembles*, Fund. Math., vol. 2 (1921), pp. 161–171.

Lewis, C. I.

[a] *Emch's calculus and strict implication*, Journ. Symb. Logic, vol. 1 (1936), pp. 77–86.

Lindenbaum, A.

[a] *Remarques sur une question de la méthode axiomatique*, Fund. Math., vol. 15 (1930), pp. 313–321.

Lusin, N.

[a] *Sur les ensembles analytiques nuls*, Fund. Math., vol. 25 (1935), pp. 109–131.

MacLane, S.

[a] *Symbolic logic*, Amer. Math. Mo., vol. 46 (1939), pp. 289–296.

Menger, K.

[a] *Der Intuitionismus*, Blätter für Deutsche Phil., vol. 4 (1930), pp. 311–325.

[b] *The new logic* (transl. by H. B. Gottlieb and J. K. Senior), Phil. of Sci., vol. 4 (1937), pp. 299–336.

Miller, E. W.

[a] *A note on Souslin's problem*, Amer. Journ. Math., vol. 65 (1943), pp. 673–678.

Miller, G. A.

[a] See collected works, Urbana, Univ. of Ill. Pr., vol. I, pp. 38–78, reprints from vols. 2 and 3 of Amer. Math. Mo.

Moore, E. H.

[a] *On the projective axioms of geometry*, Trans. Amer. Math. Soc., vol. 3 (1902), pp. 142–158.

Moore, R. L.

[a] *On the foundations of plane analysis situs*, Trans. Amer. Math. Soc., vol. 17 (1916), pp. 131–164.

[b] *A note concerning Veblen's axioms for geometry*, ibid., vol. 13 (1912), pp. 74–76.

Nagel, E.

[a] *The formation of modern conceptions of formal logic in the development of geometry*, Osiris, vol. 7 (1939), pp. 142–222.

von Neumann, J.

[a] *Eine Axiomatisierung der Mengenlehre*, Journ. für die reine u. angewandte Math., vol. 154 (1925), pp. 219–240. [Also see Berichtigung, ibid., vol. 155 (1926), p. 128.]

[b] *Die Axiomatisierung der Mengenlehre*, Math. Zeit., vol. 27 (1928), pp. 669–752.

Nicod, J.
[a] *A reduction in the number of the primitive propositions of logic*, Proc. Camb. Phil. Soc., vol. 19 (1916), pp. 32–42.

Niven, I.
[a] *Note on a paper by L. S. Johnston*, Amer. Math. Mo., vol. 55 (1948), p. 358.

Peano, G.
[a] *Sui fondamenti della Geometria*, Rivista di Matematica, vol. 4 (1894), pp. 51–90.

Quine, W. V.
[a] *Element and number*, Journ. Symb. Logic, vol. 6 (1941), pp. 135–149.
[b] *New foundations for mathematical logic*, Amer. Math. Mo., vol. 44 (1937), pp. 70–80.

Randolph, J. F., and Kac, M.
[a] *Differentials*, Amer. Math. Mo., vol. 49 (1942), pp. 110–112.

Rosenthal, A.
[a] *Über das dritte Hilbertsche Verknüpfungsaxiom*, Math. Ann., vol. 69 (1910), pp. 223–226.
[b] *Vereinfachungen des Hilbertschen Systems der Kongruenzaxiome*, Math. Ann., vol. 71 (1912), pp. 257–274.
[c] *Eine Bemerkung zu der Arbeit von Fräulin S. Weinlös: "Sur l'indépendance des axiomes de coïncidence et de la parallétité . . .,"* Fund. Math., vol. 13 (1929), pp. 304–306.

Rosser, B.
[a] *Extensions of some theorems of Gödel and Church*, Journ. Symb. Logic, vol. 1 (1936), pp. 87–91.
[b] *An informal exposition of proofs of Gödel's theorems and Church's theorem*, ibid., vol. 4 (1939), pp. 53–60.
[c] *The Burali-Forti paradox*, ibid., vol. 7 (1942), pp. 1–17.
[d] *On the many-valued logics*, Amer. Journ. Physics, vol. 9 (1941), pp. 207–212.

Russell, B.
[a] *Mathematical logic as based on the theory of types*, Amer. Journ. Math., vol. 30 (1908), pp. 222–262.
[b] *Whitehead and Principia Mathematica*, Mind, vol. 57 (1948), pp. 137–138.

Sheffer, H. M.
[a] *A set of five independent postulates for Boolean algebras*, Trans. Amer. Math. Soc., vol. 14 (1913), pp. 481–488.

Sierpinski, W.
[a] *Sur une hypothèse de M. Lusin*, Fund. Math., vol. 25 (1935), pp. 132–135.
[b] *L'hypothèse généralisée du continu et l'axiome du choix*, ibid., vol. 34 (1947), pp. 1–5.
[c] *Sur un problème de la théorie générale des ensembles équivalent au problème de Souslin*, ibid., vol. 35 (1948), pp. 165–174.

Skolem, T.
[a] *Einige Bemerkungen zur axiomatischen Begründung der Mengenlehre*, 5th Skand. Mat. Kong., Helsingfors, 1923, pp. 217–232.
[b] *Über die Grundlagendiskussionen der Mathematik*, 7th Skand. Mat. Kong., Oslo, 19–22 August 1929, Oslo, 1930, pp. 3–21.

Szele, T.
[a] *On Zorn's lemma*, Publicationes Mathematicae, vol. 1 (1950), pp. 254–256; *erratum*, ibid., p. 257.

Tarski, A.
[a]   *Sur les ensembles finis*, Fund. Math., vol. 6 (1924), pp. 45–95.
Turing, A. M.
[a]   *On computable numbers, with an application to the Entscheidungsproblem*, Proc. Lond. Math. Soc., ser. 2, vol. 42 (1937), pp. 230–265.
[b]   *A correction* (to [a]), ibid., ser. 2, vol. 43 (1937), pp. 544–546.
Veblen, O.
[a]   *A system of axioms for geometry*, Trans. Amer. Math. Soc., vol. 5 (1904), pp. 343–384.
Wang, H.
[a]   *A new theory of element and number*, Journ. Symb. Logic, vol. 13 (1948), pp. 129–137.
[b]   *A formal system of logic*, ibid., vol. 15 (1950), pp. 25–32.
Weinlös, S.
[a]   *Sur l'indépendance des axiomes de coïncidence et de parallétité dans un système des axiomes de la géométrie euclidienne à trois dimensions*, Fund. Math., vol. 11 (1928), pp. 206–221.
[b]   *Remarques à propos de la note de M. Rosenthal: "Eine Bemerkung zu der Arbeit von Frl. Weinlös . . .*, etc.," Fund. Math., vol. 15 (1930), pp. 310–312.
Wiener, N.
[a]   *A simplification of the logic of relations*, Proc. Camb. Phil. Soc., vol. 17 (1912–14), pp. 387–390.
Weyl, H.
[a]   *Mathematics and logic*, Amer. Math. Mo., vol. 53 (1946), pp. 2–13.
[b]   *A half-century of mathematics*, ibid., vol. 58 (1951), pp. 523–553.
White, L. A.
[a]   *The locus of mathematical reality; an anthropological footnote*, Phil. of Sci., vol. 14 (1947), pp. 289–303.
Wilder, R. L.
[a]   *Concerning R. L. Moore's axioms Σ_1 for plane analysis situs*, Bull. Amer. Math. Soc., vol. 34 (1928), pp. 752–760.
[b]   *The cultural basis of mathematics*, Proc. Int'l Cong. of Math'ns, Cambridge, Mass., 1950, vol. 1, pp. 258–271.
Zermelo, E.
[a]   *Beweis, dass jede Menge wohlgeordnet werden kann*, Math. Ann., vol. 59 (1904), pp. 514–516.
[b]   *Neuer Beweis für die Möglichkeit einer Wohlordnung*, ibid., vol. 65 (1908), pp. 107–128.
[c]   *Untersuchungen über die Grundlagen der Mengenlehre*, ibid., pp. 261–281.

Index of Symbols

Index of Topics and Technical Terms

Index of Names

303